Fodor's

U.S. & BRITISH
VIRGIN ISLANDS

Welcome to the U.S. & British Virgin Islands

Little did we realize that the emergence of a novel coronavirus in early 2020 would abruptly bring almost all travel to a halt. Although our Fodor's writers around the world have continued working to bring you the best of the destinations they cover, we still anticipate that more than the usual number of businesses will close permanently in the coming months, perhaps with little advance notice. We don't expect things to return to "normal" for some time. As you plan your upcoming travels to the Virgin Islands, please confirm that places are still open and let us know when we need to make updates by writing to us at this address: editors@fodors.com.

TOP REASONS TO GO

★ **Beaches:** Almost every island here has a great beach of white or golden sand.

★ **Sailing:** This archipelago is one of the world's top sailing destinations.

★ **Resorts:** You'll find everything from luxurious beachfront hideaways to simple inns.

★ **Shopping:** Bargains abound, especially in the U.S. Virgin Islands.

★ **Island Culture:** Each island has its own traditions and unique identity.

★ **Food:** From local favorites to gourmet dining rooms, you'll eat very well.

Contents

MAPS

Fodor's Features

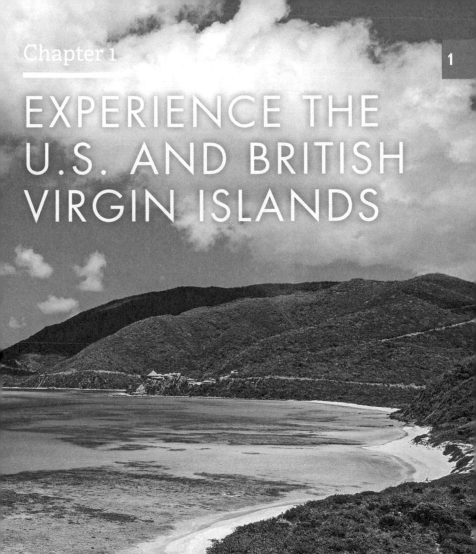

Chapter 1

EXPERIENCE THE U.S. AND BRITISH VIRGIN ISLANDS

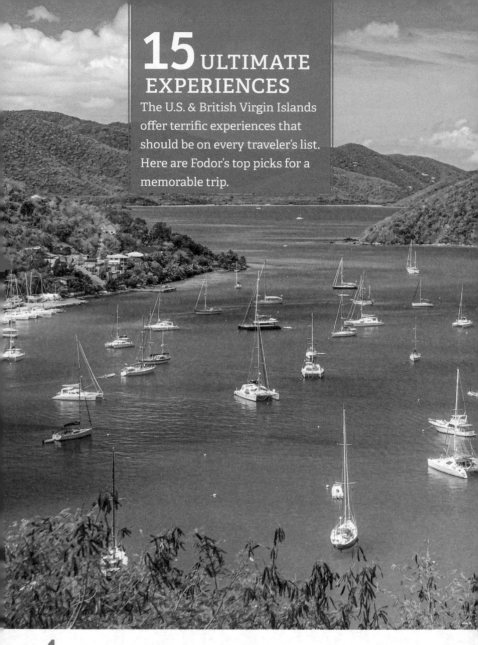

15 ULTIMATE EXPERIENCES

The U.S. & British Virgin Islands offer terrific experiences that should be on every traveler's list. Here are Fodor's top picks for a memorable trip.

1 Sail the British Virgin Islands

The best way to experience this compact archipelago is by boat. Charter a catamaran or sailboat in Tortola for a multiday adventure that includes stops at the beach bars of Jost Van Dyke, The Baths in Virgin Gorda, and reef-protected Anegada (Ch. 6–8).

2 Hike Reef Bay Trail

Three-mile Reef Bay Trail is the jewel of St. John's Virgin Islands National Park, weaving through rain forests with ancient petroglyphs carved into stone (Ch. 4).

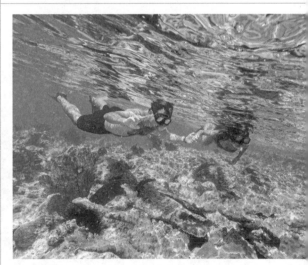

3 Snorkel at Trunk Bay

Spot vibrant coral reefs and fish along the snorkeling trail of St. John's Trunk Bay, which is fringed by one of the most spectacular beaches in the Caribbean (Ch. 4).

4 Sip a Painkiller

Try the potent mix of rum, pineapple, cream of coconut, and orange juice where it originated, the bar-lined island of Jost Van Dyke in the British Virgin Islands (Ch. 8).

5 Explore The Baths

The Baths of Virgin Gorda is the perfect beach for people who don't like the beach. You can sit on the sand if you'd like, but the real attractions are the caves created by the giant boulders on shore (Ch. 7).

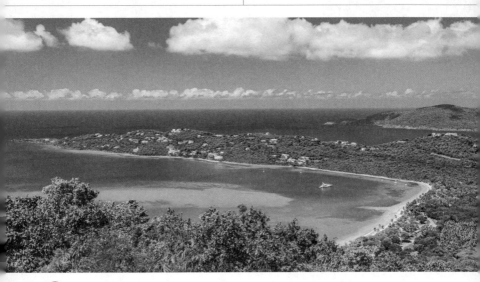

6 Hit the Beach

While there's a beautiful beach on every island, Magens Bay in St. Thomas is one of the best. It's the rare Caribbean beach with an admission fee, but it's well worth it (Ch. 3).

7 Hunt for Treasure

The sea caves of Norman Island are said to be hiding spots for buccaneer booty and even inspired Robert Louis Stevenson's *Treasure Island*. Snorkeling is a top activity (Ch. 8).

8 Ride to Paradise Point

Take a cable car ride from the heart of Charlotte Amalie, St. Thomas, to the heights of Paradise Point for a memorable view of the harbor. Salute the sunset with a Bushwacker, invented here (Ch. 3).

9 Taste Local Rum

Tour the rum factory and sample a wide range of rums at the Cruzan Rum Distillery on St. Croix, where the Nelthropp family has been making rum since the 18th century (Ch. 5).

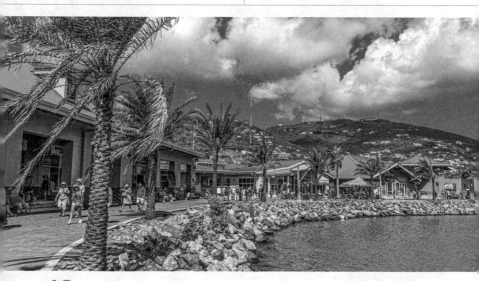

10 Shop in Charlotte Amalie

St. Thomas's capital retains some of its original Danish street layout, creating a souklike warren of streets and alleys full of duty-free shops in the heart of downtown (Ch. 3).

11 Relax at the Resort

Between island hopping, don't forget to reserve time to lounge by the pool, especially if you're at a luxurious resort like Virgin Gorda's Rosewood Little Dix Bay (Ch. 7).

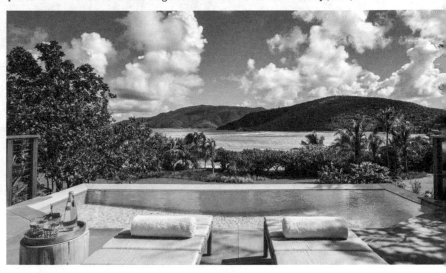

12 Learn at Annaberg Plantation

Reflect on St. John's history at the 18th-century sugar mill ruins in Virgin Islands National Park. From the striking windmill you'll get spectacular ocean views (Ch. 4).

13 Dive Among Shipwrecks

Anegada's reefs are full of dive sites, including shipwrecks dating back centuries and the awe-inspiring 1,200-foot plunge of the North Drop (Ch. 8).

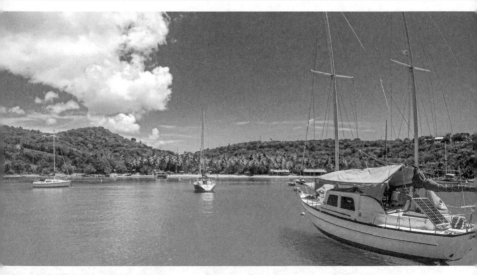

14 Day-Trip to Buck Island

A quick boat ride from Christiansted harbor in St. Croix, Buck Island is home to a great beach, reef snorkeling, and hiking and diving trails (Ch. 5)

15 Step Back in Time

The brilliant yellow walls of St. Croix's Fort Christiansvaern herald the fascinating history of Danish rule over the U.S. Virgin Islands, which lasted from 1733 to 1917 (Ch. 5).

WHAT'S WHERE

1 St. Thomas. The familiar and the foreign mingle perfectly here. Resorts run the gamut from plan and simple to luxurious, and the vibe is lively. Go for the duty-free shopping, sights, and water sports.

2 St. John. The least developed of the USVI, two-thirds of the island is a U.S. national park. With its excellent snorkeling, good restaurants, and comfortable villas and resorts, many find this the perfect island.

3 St. Croix. The largest of the U.S. Virgin Islands is 40 miles (64 km) south of St. Thomas. Choose St. Croix if you like history, good restaurants, decent shopping, and nice beaches.

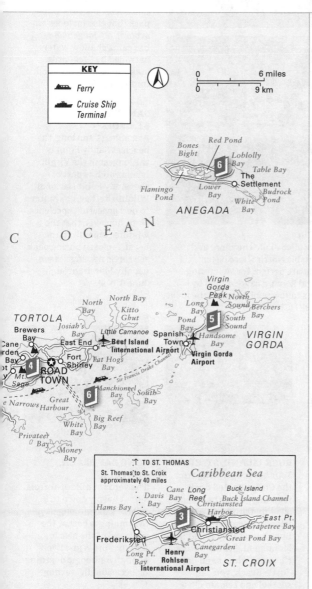

4 Tortola. A day might not be enough to tour this island because you're meant to relax while you're here. Go to Tortola if you want to do some shopping and enjoy a larger choice of good restaurants than you can find on the other British Virgins.

5 Virgin Gorda. Progressing from laid-back to more laid-back, mountainous and arid Virgin Gorda offers beautiful beaches but a more relaxed scene, with far fewer restaurants and shopping opportunities than Tortola.

6 Other British Virgin Islands. There are actually about 50 islands in the British Virgin chain, many of them completely uninhabited, but several have a single hotel or at least a beach that is popular. Set sail to Jost Van Dyke for legendary beach bars or to Anegada to snorkel past stunning reefs.

18

Best Beaches in the U.S. and British Virgin Islands

THE BATHS, VIRGIN GORDA
Massive granite boulders are piled along the shore and underwater at this unforgettable North Shore beach, creating hidden grottoes that are perfect for swimming and snorkeling. The Cathedral Room, a cave formed by intersecting boulders over a shallow pool, is one of the most photographed sights in the BVI (Ch. 7).

MAGENS BAY, ST. THOMAS
Located at the end of a long, rectangular bay, this is one of the most beautiful and popular beaches in the Caribbean. Part of a public park that also includes an arboretum, Magens Bay has calm, shallow waters patrolled by lifeguards, making it especially good for families (Ch. 3).

SANDY POINT, ST. CROIX
At 2 miles (3 km) long, the beach at Sandy Point is the longest in the Virgin Islands and, as part of the Sandy Point National Wildlife Refuge, guaranteed to be a peaceful experience. Note, however, that the wildlife comes first: the beach is closed during peak sea turtle nesting season, usually March through June (Ch. 5).

TRUNK BAY, ST. JOHN
Part of Virgin Islands National Park, Trunk Bay is stunning from above and below. Stop to enjoy the roadside view on the way to the park; then, throw down your towel on a gently arched quarter-mile of beach. An underwater snorkel trail follows a path alongside Trunk Cay, a small offshore island (Ch. 4).

BUCK ISLAND, ST. CROIX
Tour boats operating from the Christiansted dock regularly make the 1½-mile (2½-km) trip out to Buck Island, the centerpiece of Buck Island Reef National Monument. From its wide ribbon of white sand on Turtle Beach, you can snorkel and remain close to the tour boats anchored just offshore (Ch. 5).

LONG BAY BEACH, TORTOLA
The verdant hills of Tortola slope sharply down to a mile of sand at Long Bay. Swimming is best at the west end of the beach, and the surf is just lively enough for boogie boarding or, occasionally, surfing (Ch. 6).

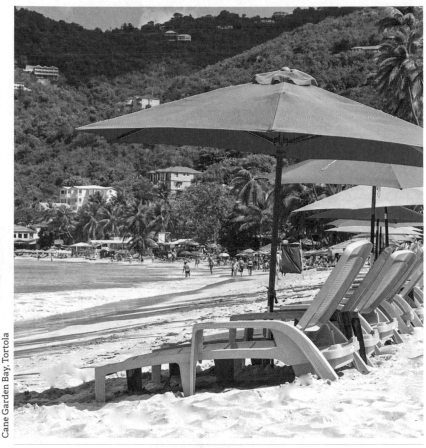

Cane Garden Bay, Tortola

CANE GARDEN BAY, TORTOLA

Stake out a place on the sand and settle in for a day swimming, snorkeling, and sunning at the shore, interrupted only by walks to nearby restaurants for drinks and snacks. As the sun settles over the horizon you can relocate to a beach bar to listen to live music, or venture into town for dinner (Ch. 6).

HAWKSNEST BEACH, ST. JOHN

If you're looking for a quiet alternative to the better-known Trunk Bay and Cinnamon Bay beaches in Virgin Island National Park, head to Hawksnest Beach on St. John's north shore for swimming and snorkeling in crystal clear waters (Ch. 4).

WHITE BAY, JOST VAN DYKE

Boaters wading ashore at White Bay Beach to get frozen drinks gave the beach's most famous bar, the Soggy Dollar Bar, its name. But don't let the daily party at White Bay's beach bars overshadow the merits of the beach itself, which has soft white sand and dazzling blue-green waters (Ch. 8).

Which Island Is Right for You?

ST. JOHN: FOR OUTDOORS ENTHUSIASTS

Virgin Islands National Park occupies 60% of St. John, including most of the island's best beaches, an extensive network of hiking trails, and fascinating historic sites, including sugar-mill ruins and a trail marked with Taíno petroglyphs (Ch. 4).

ST. CROIX: FOR FOODIES

St. Croix is full of small-town charm: even its two "cities," Christiansted and Frederiksted, are easily walkable. But the island has some big-time culinary talent paired with a well-established farm-to-table ethos, contributing to the best dining scene in the Virgin Islands—U.S. or British (Ch. 5).

TORTOLA: FOR SOCIAL BUTTERFLIES

If you love the combination of surf, sand, beach bars, and nightlife, make Cane Garden Bay on Tortola your destination. Beachfront restaurants serve local seafood, Pusser's at Myett's bar has Painkiller cocktails, and there's live music most nights at Quito's (Ch. 6).

VIRGIN GORDA: FOR EXPLORERS

Caving and diving—sometimes both at the same time—are the attractions at The Baths, a beach where giant, volcano-thrown boulders create a labyrinth onshore and an offshore playground for marine life. Navigating the caves on the beach is rewarded with hidden pools and quiet stretches of sand, while divers and snorkelers patrol the waters and venture into sunken caves in search of tropical fish and live corals. At the opposite end of the island is Gorda Peak National Park, where visitors can hike to the highest point on the "Fat Virgin" for views of North Sound and the other British Virgin Islands from the 1,370-foot summit (Ch. 7).

ANEGADA: FOR TRENDSETTERS

A low-lying coral island surrounded by reefs, Anegada is both distant and, for sailors unfamiliar with the local waters, dangerous to reach. But the isolation is a big part of the island's charm. Rent a Mini Moke for the day and set off on the dusty roads of the 14-square-mile island to discover rock iguanas at Bones Bight, cold drinks at Cow Wreck Beach and the Big Bamboo Beach Bar, and high dunes and wild waves at the Anegada Beach Club. Wreck diving is popular on the surrounding reefs, where mounds of pink conch shells make a memorable highlight of a guided snorkeling trip (Ch. 8).

1

Experience the U.S. and British Virgin Islands   WHICH ISLAND IS RIGHT FOR YOU?

St. Thomas

ST. THOMAS: FOR SHOPPERS

St. Thomas's capital city, Charlotte Amalie, is one of the best duty-free ports in the Caribbean, with narrow, Danish-era streets and alleys jammed with shops and galleries selling jewelry, liquor, rare coins pulled from shipwrecks, and locally made gifts (Ch. 3).

NORMAN ISLAND: FOR TREASURE SEEKERS

Norman Island has a real-life history as a pirates' hideout—people still search the island's caves for buried treasure. You're more likely to discover shimmering fish than gold, but it's worth lingering to enjoy the nearby Pirate's Bight restaurant and *Willy T* floating bar (Ch. 8).

GUANA ISLAND: FOR NATURE LOVERS

Access to a world-renowned nature sanctuary and conservation program is included in the price of a stay at Guana Island, a luxury all-inclusive resort with private villas scattered across a lush island covered in rain forest. Guests can meet the locals (green iguanas, geckos, and red-legged tortoises) while hiking the island's 12 miles of hiking trails or relaxing at one of seven beaches (Ch. 8).

COOPER ISLAND: FOR RUM DRINKERS

One of the best rum bars in the Caribbean resides at Cooper Island's small ecoresort across Sir Francis Drake channel from Tortola. Visitors can sample from a collection of more than 280 rums and chase it with a beer from the on-site Cooper Island Brewing Company (Ch. 8).

JOST VAN DYKE: FOR BAR CRAWLERS

No yacht tour of the BVI would be complete without anchoring at Jost Van Dyke for a pub crawl of the island's beach bars. The Soggy Dollar in White Bay is the famous home of the potent Painkiller rum punch; Foxy's in Great Harbour has great live music (Ch. 8).

Weddings and Honeymoons

There's no question that the Virgin Islands are a popular destination for a honeymoon. Romance is in the air here, and the white, sandy beaches, turquoise water, swaying palm trees, balmy tropical breezes, and perpetual summer sunshine put people in the mood for love. It's easy to understand why the Virgin Islands are fast becoming a popular wedding destination as well. They are easy to reach from the United States and offer a broad array of hotels and resorts. A destination wedding is no longer exclusive to celebrities and the superrich. You can plan a simple ceremony right on the beach or use your resort's chapel. Every large resort has a wedding planner, and there are independent wedding planners as well. Although the procedures in the British Virgin Islands are a little different, planning your wedding is relatively simple regardless of where you are.

GETTING MARRIED IN THE USVI

You must first apply for a marriage license at the Superior Court (in either St. Thomas or St. Croix; St. John has no court office). The fee for the application and license is $200. You have to wait eight days after the clerk receives the application to get married, and licenses must be picked up in person on a weekday, though you can apply by mail. To make the process easier, most couples hire a wedding planner. If you plan to get married at a large resort, most have planners on staff to help you with the paperwork and all the details, but if you're staying in a villa, at a small hotel or inn, or are arriving on a cruise ship, you'll have to hire your own.

The wedding planner will help you organize your marriage-license application as well as arrange for a location, flowers,

music, refreshments, and whatever else you want to make your day special. The wedding planner will also hire a clergyman if you'd like a religious service or a nondenominational officiant if you prefer. Indeed, many wedding planners are licensed by the territory as nondenominational officiants and will preside at your wedding.

WEDDING PLANNERS Anne Marie Weddings 340/626–4658, 888/676–5701 ⊕ www.stjohnweddings.com. **Weddings the Island Way** 340/777–6505, 800/755–5004 ⊕ www.weddingstheislandway. com.

GETTING MARRIED IN THE BVI

Getting married in the BVI is a breeze, but you must make advance plans. To make things go more smoothly, hire a wedding planner to guide you through the ins and outs of the BVI system. Many hotels also have wedding planners on staff to help organize your event. Hotels often offer packages that include the ceremony; accommodations for you, your wedding party, and your guests; and extras like massages, sailboat trips, and champagne dinners.

You must apply in person for your license ($220) weekdays at the Registrar General's office in Road Town, Tortola, and wait three days to pick it up at the registrar's office there. If you plan to be married in a church, announcements (called *banns* locally) must be published for three consecutive Sundays in the church bulletin. Only the registrar or clergy can perform ceremonies. The registrar charges $120 at the office and $220 at another location. No blood test is required.

HOW TO DRESS

In the Virgin Islands, basically anything goes, from long, formal dresses with trains to white bikinis. Floral sundresses are fine, too. For the men, tuxedos are not the norm; a pair of solid-colored slacks with a nice shirt is. If you're planning a wedding on the beach, barefoot is the way to go.

If you decide to marry in a formal dress and tuxedo, you're better off making your selections at home and hand-carrying them aboard the plane. Yes, it can be a pain, but ask your wedding-gown retailer to provide a special carrying bag. After all, you don't want to chance losing your wedding dress in a wayward piece of luggage. And when it comes to fittings, again, that's something to take care of before you arrive in the Virgin Islands.

YOUR HONEYMOON

Do you want champagne and strawberries delivered to your room each morning? A breathtaking swimming pool in which to float? A five-star restaurant in which to dine? Then a resort is the way to go. If you're on a tight budget or don't plan to spend much time in your room, there are also plenty of cheaper small inns and hotels throughout the USBVI to choose from. On the other hand, maybe you want your own private home in which to romp naked—or just laze around recovering from the wedding planning. Maybe you want your own kitchen in which to whip up a gourmet meal for your loved one. In that case, a private villa rental is the answer. That's another beautiful thing about the Virgin Islands: the lodging accommodations are almost as plentiful as the beaches, and there's bound to be one to match your tastes and your budget.

POPULAR HONEYMOON RESORTS

If you are looking for some serious time together with few distractions, you can always head to one of the private-island resorts in the BVI. **Guana Island** is luxurious, but **Cooper Island Beach Club** offers both privacy and moderate prices.

Many honeymooners choose the laid-back style of **Estate Lindholm** on St. John or the **Rosewood Little Dix Bay** on Virgin Gorda. Those looking for more creature comforts might consider the **Ritz-Carlton** on St. Thomas or the **Buccaneer Beach & Golf Resort** on St. Croix (which has a good golf course). The **Sugar Mill Hotel** on Tortola is simple and small but still gracious, while the **Scrub Island Resort** on Scrub Island, a 10-minute ferry ride from Tortola's Trellis Bay dock, offers the privacy advantages of a villa with some hotel amenities. St. Thomas's **Bolongo Bay Beach Resort,** though also popular with families, has an on-site wedding coordinator and is the island's only true all-inclusive resort.

Ferry Routes and Travel Times

ATLANTIC OCEAN

Great Harbour

JOST VAN DYKE
Inter Island Boat Service
New Horizon

**CHARLOTTE AMALIE–
CRUZ BAY**
Varlack Ventures

ST. THOMAS

Cyril E. King
International
Airport

CHARLOTTE
AMALIE

45 min.

35 min.

50 min.

ST. JOHN

Crown Bay

10 min.

MARRIOTT
Reefer

Cruz Bay

Phillips' landing

Marriott
12 min.

Red Hook
15 min.

RED HOOK–CRUZ BAY
PASSENGER ONLY
Varlack Ventures
CAR BARGE
Boyson Inc.
Global Marine
Love City

WATER ISLAND
Water Island
Ferry

45 min.

120 min.

← **PUERTO RICO**
Transportation
Services STT

Caribbean Sea

0   6 miles

0   9 km

*St. Croix Island is made to fit for this diagram.
It is not true to scale.

Christiansted

ANEGADA
Smith's Ferry

The
Settlement

60 min.

ROAD TOWN
Road Town Fast Ferry
Native Son
Smith's Ferry
Speedy's

Beef Island
International
Airport

Virgin Gorda
Airport

East End

BEEF IS.

45 min.

VIRGIN GORDA
Inter Island Boat Service
Smith's Ferry
Speedy's

10 min.

Spanish
Town

TORTOLA
ROAD TOWN ✪

EAST END
North Sound Express

West End

20 min.

30 min.

WEST END
Inter Island
Boat Service
Native Son
Smith's Ferry

Great
Harbour

PETER ISLAND
Peter Island Ferry

FERRY SCHEDULES:
U.S. Virgin Islands ⊕ *www.vinow. com/stjohn/getting_there*

British Virgin Islands ⊕ *www. bviwelcome.com/ferries.php*

FERRY COMPANIES:
Boyson Inc. General II and Mister B (St. John car barge) ☎ 340/776-6294

Global Marine's Tug Life aka Roanoke (St. John car barge) ☎ 340/779-1739

Inter-Island Boat Service (St. Thomas/St. John/Jost Van Dyke/ Tortola/Virgin Gorda) ☎ 340/776-6597 in St. John, 284/495-4166 in Tortola

Love City Car Ferries' Captain Vic (St. John car barge) ☎ 340/779-4000

Native Son ☎ 340/774-8685 in St. Thomas, 284/495-4617 in Tortola ⊕ *www.nativesonferry.com*

New Horizon Ferry Service ☎ 284/495-9278 in Tortola

Norman Island Ferry ☎ 284/443-1305 in Tortola ⊕ *www.pirates-bight.com/gettinghere.htm*

North Sound Express ☎ 284/495-2138 in Tortola

Peter Island Ferry (Peter Island Resort) ☎ 284/495-2000 in Tortola ⊕ *www.peterisland.com*

QEIV Ferry (St. Croix – St. Thomas) ☎ 340/473-1322 ⊕ *www. qe4ferry.com*

Reefer (Marriott Frenchman's Reef/Morningstar Beach) ☎ 340/776-8500 in St. Thomas ⊕ *www.marriottfrenchmansreef.com*

Road Town Fast Ferry ☎ 284/494-2323 in Tortola, 340/777-2800 in St. Thomas ⊕ *www.roadtownfastferry.com*

Smith's Ferry ☎ 340/775-7292 in St. Thomas, 284/494-4454 in Tortola ⊕ *www.bviferryservices.com*

Speedy's Ferries ☎ 284/494-6154 in Tortola ⊕ *www.bviferries.com*

Varlack Ventures (St. John) 340/776-6412 in St. John ⊕ *www.varlack-ventures.com*

Water Island Ferry (Water Island) ☎ 340/690-4159

Island Finder

	ST. THOMAS	ST. JOHN	ST. CROIX	TORTOLA	VIRGIN GORDA	JOST VAN DYKE	ANEGADA
APPEAL							
Crowds	●	◑	◑	◑		◑	
Urban Development	●	◑	●	◑			
Family-friendly	●	●	◑	●	◑		◑
BEACHES							
Beautiful	◑	●	◑	◑	◑	●	●
Deserted		●	◑	◑	●	◑	●
ENTERTAINMENT							
Cultural and Historic Sights	●	◑	◑	◑			
Fine Dining	●	◑	◑	◑	◑		
Nightlife	◑	◑	◑	◑		●	
Shopping	●	◑	◑	◑			
Casinos	●	◑				◑	
LODGING							
Luxury Resorts	●	◑	◑	◑	●		
Moderately Priced Resorts	●		●	◑	◑	◑	◑
Small Inns	●	◑	●	◑			◑
NATURE							
Wildlife	◑	●	◑	◑	●	◑	◑
Ecotourism	◑	●	◑	◑	●		
SPORTS							
Golf	●		◑				
Scuba Diving	●	◑	●	●	●	◑	●
Snorkeling	●	●	◑	●	●	●	●
Fishing	●	◑	●	◑	●		◑

● : noteworthy; ◑ : some; blank space: little or none

Chapter 2

TRAVEL SMART

Updated by
Carol Bareuther

★ **CAPITAL**
USVI: Charlotte Amalie, St. Thomas

BVI: Road Town, Tortola

♛ **POPULATION**
USVI: 105,000

BVI: 31,000

💬 **LANGUAGE**
English

$ **CURRENCY**
USVI & BVI: U.S. Dollar

☎ **AREA CODE**
USVI: 340

BVI: 284

⚠ **EMERGENCIES**
USVI: 911

BVI: 999

🚗 **DRIVING**
USVI & BVI: On the left

⚡ **ELECTRICITY**
USVI: 120 volts/60 cycles; plugs are U.S. standard two- and three-prong

BVI: 110 volts/60 cycles; plugs are standard two- and three-prong

🕐 **TIME**
Atlantic Standard Time zone (one hour later than EST; the same during daylight savings time)

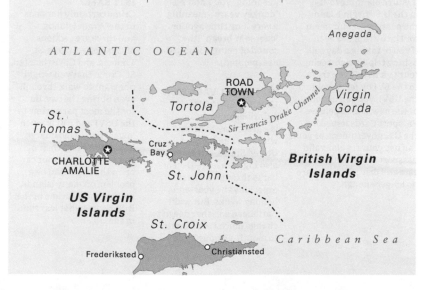

Know Before You Go

The U.S. Virgin Islands—St. Thomas, St. Croix, and St. John—operate under the American flag as a U.S. territory, while the British Virgin Islands—Tortola, Virgin Gorda, Jost Van Dyke, Anegada, and surrounding islands—are part of the British Commonwealth. Yet, the proximity between the two countries (at one point less than a mile, between St. John and Tortola), and centuries of cultural ties mean there are many characteristics all the islands have in common. Here's what you need to know before your trip.

YOU MIGHT NEED A PASSPORT

U.S. citizens don't need a passport to enter the U.S. Virgin Islands, but it's important to carry some type of government-issued photo ID like a driver's license or an original birth certificate (not a photocopy). However, U.S. and U.K. citizens must have a passport to enter the British Virgin Islands. Even if you're planning to stay in the U.S. Virgin Islands, the passport requirement for the BVI applies even if you're taking a day sail, fishing trip, or sightseeing tour to a BVI. If you travel to the BVI by ferry from the USVI, you can use one of the new, less expensive Passport Cards issued by the U.S. government, or you can use your regular valid passport. But a birth certificate and driver's license are no longer enough.

ENGLISH IS THE OFFICIAL LANGUAGE

English is the official language of both the U.S. and British Virgin Islands. However, don't be surprised to hear locals engaged in conversation and think they are speaking a foreign language. Virgin Islands Creole is based on the English language, but it's a dialect all its own. You might hear "yuh chek?" (meaning "you know?"), "donkey years" (meaning a very long time ago), or "cheese 'n' bread" (the sound of being surprised or exasperated).

DON'T JUST VACATION IN HIGH SEASON

A Caribbean vacation is a great way to escape winter in much of the United States, but this is also high season—December 15 through April 15, especially the year-end holiday weeks. But wait! Caribbean weather doesn't change much from month to month, although late summer and early fall are generally more humid. So, whenever you're in the mood to escape, don't hesitate. Low season, which is really most of the year, can be quiet, but with lower prices for accommodations and flights. The only caveat: hurricanes are at their peak in September and October.

CORAL REEF–SAFE SUNSCREEN IS A MUST

In fact, it's the law in the Virgin Islands as of 2020. Coral reefs are dying at an alarming rate, and one of the major contributors is sunscreen, more specifically the chemicals oxybenzone and octinoxate. Luckily, numerous companies like Sun Bum, Blue Lizard, and Thinksport offer reef-safe alternatives. If you forget to pack sunscreen, reef-safe products are available at drug, department, and grocery stores. Either way, check those labels before you buy your next bottle.

IS IT SAFE?

Crime certainly happens in the Virgin Islands, and there are sections of Charlotte Amalie, St. Thomas, and Christiansted, St. Croix, that you would not want to walk through even during the day. But, for the most part, crime in the USVI and BVI is much lower than in most large U.S. cities. Petty theft of belongings from your car or on the beach can be a problem on many islands, but in general crime in the BVI is somewhat less than in the USVI.

BRING A REUSABLE WATER BOTTLE

The average temperature in the Caribbean is around 80°F, so it's no wonder people are always drinking (this is the capital of fruity, frozen cocktails after all), and using plastic straws and cups and disposable water bottles. Unfortunately, these are also major contributors to the garbage found on the Caribbean's famous beaches. Numerous properties are starting to do away with plastic straws and offer alternatives to plastic water bottles, but why not bring your own bottle (or straw)?

BRING U.S. DOLLARS

The U.S. dollar is the official currency of both the U.S. and British Virgin Islands. Many vendors, even in the BVI, won't accept pounds or euros.

RENT A VEHICLE

If you're staying in a remote location, but plan to explore, eat out, or visit distant sights or beaches, consider renting a vehicle—car, jeep, or scooter. Be aware, though, that driving can be a challenge on narrow, winding roads on mountainous islands—especially at night. Taxis and inexpensive public buses (or private vans that operate like buses) are always an option, and drivers are generally well informed and will take you where you want to go, when you want to go, for as long as you wish, at an hourly rate. There are no ride-share services like Lyft or Uber in the USBVI.

DRIVE ON THE LEFT

Like currency, it's one size fits all in both the U.S. and British Virgin Islands: drive on the left side of the road. In the USVI, this is a holdover from when the Danes owned the islands. In the BVI, it's the norm from the United Kingdom. However, cars in both territories are typically imported from the United States, meaning although driving is on the left side of the road, the steering wheel is on the left, too.

USE FORMAL GREETINGS

Always start any encounter with a "good morning," "good afternoon," "good day," or "good night" before you ask a question. Virgin Islanders like formality and respect. Most also like to be called by their surname rather than first name. If you do use someone's first name, it's nice to put a Ms., Mrs., or Mr. in front of it. Do this, and you'll experience Virgin Islanders legendary friendliness and hospitality.

YES, YOU SHOULD TIP

Sometimes you'll see a service charge of about 10% on your restaurant bill (especially in the BVI); when this is the case, tip a little extra (about 5%). Otherwise, tip as you would at home, about 15% to 20%. Many hotels and resorts in the Virgin Islands add a hefty service charge of 10% to 15%, but that money doesn't always find its way to the staff. It's not inappropriate to leave $2 or $3 per day for the maid or to give $1 per bag to the bellhop. Tip taxi drivers in the USVI about 15% of the fare.

FOOD IS EXPENSIVE

You should expect to pay at least 30% more for groceries in the Virgin Islands than you would at home, and on some of the smaller islands, you'll pay an even larger premium. But there are good, U.S.–style supermarkets on St. Thomas and St. Croix, and decent markets on St. John and Tortola.

THERE'S JUST ONE ALL-INCLUSIVE RESORT

The Sugar Bay Resort on St. Thomas is the only true all-inclusive resort in the Virgin Islands. Some of the private-island resorts in the BVI do offer full-meal or all-inclusive plans, but they are as far from the typical all-inclusive resort experience as you could possibly imagine. Few resorts (even those that do offer meal plans) include alcoholic drinks, as you'd find at an all-inclusive resort in the Dominican Republic or Jamaica.

THERE ARE NO NUDE BEACHES

Be sure to pack more than your birthday suit. It's against the law in both the U.S. and British Virgin Islands to go nude in public places like the beaches. The beaches are where many local families, especially those with young children, go to spend the day.

Getting Here

While St. Croix has a four-lane highway and St. Thomas has multiple lanes running along the Charlotte Amalie waterfront, the other islands in the region have only paved two-lane main roads that twist and turn up and down the hillsides. Potholes are common. Once you get into neighborhoods, most roads are paved, but particularly on St. John and in the British Virgin Islands you may find some that are still dirt or gravel. Planes connect the larger islands, but travel to St. John and the smaller BVI is only by ferry. Ferries also connect the larger islands with the smaller ones and with each other.

■TIP➜ Ask the local tourist board about hotel and local transportation packages that include tickets to special events.

 Air

It's fairly easy to get to St. Thomas from the United States, with many nonstop flights. From New York to St. Thomas or San Juan, Puerto Rico, it takes about four hours; from Miami to St. Thomas or San Juan it's about three hours. There's no air service to St. John. For St. Croix, you usually connect in either Miami, San Juan, or St. Thomas. The only air service to the British Virgin Islands is through Tortola (always a connecting flight on a smaller plane). Flights between St. Thomas and Tortola take 15 minutes.

Reconfirming your flights on interisland carriers is a good idea, particularly when you're traveling to the smallest islands. You may be subjected to a carrier's whims: if no other passengers are booked on your flight, you may be asked to take another flight later in the day, or your plane may make unscheduled stops to pick up more passengers or cargo. It's all part of the excitement—and unpredictability—of travel in the Caribbean.

In addition, regional carriers use small aircraft with limited baggage space, and they often impose weight restrictions; travel light, or you could be subject to outrageous surcharges or delays on very large or heavy luggage, which may have to follow on another flight. If you have an afternoon flight, check your bags in early in the morning (keep a change of clothes in a carry-on), then go back to the beach for one last lunch, returning to the airport two hours before your flight departs. It makes for much easier traveling, saves time, and you get your last beach fix.

AIRPORTS

The major airports are Terrance B. Lettsome International Airport on Beef Island, Tortola; Cyril E. King Airport on St. Thomas; and Henry Rohlsen Airport on St. Croix, which is on the southwestern side of the island, near Christiansted. There's a small airport (so small that it doesn't have a phone number) on Virgin Gorda.

Ground transportation options are covered in the Essentials sections in individual island chapters.

FLIGHTS

There are nonstop and connecting flights, usually through San Juan, Puerto Rico, from the U.S. mainland to St. Thomas and St. Croix, with connecting ferry service from St. Thomas to St. John. There are no nonstop flights to the BVI from the United States; you must connect in San Juan or St. Thomas for the short hop over to Tortola or Virgin Gorda.

American Airlines is the biggest air carrier to the Virgin Islands, with several nonstop flights a day from Boston, New York, and Miami to St. Thomas and several connecting flights through San Juan. American also flies nonstop to St. Croix from Miami. The frequency of flights is seasonal.

US Airways has nonstop flights from Philadelphia and Charlotte, North Carolina. Spirit Airlines flies nonstop every day from Fort Lauderdale. Delta flies nonstop from Atlanta. United also flies nonstop from Chicago, Newark, and Washington, D.C. JetBlue flies direct from Boston but connects to many points on the mainland through San Juan.

Although connecting through San Juan is your best bet for getting to Tortola or Virgin Gorda, you can also fly from St. Thomas and St. Croix to Tortola and Virgin Gorda on Air Sunshine and Cape Air. Seaborne flies direct from San Juan to St. Thomas, St. Croix, Tortola, and Virgin Gorda, and between St. Thomas and St. Croix.

Some islands in the British Virgin Islands are accessible only by small planes operated by local or regional carriers. International carriers will sometimes book those flights for you as part of your overall travel arrangements, or you can book directly with the local carrier.

ⓑ Boat and Ferry

Ferries travel between St. Thomas and St. John as well as between St. Thomas and St. Croix. You can also travel by ferry from both St. Thomas and St. John to the British Virgin Islands, and between the British Virgin Islands themselves. The companies run regularly scheduled trips, departing from Charlotte Amalie or Red Hook on St. Thomas; Cruz Bay, St. John; West End, Road Town, or Beef Island on Tortola; Spanish Town or North Sound on Virgin Gorda; and Jost Van Dyke. There's also regularly scheduled service between Tortola, Virgin Gorda, and Anegada a few times a week. Schedules change, so check with your hotel or villa manager to find out the latest. The ferry companies

are all regulated by the U.S. Coast Guard, and prices are about the same, so there's no point in trying to organize your schedule to take one company's ferries rather than another's. Just show up at the dock to buy your ticket on the next ferry departing for your destination. If it all seems confusing—and it can be very confusing for travel to or around the BVI—just ask a local who's also buying a ticket. They know the ropes.

Although you might save a few dollars flying into St. Thomas if you're headed to the BVI, it's much easier to connect through San Juan for a flight to Tortola or Virgin Gorda. If you're headed to St. John or to points like North Sound, Virgin Gorda, or Jost Van Dyke, you'll have to hop a ferry regardless. If you're splitting your vacation between the U.S. and British Virgin Islands, ferries are the perfect way to get from one to another. You'll also get a bonus: views of the many small islands that dot the ferry route.

Dolphin Water Taxi runs from St. Thomas to St. John and many points in the BVI. You'll avoid the often crowded ferries, the crew will handle your luggage and navigate customs in the BVI, and you'll arrive at your destination feeling relaxed; however, you'll pay significantly more for the convenience.

There's frequent daily service from both Red Hook (15 to 20 minutes, $8.15 each way plus $4 for each piece of luggage) and Charlotte Amalie (45 minutes, $13 each way plus $4 for each piece of luggage) to Cruz Bay. The more frequent ferry from Red Hook to St. John leaves at 6:30 am and hourly starting at 8 am, the last at midnight; from St. John back to Red Hook, the first ferry leaves at 6 am, the last at 11 pm. About every hour there's a car ferry, which costs $50 (plus $3 port charges) round-trip; you should arrive at least 25 minutes before

Getting Here

departure. From Charlotte Amalie the first ferry to St. John leaves at 10 am, the last at 5:30 pm; from St. John to Charlotte Amalie, the first ferry leaves at 8:45 am, the last at 3:45. The ferry between Charlotte Amalie and St. John is prone to cancellations, particularly in the slower fall months.

Reefer is the name given to both of the brightly colored 26-passenger skiffs that run between the Charlotte Amalie waterfront and Marriott Frenchman's Cove hotel every day on the half hour from 8 to 5. It's a good way to beat the traffic (and is about the same price as a taxi) and dine out at one of the resort's restaurants. The one-way fare is $7 per person, and the trip takes about 15 minutes.

There's daily service between Charlotte Amalie or Red Hook, on St. Thomas, and West End or Road Town, Tortola, BVI, by either Smith's Ferry or Native Son, and to Virgin Gorda, BVI, by Smith's Ferry. The round-trip fare is $55–$65 and the trip from Charlotte Amalie takes 45 minutes to an hour to West End and up to 90 minutes to Road Town; from Red Hook the trip is only a half hour.

There's also frequent service from Cruz Bay to Tortola aboard an Inter-Island Boat Service ferry. The half-hour trip costs $55 round-trip; bring your passport if you plan to go to BVI (it's now required for all travel there).

The 1½-hour trip from Charlotte Amalie to Virgin Gorda costs $40 one way and $70 round-trip. From Red Hook and Cruz Bay, Inter-Island offers service on Thursday and Sunday; Speedy's offers service on Tuesday, Thursday, and Saturday.

On Monday, Tuesday, Wednesday, Friday, Saturday, and Sunday a ferry operates between Red Hook, Cruz Bay, and Jost Van Dyke; the trip takes 45 minutes and costs $100 per person round-trip.

Car

RENTAL CARS

Unless you plan to spend all your days at a resort or plan to take taxis everywhere, you'll need a rental car at least for a few days. While driving is on the left, you'll drive an American-style car with the steering wheel on the left. Traffic doesn't move all that fast in most USBVI locations, so driving on the left is not that difficult to master.

If you're staying on St. Thomas or St. Croix and don't plan to venture far off the main roads, you won't need a four-wheel-drive vehicle. On St. John and in the BVI, a four-wheel-drive vehicle is useful to get up steep roads when it rains. Many rental homes in St. John and the BVI are on unpaved roads, so a four-wheel-drive vehicle with high clearance may be a necessity if you rent a villa. While rental agencies don't usually prohibit access to certain roads, use common sense; if the road looks too bad, turn around.

Most car-rental agencies won't rent to anyone under age 25 or over age 75.

Some car-rental agencies offer infant car seats for about $5 a day, but check and check again right before you leave for your trip to make sure one will be available. If you don't use one, you may get a ticket since the law requires their use. You might consider bringing your own car seat from home.

Book your rental car well in advance during the winter season. Vehicles are particularly scarce around the busy Christmas to New Year's and Presidents' Day holidays. If you don't reserve, you might find yourself without wheels. Prices will be higher during the winter season.

Rates range from $50 a day ($300 a week) for an economy car with air-conditioning, automatic transmission, and unlimited mileage to as much as $110 a day ($720 a week) for a four-wheel-drive vehicle. Both the USVI and the BVI have major companies (with airport locations) as well as numerous local companies (near the airports, in hotels, and in the main towns), which are sometimes cheaper. Most provide pick-up service; some ask that you take a taxi to their headquarters.

A driver's license from the United States or other countries is fine in the USVI and the BVI.

RENTAL CAR INSURANCE

Everyone who rents a car wonders whether the insurance that the rental companies offer is worth the expense. No one—including us—has a simple answer. If you own a car, your personal auto insurance may cover a rental to some degree, though not all policies protect you abroad; always read your policy's fine print. If you don't have auto insurance, then seriously consider buying the collision- or loss-damage waiver (CDW or LDW) from the car-rental company, which eliminates your liability for damage to the car. Some credit cards offer CDW coverage, but it's usually supplemental to your own insurance and rarely covers SUVs, minivans, luxury models, and the like. If your coverage is secondary, you may still be liable for loss-of-use costs from the car-rental company. But no credit-card insurance is valid unless you use that card for *all* transactions, from reserving to paying the final bill. All companies exclude car rental in some countries, so be sure to find out about the destination to which you are traveling. It's sometimes cheaper to buy insurance as part of your general travel insurance policy.

GASOLINE

Gas is up to $1 to $2 more per gallon than in the United States. USVI stations sell gas by the gallon; BVI stations sell it by the liter or the gallon, depending on the station. Most stations accept major credit cards, but don't count on that. Some stations have a pump-it-yourself policy, but it's still easy to find one with attendants, except on St. John. There's no need to tip unless they change a tire or do some other quick mechanical chore. You'll have to ask for a handwritten receipt if you're not paying by credit card. On smaller islands stations may be closed on Sunday.

PARKING

Parking can be tight in towns across the USBVI. Workers grab up the street parking, sometimes arriving several hours early to get prime spaces. It's particularly difficult to find parking in Cruz Bay, St. John. There are free public lots scattered around town, but they're usually filled by folks taking the ferry to St. Thomas. However, you can often find a spot in the public lot across from the tennis courts, but it's a 10-minute walk to the heart of Cruz Bay. Your rental-car company probably will allow you to park in its lot. Charlotte Amalie, St. Thomas, has a paid parking lot next to Fort Christian. A machine takes your money—$2 for the first hour and $6 for all day. In Christiansted, St. Croix, you'll find a public parking lot on Strand Street. Since the booth isn't staffed, there's no charge. There's also a public lot near Fort Christiansvaern, but that lot is locked at 4:30 pm. It costs $2 for the first hour, and $6 for all day. Tortola has several free parking lots near the waterfront, but daytime parking is a nightmare unless you get there early. On Virgin Gorda there's a free lot at Virgin Gorda Yacht Harbor. There are no parking meters anywhere in the USBVI. Even if you're desperate for a parking space in the USVI, don't park in a handicapped space without a sticker—unless you want to pay a $1,000 fine.

Getting Here

ROADSIDE EMERGENCIES

To reach police, fire, or ambulance, dial 911 in the USVI and 999 or 911 in the BVI. There are no emergency-service companies such as AAA in the USBVI. Before driving off into the countryside, check your rental car for tire-changing equipment, including a spare tire in good condition.

ROAD CONDITIONS

Island roads are often narrow, winding, and hilly. Those in mountainous regions that experience heavy tropical rains are also potholed and poorly maintained. Streets in towns are narrow, a legacy of the days when islanders used horse-drawn carts. Drive with extreme caution, especially if you venture out at night. You won't see guardrails on every curve, although the drops can be frighteningly steep. And pedestrians and livestock often share the roadway with vehicles.

You'll face rush-hour traffic on St. Thomas (especially in Charlotte Amalie); on St. Croix (especially in Christiansted and on Centerline Road); and on Tortola (especially around Road Town). All the larger towns have one-way streets. Although they're marked, the signs may be obscured by overhanging branches and other obstacles.

RULES OF THE ROAD

Driving in the Virgin Islands can be tricky. Traffic moves on the left in *both* the USVI and BVI. Almost all cars are American, which means the driver sits on the side of the car next to the road's edge, a position that makes some people nervous.

Buckle up before you turn the key. Police in the USVI are notorious for giving $50 tickets to unbelted drivers and front-seat passengers. The police are a bit lax about driving under the influence, but why risk it? Take a taxi or appoint a designated driver when you're out on the town.

Traffic moves at about 10 mph in town; on major highways you can fly along at 50 mph. On other roads, the speed limit may be less. Main roads in the USVI carry route numbers, but they're not always marked, and locals may not know them. (Be prepared for such directions as, "Turn left at the big tree.") Few USVI secondary roads have signs; BVI roads aren't very well marked either.

Ride-Sharing

There are no formal ride-share companies operating in the Virgin Islands at this time.

Scooter

Scooters can be a fun way to get around these islands, and many places offer day rates. Just remember to pay attention to road rules: on both island groups you drive on the left—and wear sunblock and a helmet. A valid driver's license and cash deposit or credit card may be required.

Taxi

Taxis rates are set by the government, and you'll pay extra for your bags. Fares vary by destination and the number of people in the taxi, but count on paying $7 per person from Cyril E. King Airport on St. Thomas to Charlotte Amalie; $16 per person from Henry Rohlsen Airport on St. Croix to Christiansted; and $27 per person from Terrance E. Lettsome Airport on Beef Island, Tortola, to Road Town. Tip taxi drivers 15%.

Essentials

Dining

Everything from fast food to fine cuisine in elegant settings is available in the USBVI, and prices run about the same as what you'd pay in New York or any other major city. You'll find global chains such as McDonald's, Pizza Hut, KFC, and more on St. Thomas and St. Croix alongside authentic nonchain restaurants with kid-friendly menus. Resorts that cater to families always have a casual restaurant, but there are delis and other restaurants across the USBVI that offer something for everyone on their menus. Most chefs at top-of-the-line restaurants and even some small spots went to a major culinary school, which means innovative and interesting cuisine. Don't be afraid to sample local dishes at the roadside restaurants and food trucks on all the islands. More and more restaurants have vegetarian offerings on their menus, though true vegetarian restaurants are hard to find. The restaurants we list are the cream of the crop in each price category.

Unless otherwise noted, the restaurants listed are open daily for lunch and dinner.

RESERVATIONS AND DRESS

In many places in the Caribbean reservations are expected, particularly at nicer restaurants. We mention reservations only when they are essential (there's no other way you'll ever get a table) or when they're not accepted. For popular restaurants, book as far ahead as you can (often a month or more), and reconfirm as soon as you arrive. Large parties should always call ahead to check the reservations policy. We mention dress only when men are required to wear a jacket or a jacket and tie. Beach attire is universally frowned upon in restaurants throughout the Caribbean.

WINES, BEER, AND SPIRITS

Top-notch restaurants offer good selections of fine wines. Beer and spirits are available on all islands at all kinds of restaurants and roadside stands, but you may not find the brand you prefer. Cruzan Rum, manufactured in St. Croix, is available across the USBVI. Alcoholic beverages are available from the smallest corner rum shop to the fanciest resort at all hours of the day and night. The only prohibition comes during the day on Good Friday, when no one can sell drinks.

Health

Water in the USBVI is generally safe to drink. Mosquitoes can be a problem here, particularly after a spate of rain showers. Insect repellent is readily available, but you may want to bring something from home, because it's more expensive in the Virgin Islands. Dengue fever and the Chikungunya virus are a particular concern.

Less dangerous, but certainly a nuisance, are the little pests from the sand-flea family known as no-see-ums. You don't realize you're being had for dinner until it's too late, and these bites itch, and itch, and itch. No-see-ums start getting hungry around 3 pm and are out in force by sunset. They're always more numerous in shady and wooded areas. Take a towel along for sitting on the beach, and keep reapplying insect repellent.

Beware of the manchineel tree, which grows near the beach and has green apple-like fruit that is poisonous and bark and leaves that burn the skin.

Even if you've never been sunburned in your life, believe the warnings and use sunscreen in the USBVI. Start with at least an SPF of 15 and keep it on. Rays are most intense between 11 and 2, so

Essentials

move under a seagrape tree (although you can still burn here) or, better yet, take a shady lunch break. You can also burn in this part of the world when it's cloudy, so putting sunscreen on every day no matter what the weather is the best strategy. When packing sunscreen, be sure it's reef safe or a product without any of the three O's: oxybenzone, octinoxate, and octocrylene, as the USVI banned use of these products as of March 30, 2020.

COVID-19

A novel coronavirus brought all travel to a virtual standstill in the first half of 2020. Although the illness is mild in most people, some experience severe and even life-threatening complications. Once travel started up again, albeit slowly and cautiously, travelers were asked to be particularly careful about hygiene and to avoid any unnecessary travel, especially if they are sick.

Older adults, especially those over 65, have a greater chance of having severe complications from COVID-19. The same is true for people with weaker immune systems or those living with some types of medical conditions, including diabetes, asthma, heart disease, cancer, HIV/AIDS, kidney disease, and liver disease.

Starting two weeks before a trip, anyone planning to travel should be on the lookout for some of the following symptoms: cough, fever, chills, trouble breathing, muscle pain, sore throat, new loss of smell or taste. If you experience any of these symptoms, you should not travel at all.

And to protect yourself during travel, do your best to avoid contact with people showing symptoms. Wash your hands often with soap and water. Limit your time in public places, and, when you are out and about, wear a cloth face mask that covers your nose and mouth. Indeed, a mask may be required in some places,

such as on an airplane or in a confined space like a theater, where you share the space with a lot of people.

You may wish to bring extra supplies, such as disinfecting wipes, hand sanitizer (12-ounce bottles were allowed in carry-on luggage at this writing), and a first-aid kit with a thermometer.

Given how abruptly travel was curtailed in March 2020, it is wise to consider protecting yourself by purchasing a travel insurance policy that will reimburse you for any costs related to COVID-19–related cancellations. Not all travel insurance policies protect against pandemic-related cancellations, so always read the fine print.

OVER-THE-COUNTER REMEDIES

Over-the-counter medications like aspirin, Tylenol, and Mylanta are readily available in the USBVI. You can find a big selection of these products at grocery and drug stores across the USBVI. You can find a smaller selection (and considerably higher prices) on the smaller islands.

IMMUNIZATIONS

No vaccinations are required to visit the USBVI. The most serious tropical disease prevalent here is dengue fever, which has no vaccine.

 # Lodging

Decide whether you want to pay the extra price for a room overlooking the ocean or the pool. At less expensive properties location may mean a difference in price of only $10 to $20 per night; at luxury resorts, however, it could amount to as much as $100 or more per night. Also find out how close the property is to a beach. At some hotels you can walk barefoot from your room onto the sand; others are across a road or a 10-minute drive away.

Nighttime entertainment is often alfresco in the USBVI, so if you go to bed early or are a light sleeper, ask for a room away from the dance floor. Air-conditioning isn't a necessity on all islands, many of which are cooled by trade winds, but it can be a plus if you enjoy an afternoon snooze or are bothered by humidity. Breezes are best on upper floors, particularly corner rooms. If you like to sleep without air-conditioning, make sure that windows can be opened and have screens; also make sure there are no security issues with leaving your windows open. If you're staying away from the water, make sure the room has a ceiling fan and that it works. Even in the most luxurious resorts, there are times when things simply *don't* work; it's a fact of Caribbean life. No matter how diligent the upkeep, humidity and salt air quickly take their toll, and cracked tiles, rusty screens, and chipped paint are common everywhere.

The lodgings we list are the cream of the crop in each price category. When pricing accommodations, always ask what's included and what costs extra.

APARTMENT AND VILLA RENTALS

Villas—whether luxurious or modest— are popular lodging options on all the Virgin Islands.

Renting a villa lets you settle in. You can have room to spread out, you can cook any or all of your meals, and you can have all the privacy you desire. Since most villas are in residential neighborhoods, your neighbors probably won't appreciate late-night parties or your children playing too loudly in the swimming pool. And you may be disturbed by your neighbor's weekend yard maintenance. That said, there's no better way to experience life in the USBVI.

Many villas are set up specifically for the rental market with bedrooms at opposite ends of the house. This makes

them perfect for two couples who want to share an accommodation but still prefer some privacy. Others with more bedrooms are sized right for families. Ask about the villa layout to make sure young children won't have to sleep too far away from their parents. Villas with separate bedroom buildings are probably not a good idea unless your children are in their teens.

Most villas are owned by people who live somewhere else but hire a local management company to attend to the details. Depending on the island and the rental, the manager will either meet you at the ferry or airport or will give you directions to your villa. Most of the companies offer the same services with similar degrees of efficiency.

You can book your villa through the numerous agencies that show up on the Internet, but they're usually not based on the island you want to visit. Booking through an island-based manager means that you can talk to a person who knows the villa and can let you know whether it meets your specifications. Your villa manager can also arrange for a maid, a chef, and other staffers to take care of myriad other details to help make your vacation go smoothly. They're only a phone call away when something goes wrong or you have a question.

Catered To Vacation Homes focuses on St. John. Vacation St. Croix is based on St. Croix. McLaughlin-Anderson has rentals across the USBVI.

HOTELS

Hotels range from luxury beachfront resorts, where the staff caters to your every whim and where you'll find plenty of activities to keep you busy, to small, locally owned hillside hotels with great views that cater to more independ-ent-minded visitors. They're priced

Essentials

accordingly. At the smaller inland properties you'll probably want to rent a car to get out to the island's best beaches and interesting restaurants.

The USBVI are quite Americanized thanks to television and the influx of U.S. visitors, but some traditional Caribbean customs still apply. Common courtesy is particularly important in the islands, so always say hello when you enter a store and make some small talk before getting down to business. Also, watch out for cars that stop suddenly in the middle of the road for chats with passersby and be aware that nothing, and we mean nothing, ever starts on time.

⑤ Money

Prices quoted are in U.S. dollars, which is the official currency on all the islands. Major credit cards are accepted at many establishments.

Prices *in this guide* are given for adults. Reduced fees are almost always available for children.

ATMS AND BANKS

You can find ATMs at most banks in the USBVI. The ATM at FirstBank, the only one on St. John, sometimes runs out of cash on long holiday weekends.

Packing

A pocket LED flashlight to deal with the occasional power outage, bug repellent for mosquitoes, sunglasses, a hat, and sunscreen are essentials for any USBVI vacation. If you forget something, those items are available at stores across the USBVI, but are usually more expensive than what you would pay at home. Pharmacies can fill prescriptions with a call to your home drug store, but this may be the

week the drug shipment didn't arrive. It's always safer to bring everything you need. Dress is casual even at the most expensive resorts, but men are usually required to wear a collared shirt in dining rooms. For dinner out women typically wear what the locals call "island fancy" (a flowy skirt and nice top will do). Bring your bathing suit, a cover-up, sandals, sturdy walking shoes if you're a hiker, beach shoes if you plan on strolling those luscious strands of sand, and a sweater or fleece if you're visiting in the winter when the nights are cool. In these days of packing light, rent snorkel gear on the island rather than bringing it unless you have a prescription mask. Shorts and T-shirts will do everywhere during the day. Don't forget a good book for whiling away those afternoons in the beach chair and your camera for bringing home those USBVI memories.

🪪 Passports and Visas

For U.S. citizens, a passport is *not* required to visit the U.S. Virgin Islands, though you must still provide proof of citizenship by showing an original birth certificate with a raised seal as well as a government-issued photo ID. There are no immigration procedures upon arriving in St. Thomas or St. Croix for anyone arriving on planes from the U.S. mainland or Puerto Rico, but on your return you will clear immigration and customs before boarding your flight.

If you visit the BVI by ferry from the USVI, you must go through customs and immigration procedures and prove your citizenship. U.S. citizens must have a passport to enter the BVI by ferry.

If you fly into the BVI, you must go through customs and immigration upon arrival and have a valid passport. Aside from paying the departure tax, there are no special departure procedures.

✚ Safety

In the USVI ask hotel staff members about the wisdom of venturing off the beaten path. Although it may seem like a nice night for a stroll back to your hotel from that downtown restaurant, it's better to take a taxi than face an incident. The BVI has seen less crime than its neighbors to the west, but again, better safe than sorry.

Follow the same precautions that you would anywhere. Look around before using the ATM. Keep tabs on your wallet or bag; put it on your lap—not the back of your chair—in restaurants. Stow valuable jewelry or other items in the hotel safe when you leave your room; hotel and villa burglaries do occur infrequently. Deserted beaches on St. John and the BVI are usually safe, but think twice about stopping at that strand of lonely sand on St. Croix and St. Thomas. Hotel or public beaches are your best bets. Never leave your belongings unattended at the beach or on the seats of your rental car. Be sure to lock the doors on your rental villa or hotel room.

Ⓢ Taxes

There's no sales tax in the USVI, but there's a 12.5% hotel-room tax; most hotels also add a 10% service charge to the bill. The St. John Accommodations Council members ask that hotel and villa guests voluntarily pay a $1 per day surcharge to help fund school and community projects and other good works. Many hotels add additional energy surcharges and the like, so ask about any additional charges, but these are not government-imposed taxes.

In the BVI the departure tax is $20 per person by boat and $20 per person by plane. There is also a $15 departure tax from the USVI when traveling to the BVI. There are separate booths at the airport and at ferry terminals to collect this tax, which must be paid in cash in U.S. currency. Most hotels in the BVI add a service charge ranging from 10% to 18% to the bill. A few restaurants and some shops tack on an additional 10% charge if you use a credit card. There's no sales tax in the BVI. However, there's a 10% government tax on hotel rooms.

Ⓢ Tipping

Many hotels in the USVI add a 10% to 15% service charge to cover the services of your housekeeping and other staff. However, some hotels use part of that money to fund their operations, passing only a portion of it on to the staff. Check to determine the hotel's policy. If you discover you need to tip, give bellhops and porters $1 to $2 per bag and housekeepers $3 or $5 per day. Special errands or requests of hotel staff always require an additional tip. At restaurants bartenders and waiters expect a 15%–20% tip, but always check your tab to see whether service is included. Taxi drivers in the USVI should get a 15% tip.

In the BVI tip porters and bellhops $1 per bag. Sometimes a service charge of 15% is included on restaurant bills; it's customary to leave another 5% if you liked the service. If no charge is added, 15% is the norm. Cabbies normally aren't tipped because most own their cabs; add 10% to 15% if their service is great.

Essentials

● Visitor Information

Stop by the tourism department's local offices for brochures on things to do and places to see. The offices are open only weekdays from 8 to 5, so if you need information on the weekend or on one of the territory's many holidays, you're out of luck. *(For locations, see Visitor Information in the Essentials section of each chapter.)*

● When to Go

The Caribbean high season is traditionally winter—from December 15 to April 15— when you're guaranteed the most entertainment at resorts and the most people with whom to enjoy it. It's also the most fashionable, the most expensive, and the most popular time to visit—and most hotels are heavily booked. You must make reservations at least two or three months in advance for the very best places (sometimes a year in advance for the most exclusive spots). Hotel prices can drop 20% to 50% after April 15; airfares and cruise prices also fall. Saving money isn't the only reason to visit the Caribbean during the off-season. Many islands now schedule their carnivals, music festivals, and other events during the off-season. Late August, September, October, and early November are the least crowded—but the weather then is the most unpredictable. Some hotels and resorts actually close during September and October.

CLIMATE

The Caribbean climate is fairly constant. The average year-round temperatures for the region are 78°F to 88°F. The temperature extremes are 65°F low, 95°F high; but, as everyone knows, it's the humidity, not the heat, that makes you suffer— especially when the two go hand in hand. The high-season months of December through April generally provide warm, sunny days with little humidity. The off-season months, particularly August through November, are the most humid. As part of the late-fall rainy season, hurricanes occasionally sweep through the Caribbean. Check the news daily and keep abreast of brewing tropical storms. The rainy season consists mostly of brief showers interspersed with sunshine. You can watch the clouds thicken, feel the rain, then have brilliant sunshine dry you off, all while remaining on your lounge chair. A spell of overcast days or heavy rainfall is unusual.

HURRICANE SEASON

The Atlantic hurricane season lasts from June 1 through November 30, but it's fairly rare to see a large storm in either June or November. Most major hurricanes occur between August and October, with the peak season in September.

Avoiding Storms. Keep in mind that hurricanes are more common the farther north in the Caribbean you go. The U.S. and British Virgin Islands experienced first-ever back-to-back Category 5 hurricanes in 2017. Tourism departments in both jurisdictions are good about keeping tabs on visitors' safety and security and organizing evacuations both prior to and after major storms.

Airlines. Airports are usually closed during hurricanes and flights are canceled, which results in a disruption of the steady flow of tourists in and out of affected islands. If you are scheduled to fly into an area where a hurricane is expected, check with your airline regularly and often. If flights are disrupted, airlines will usually allow you to rebook for a later date. You will not get a refund if you have booked a nonrefundable ticket nor, in most cases, will you be allowed to change your ticket to a different destination; rather, you will be expected to reschedule your trip for a later date.

Hotels and Resorts. If a hurricane warning is issued and flights to your destination are disrupted, virtually every USBVI resort will waive cancellation and change penalties and allow you to rebook your trip for a later date. Some will allow you to cancel if a hurricane threatens to strike, even if flights aren't canceled. Some will give you a refund if you have prepaid for your stay, while others will expect you to rebook your trip for a later date.

Travel Insurance. If you plan to travel to the USBVI during the hurricane season, it is wise to buy travel insurance that allows you to cancel for any reason. This kind of coverage can be expensive (up to 10% of the value of the trip); but if you have to prepay far in advance for an expensive vacation package, the peace of mind may be worth it. Just be sure to read the fine print; some policies don't kick in unless flights are canceled and the hurricane strikes, something you may not be assured of until the day you plan to travel. To get a complete cancellation policy, you must usually buy your insurance within a week of booking your trip. If you wait to purchase insurance until after the hurricane warning is issued, it will be too late.

Track Those Hurricanes. To keep a close eye on the Caribbean during hurricane season, several websites track hurricanes as they progress: ⊕ *www. accuweather.com*, ⊕ *hurricanetrack. com*, ⊕ *www.nhc.noaa.gov*, and ⊕ *www. weather.com*.

2

Travel Smart ESSENTIALS

On the Calendar

The USBVI's top seasonal events are listed here, and any one of them could provide the stuff of lasting memories. Contact local tourism authorities for exact dates and for more information.

January

Bordeaux Farmers Rastafari Agricultural & Cultural Vegan Food Fair. On St. Thomas, this annual three-day event over the Martin Luther King Jr. holiday weekend features locally grown produce, vegan foods, handicrafts, live music, and much more.

February

Celebration of Love. On Valentine's Day, St. John always hosts a free vow-renewal ceremony right on the beach at Trunk Bay.

St. Croix Agriculture and Food Fair. Every February, St. Croix celebrates its natural bounty with this food fair, also called "AgriFest." ⊕ www.viagrifest.org

Sweetheart of the Caribbean and Classic Yacht Regatta. The BVI's West End Yacht Club hosts this regatta over Valentine's Day weekend.

March

BVI Spring Regatta and Sailing Festival. More than 60 boats from the Caribbean, the United States, and Europe participate in three days of racing, with parties and sailing competitions on Tortola and Virgin Gorda. ⊕ www.bvispringregatta.org

St. Patrick's Day Parade. Locals and visitors alike gather in downtown Christiansted on St. Croix for the annual parade, complete with floats, bands, and green-costumed, stilt-walking Mocko Jumbies.

St. Thomas International Regatta. During late March, the St. Thomas Yacht Club hosts this regatta, which pulls in yachties from all over. ⊕ stthomasinternationalregatta.com

VI Jam Fest. Musicians from all over play for three days in venues across the U.S. Virgin Island of St. John. ⊕ www.vijamfest.com

April

Carnival, St. Thomas. Expect to see plenty of Mocko Jumbies, St. Thomas's otherworldly stilt walkers, during Carnival, which takes place right after Easter. ⊕ www.vicarnivalschedule.com/stthomas

Foxy's Wood Boat Regatta. Bringing together myriad older wooden boats for two days of racing excitement, this regatta on Jost Van Dyke has been sponsored by Foxy's and Tortola's West End Yacht Club for well over 30 years.

St. Croix Food and Wine Experience. Foodies will prosper when local restaurateurs get together for this four-day celebration of all things food related. One of the highlights is "A Taste of St. Croix," a special one-night event when the top restaurants on the island serve up their top dishes; the event often sells out the same day the highly coveted tickets become available. ⊕ stxfoodandwine.com

May

BVI Poker Run. North Sound, Virgin Gorda, is the start and finish of the run, where over 200 powerboats participate, culminating with a big beach party and live music at the finish.

June

International Optimist Regatta. The regatta happens on St. Thomas, with over 100 8- to 15-year-old junior sailors from around the world racing their 8-foot single-sail dinghies. ⊕ *stthomasyachtclub.org*

July

Carnival, St. John. The island celebrates with plenty of street celebrations and a huge parade on the 4th of July. ⊕ *www.vicarnivalschedule.com/stjohn*

July Open Tournament. The Virgin Islands Game Fishing Club hosts this event early in the month. There are categories for serious marlin anglers, just-for-fun fishermen, and even kids who want to try their luck from docks and rocks. ⊕ *www.vigfc.com*

August

Emancipation Festival, BVI. Also known as August Festival, the event celebrates the abolition of slavery in the Danish West Indies in 1848.

Texas Society of the Virgin Islands Chili Cookoff. St. Thomas's Brewers Bay Beach fills with themed booths on the third Sunday of the month for this annual cookoff.

October

The Moorings Interline Regatta, BVI. Kick off the boat-racing season with this annual regatta in the Caribbean's sailing capital. ⊕ *www.moorings.com/regattas-and-events/interline-regatta*

November

Annual Coral Bay Thanksgiving Regatta. On Thanksgiving weekend, the regatta brings together boat owners for a two-day race event sponsored by the Coral Bay Yacht Club.

Beauty & The Beast Triathlon. The St. Croix event attracts international-class athletes as well as amateurs for a 1.24-mile (2-km) swim, a 13.1-mile (21-km) run, and a 56-mile (90-km) bike ride; it includes a climb up the Beast on Route 69. ⊕ *www.stxtriathlon.com*

BVI Food Fete. From rum fests to seafood soirees and tastes of all the islands, the monthlong party is paradise for food lovers. ⊕ *bvifoodfete.com*

December

Crucian Christmas Festival, St. Croix. A nearly monthlong celebration coincides with the island's Christmas Carnival, ending January 6 with a huge parade. ⊕ *www.vicarnivalschedule.com*

Foxy's Old Year's Night Celebration. Ring in the New Year at Foxy's on Jost Van Dyke, where the annual party has been consistently ranked as one of the top 10 New Year's Eve parties in the world.

Contacts

Air

AIRPORT INFORMATION
Cyril E. King Airport. (*STT*).
✉ *Rte. 30, Lindbergh
Bay* ☎ *340/774–5100.*
Henry Rohlsen Airport.
(*STX*). ✉ *Airport Rd., off
Rte. 66, Christiansted*
☎ *340/778–1012.*

INTERISLAND CARRIERS
Air Sunshine. ☎ *800/327–
8900, 954/434–8900,
284/340–9999 in
Tortola, 284/495–8900
in BVI, 284/495–8989 in
Virgin Gorda* ⊕ *www.
airsunshine.com.* **Cape
Air.** ☎ *800/227–3247,
508/771–6944 outside
the U.S./USVI* ⊕ *www.
capeair.com.* **Fly BVI.**
☎ *284/340–1747 in BVI,
800/865–7652 toll-free,
706/550–1747 in U.S.* ⊕ *fly-
bvi.com.* **LIAT.** ☎ *888/844–
5428, 866/549–5428 in
Puerto Rico and USVI,
268/480–5601 in BVI*
⊕ *www.liat.com.* **Seaborne
Airlines.** ☎ *787/946–7800,
866/359–8784* ⊕ *www.
seaborneairlines.com.*

🛥 Ferry

Dolphin Water Taxi.
☎ *340/774–2628* ⊕ *www.
dolphinshuttle.com.*
**Inter-Island Boat Ser-
vice.** ☎ *340/776–6597*
⊕ *www.interislandboat-
services.com.* **Native
Son.** ☎ *340/774–8685 in
St. Thomas (Charlotte
Amalie), 284/495–4617*

*in Tortola (West End),
284/494–5674 in
Tortola (Road Town),
340/775–3111 in St.
Thomas (Red Hook)*
⊕ *www.nativesonferry.
com.* **New Horizon Ferry
Service.** ☎ *284/499–0952,
284/542–5959* ⊕ *www.
newhorizonferry.com.*
Norman Island Ferry.
☎ *284/443–1305* ⊕ *www.
piratesbight.com/getting-
here.htm.* **Road Town Fast
Ferry.** ☎ *284/494–2323 in
Tortola, 340/777–2800 in
St. Thomas, 284/340–3976
reservations* ⊕ *www.road-
townfastferry.com.* **Smith's
Ferry.** ☎ *340/775–7292 in
St. Thomas, 284/494–4454
in Tortola (Road Town),
284/495–4495 in Tortola
(West End)* ⊕ *www.bvifer-
ryservices.com.* **Speedy's
Ferries.** ☎ *284/495–5235,
284/495–5779, 284/495–
5240, 284/442–5240 Virgin
Gorda, 284/494–6154 Tor-
tola, 284/495–7141 Beef
Island, 340/714–5240 St.
Thomas* ⊕ *www.bviferries.
com.*

🚗 Car

Cool Breeze Car Rental.
☎ *340/776–6588* ⊕ *www.
coolbreezecarrental.com.*
Itgo Car Rental. ✉ *Mill Mall,
Wickham's Cay I, Road
Town* ☎ *284/494–5150,
284/494–2639* ⊕ *www.
itgobvi.com.* **Judi of
Croix.** ☎ *340/773–2123,
877/903–2123* ⊕ *www.*

judiofcroix.com. **L&S Jeep
Rental.** ☎ *284/495–5297*
⊕ *www.landsjeeprental.
com.* **St. John Car Rental.**
✉ *Bay St., near Wharf-
side Village, Cruz Bay*
☎ *340/776–6103* ⊕ *www.
stjohncarrental.com.*

🛏 Lodging

**VILLA MANAGEMENT
COMPANIES Catered to
Vacation Homes.** ✉ *Mar-
ketplace Suite 206,
5206 Enighed, Cruz
Bay* ☎ *340/776–6641,
800/424–6641* ⊕ *www.
cateredto.com.* **Vacation
St. Croix.** ✉ *400 La Grande
Princess, Christiansted*
☎ *340/718–0361* ⊕ *www.
vacationstcroix.com.*

📍 Visitor Information

BVI Tourist Board.
☎ *212/563–3117, 800/835–
8530 in the U.S.* ⊕ *www.
bvitourism.com.* **USVI Tourist Board.** ☎ *800/372–8784*
⊕ *www.visitusvi.com.*

Chapter 3

ST. THOMAS

Updated by
Carol Bareuther

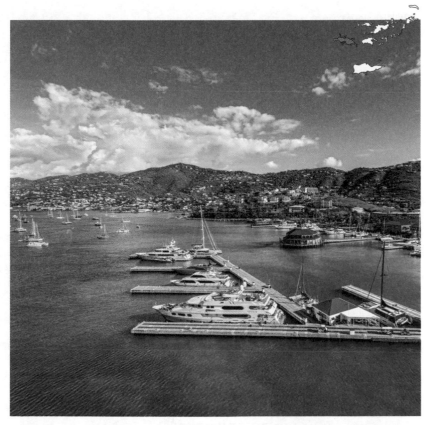

⊙ Sights	🍴 Restaurants	🛏 Hotels	💼 Shopping	🍸 Nightlife
★★★☆☆	★★★★☆	★★★★☆	★★★★★	★★☆☆☆

WELCOME TO ST. THOMAS

TOP REASONS TO GO

★ **Shop 'til you drop:** Find great deals on duty-free jewelry, timepieces, and electronics along Charlotte Amalie's Main Street—but don't forget to pick up some locally made crafts as well.

★ **Tell fish stories:** Go in search of magnificent blue marlins and other trophy-worthy fish in the waters around St. Thomas from June through October.

★ **Get your sea legs:** Charter a yacht (or just take a regularly scheduled day sail) to cruise between the islands any time of year. It's a short hop to the British Virgin Islands from St. Thomas.

★ **Step back in time:** Take a self-guided walking tour of the historic sights in Charlotte Amalie, including Fort Christian, Government House, and the Synagogue, to imagine life when Denmark ruled the islands.

★ **Take a dip:** Swim at Magens Bay, considered by many to be one of the most beautiful beaches in the world.

ATLANTIC OCEAN

Picara Pt.

Hans
Lollick

The General
Rogers

Magens
Bay

Lovelund Bay

Mandal Pt.

Thatch
Cay

Grass Cay and
Congo Cay

Mahogany Run
Golf Course

Magens
Bay

42

Tutu Bay

Coki Beach

Signal
Hill

Matolie

Mandal

Lindquist Beach

40

Frenchtown

Charlotte Amalie

38

Frydendal

TO
Cabes Pt.
XXXX
38

St. Thomas
Harbor

Tutu

Sapphire Beach
Redhook Bay

Paradise
Pt.

Vessup
Beach

TO
ST. JOHN

Hassel
Island

32

Morning
Star Beach

30

Red Hook

Cow and
Calf Rocks

Limestone
Bay

Nadir

Great
Bay

Great
St. James
Island

TO
XXXX

Coculus
Pt.

Jersey Bay

Secret
Harbour

St. James
Bay

Long Pt.

Little
St. James
Island

TO
ST. JOHN

Frenchcap

Caribbean Sea

0   2 miles

0   3 km

EATING AND DRINKING WELL IN THE VIRGIN ISLANDS

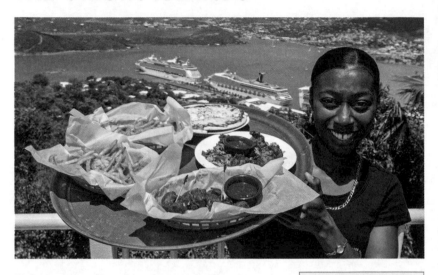

Take a mix of local and imported ingredients—everything from papaya to salt cod. Blend this with the cooking styles of the indigenous Ciboney, Carib, and Arawak peoples, plus those who immigrated from Africa, Europe, Asia, and beyond, and you have the rich melting pot that is traditional Virgin Islands cuisine.

Despite its American-flag status and the abundant fast-food and Continental-style restaurants that dominate the islands, the traditional cuisine of the Virgin Islands still maintains a foothold here. The best places to sample the authentic flavors of the islands are local restaurants, bakeries, and mobile food vans, as well as the many food fairs and fish fries that take place throughout the year. When you order an entrée—a "plate of food" as a meal is called—it will often be accompanied by a green salad and a choice of three filling, starchy side dishes, all packed with fresh ingredients and bold flavors. —Carol Bareuther

SNACKS

Be sure to try the popular **Caribbean pate** *(pah-teh)*, a triangular fried pastry stuffed with spicy ground beef, conch, or salted fish. And nothing beats **mango-ade**, **passion fruit punch**, or **soursop juice** to tame the heat (pates often boast a touch of fiery Scotch bonnet peppers among their ingredients). For a tamer snack, look for **johnnycakes** (fried cornmeal cakes) or hush puppy–like **conch fritters.** Another refresher is **coconut water**, the nectar of cracked coconuts.

FRUIT

Tropical fruits are abundant throughout the islands. Make sure to sample juicy, sweet mangoes, floral-scented papaya (great with a squeeze of lime), tart star fruit (bite into it or slice it up), and finger-long fig bananas, which are sweeter than stateside-purchased varieties. Other favorites include soursop, passion fruit, coconuts (both young and mature), guava, and pineapple.

VEGETABLES

Common vegetables include okra, spinach and other greens, sweet potatoes, eggplants, green plantains, and gnarly root vegetables like tannia, cassava, and boniato. *Kallaloo* is a popular soupy vegetable stew made with spinach and okra, seasoned with fresh herbs, and further flavored with crab, fish, or ham.

SEAFOOD

Popular fish varieties include snapper, grouper, yellowtail, mahimahi, and wahoo, which are often fried or grilled and served whole. Lobster and conch also are prevalent, the latter appearing in everything from ceviche salads to soups. The unofficial national dish for the Virgin Islands is "fish and fungi," simmered fish with okra-studded cornmeal mush.

MEAT

Meat plays a prominent role in soups on the islands. Goat water (mutton stew) and souse (pig-foot stew) make hearty meals, and are typically served with dumplings or bread. Curried goat is a classic dish worth a taste. For something less spicy, try simply prepared chicken and rice.

STARCHES

Don't be thrown off by unexpected naming conventions. For example, "peas and rice" may be made with red beans, kidney beans, or black beans (no peas). Potato stuffing, a mix of mashed white potatoes, tomato sauce, and seasonings, isn't used to stuff anything. And "fungi" (fun-gee) is not mushrooms, but a polentalike dish of African origin made from cornmeal studded with chopped okra. More straightforward are the fried plantains, and boiled sweet potatoes, yams, and tannia.

DRINKS

Rum, made from sugarcane, has a significant history in the Virgin Islands, dating back to the rise of sugarcane plantations in the mid-1700s. Rum is still produced here, and it's available in numerous styles (and flavors). For a lower-proof sipper, try *mauby*, a bitter, root beer–like drink made from the bark of the mauby tree.

Because it's the transportation hub of the Virgin Islands, most visitors land on hilly St. Thomas even if they don't linger. Visitors who stay longer may be drawn by the legendary shopping and the wide variety of water sports, activities, beaches, and accommodations. The bustling port of Charlotte Amalie is the main town, while Red Hook sits on the eastern tip. The west end of the island is relatively wild, and hotels and resorts rim the southern and eastern shores.

If you fly to the 32-square-mile (83-square-km) island of St. Thomas, you land at its western end; if you arrive by cruise ship, you come into one of the world's most beautiful harbors. Either way, one of your first sights is the town of Charlotte Amalie. From the harbor you see an idyllic-looking village that spreads into the lower hills. If you were expecting a quiet hamlet with its inhabitants hanging out under palm trees, you've missed that era by about 300 years. Although other islands in the USVI developed plantation economies, St. Thomas cultivated its harbor, and it became a thriving seaport soon after it was settled by the Danish in the 1600s.

The success of the naturally perfect harbor was enhanced by the fact that the Danes—who ruled St. Thomas with only a couple of short interruptions from 1666 to 1917—avoided involvement in some 100 years' worth of European wars. Denmark was the only European country with colonies in the Caribbean to stay neutral during the War of the Spanish Succession in the early 1700s. Accordingly, products of the Dutch, English, and French islands—sugar, cotton, and indigo—were traded through Charlotte Amalie, along with regular shipments of slaves (emancipation came in 1848). When the Spanish wars ended, trade fell off, but by the end of the 1700s Europe was at war again, Denmark again remained neutral, and St. Thomas continued to prosper. Even into the 1800s, while the economies of St. Croix and St. John foundered with the market for sugarcane, St. Thomas's economy remained vigorous. This prosperity led to the development of shipyards, a well-organized banking system, and a large merchant class. In 1845 Charlotte Amalie had 101 large importing houses owned by the English, French, Germans, Haitians, Spaniards, Americans, Sephardim, and Danes.

Charlotte Amalie is still one of the world's most active cruise-ship ports. On almost any day at least one and sometimes as many as eight cruise ships are tied to the docks or anchored outside the harbor. Gently rocking in the shadows of these giant floating hotels are just about every other kind of vessel imaginable: sleek sailing mono- and multihulls that will take you on a sunset cruise complete with rum punch and a Jimmy Buffett soundtrack, private megayachts that spirit busy executives away, and barnacle-bottom sloops—with laundry draped over the lifelines—that are home to world-cruising ramblers. Huge container ships pull up in Subbase, west of the harbor, bringing in everything from breakfast cereals to tires. Anchored right along the waterfront are down-island barges that ply the waters between the Greater Antilles and the Leeward Islands, transporting goods like refrigerators and disposable diapers.

The waterfront road through Charlotte Amalie was once part of the harbor. Before it was filled in to build the highway, the beach came right up to the back door of the warehouses that now line the thoroughfare. Two hundred years ago those warehouses were filled with indigo, tobacco, and cotton. Today the stone buildings house silk, crystal, linens, and leather. Fragrances are still traded, but by island beauty queens in air-conditioned perfume palaces instead of through open market stalls. The pirates of old used St. Thomas as a base from which to raid merchant ships of every nation, though they were particularly fond of the gold- and silver-laden treasure ships heading to Spain. Pirates are still around, but today's versions use St. Thomas as a drop-off for their contraband: illegal immigrants and drugs.

Planning

Getting Here and Around

AIR
American, Delta, JetBlue, Spirit, and United fly to St. Thomas from the United States. Cape Air and Seaborne Airlines fly from San Juan.

BUS
On St. Thomas the island's large buses make public transportation a very comfortable—though slow—way to get from east and west to Charlotte Amalie and back (service to the north is limited). Buses run about every 30 minutes from stops that are clearly marked with Vitran signs. Fares are $1 between outlying areas and town and 75¢ for journeys within town. Some open-air safari cabs also follow the bus routes, and these drivers charge $1 for short trips in town—hence their nickname "dollar buses"—or $2 for longer trips to places like Tutu or Red Hook.

CAR
You will want to rent a car if you are staying in a private villa, but if you are staying in a hotel on the beach, you can usually get by with taxis, though getting a taxi every day can be expensive. If you are a family or group of four, then a car can be a more cost-effective solution since taxi rates are per person.

Traffic can be bad, especially in Charlotte Amalie at rush hour (7 to 9 and 4:30 to 6). If you need to get from an East End resort to the airport during these times, find the alternate route (starting from the East End, Route 38 to 42 to 40 to 33) that goes up the mountain and then drops you back onto Veterans Highway. All drivers should get a copy of *Road Map St. Thomas–St. John*, available on the island anywhere you find maps and guidebooks. In addition, most GPS units will work in the Virgin Islands and some car-rental agencies will rent out GPS devices.

CAR RENTALS

Major car-rental companies, including Avis, Budget, and Hertz, have locations at the airport; Avis and Budget also have branch offices. Local rental companies include Discount Car Rental and Paradise Rental Car.

CONTACTS Avis. ✉ *Cyril E. King Airport, 70 Lindbergh Bay, Lindbergh Bay ✈ 4 miles (6½ km) west of Charlotte Amalie* ☎ *340/774–1468* ⊕ *www.avis. com.* **Budget.** ✉ *Cyril E. King Airport, 70 Lindbergh Bay, Lindbergh Bay ✈ 4 miles (6½ km) west of Charlotte Amalie* ☎ *340/776–5774* ⊕ *www.budgetstt. com.* **Discount Car Rental.** ✉ *Cyril E. King Airport, 70 Lindbergh Bay ✈ 4 miles (6½ km) west of Charlotte Amalie; car rental is located adjacent to the entrance road of the airport, 1 min from the terminal* ☎ *340/643–4222, 877/478–2833* ⊕ *www. discountcar.vi.* **Hertz.** ✉ *Cyril E. King Airport, 70 Lindbergh Bay, Lindbergh Bay ✈ 4 miles (6½ km) west of Charlotte Amalie* ☎ *340/774–1879* ⊕ *www.hertz. com.* **Paradise Rental Car.** ✉ *Cyril E. King Airport, 70 Lindbergh Bay* ☎ *340/643– 2692* ⊕ *www.pdiseinc.com.*

ScooterVI

Scooters and motorbikes for rent by the day ($65–$75) or week ($230–$245). Rental fee includes helmet, tank of gas, and island map. ✉ *9717 Estate Thomas No. 1, Rte. 30, Havensight ✈ Across from the main Havensight Mall gate, between Al Cohen Mall and Guardian Insurance Plaza* ☎ *340/774–5840* ⊕ *www. scootervi.com.*

FERRY

There's frequent service from St. Thomas to St. John and Tortola, and less frequent service to Virgin Gorda and Jost Van Dyke. Virgin Islands ferry schedules are published on the website of ⊕ *www.VInow.com.* There's also a ferry from Charlotte Amalie's waterfront to Marriott's Frenchman's Cove resort. In St. Thomas, ferries leave from both Charlotte Amalie and Red Hook. Remember that a passport is now required to travel between the USVI and BVI by ferry. Schedules change, so you should confirm current schedules with the ferry companies.

CONTACTS VInow.com. ⊕ *www.vinow. com.*

TAXI

USVI taxis charge per person and have set prices. Drivers usually take multiple fares, especially from the airport, ferry docks, and the cruise-ship terminal. Most taxis are either safari-style or enclosed, air-conditioned vans. They can be hailed on the street (especially in town and near major shopping malls and attractions) and can also be called by telephone. There are taxi stands in Charlotte Amalie across from Emancipation Garden (in front of Little Switzerland, behind the post office) and along the waterfront. V.I. Taxi Association has exclusive rights to pick up customers at Cyril E. King Airport, Havensight Cruise Ship Dock, Yacht Haven Grande, Marriott's Frenchman's Cove resort, and Sapphire Beach Resort. *There is no Uber, Lyft, or other ride-share option here.*

CONTACTS Dial-A-Ride St. Thomas. ✉ *Knud Hansen Complex, 1303 Hospital Ground, adjacent to Lionel Roberts Stadium* ☎ *340/776–1277.* **East End Taxi.** ✉ *Urman Victor Fredericks Marine Terminal, 6117 Red Hook Quarters, off Rte. 38, Red Hook* ☎ *340/775–6974.* **Islander Taxi Services.** ✉ *Fortress Storage, Bldg. K, Suite 2025, at the intersection of Rtes. 313 and 38, Charlotte Amalie* ☎ *340/774–4077* ⊕ *www.islandertaxiservice.com.* **Virgin Islands Taxi Association.** ✉ *68A Estate Contant, Charlotte Amalie* ☎ *340/774– 4550, 340/774–7457* ⊕ *vitaxiassociation. com.*

Essentials

BANKS
The major banks on St. Thomas are First Bank, Banco Popular, and Oriental (formerly Scotia Bank), each of which has several branches in convenient locations.

BEACHES
All 44 St. Thomas beaches are open to the public, although you can reach some of them only by walking through a resort. Hotel guests frequently have access to lounge chairs and floats that are off-limits to nonguests; for this reason, you may feel more comfortable at one of the beaches not associated with a resort, such as Magens Bay (which charges an entrance fee to cover beach maintenance) or Coki Beach. Whichever one you choose, remember to remove your valuables from the car and keep them out of sight when you go swimming.

HOTELS
You can let yourself be pampered at a luxurious resort on the eastern end of the island, many of which are self-contained and feel like islands unto themselves. Or, if your means are more modest, you can find cheaper hotels in lovely settings throughout the island. There are also guesthouses and inns with great views (if not a beach at your door) and great service at about half the cost of what you'll pay at the beachfront pleasure palaces. Many of these are west and north of Charlotte Amalie or in the overlooking hills—ideal if you want the peace and quiet afforded by a lush, junglelike landscape. There are also inexpensive lodgings (most right in town) that are perfect if you just want a clean room to return to after a day of exploring or beach bumming. East End condominium complexes are popular with families, and close to the ferry dock in Red Hook that makes island-hopping to St. John or the British Virgin Islands a breeze. Although condos are pricey, they have full kitchens, and you can definitely save money by cooking for yourself—especially if you bring some of your own nonperishable food. Though you may spend some time laboring in the kitchen, many condos ease your burden with daily maid service and on-site restaurants; a few also have resort amenities, including pools and tennis courts. There is also a selection of Airbnbs for rent, from studios to five- and six-bedroom homes.

Hotel reviews have been shortened. For full information, visit Fodors.com.

PRIVATE VILLAS
St. Thomas has a wide range of private villas, from modest two-bedroom houses to luxurious five-or-more-bedroom mansions. Most will require that you book for seven nights during high season, five in low season. A minimum stay of up to two weeks is often required during the holiday season.

You can arrange private villa rentals through various agents that represent luxury residences and usually have both websites and brochures that show photos of the properties they represent. Some are suitable for travelers with disabilities, but be sure to ask specific questions regarding your own needs.

Calypso Realty
☎ 340/774–1620, 800/747–4858 ⊕ www.calypsorealty.com.

McLaughlin-Anderson Luxury Caribbean Villas
Handling rental villas throughout the U.S. Virgin Islands, British Virgin Islands, and Grenada, McLaughlin-Anderson has a good selection of complexes in St. Thomas's East End. ☎ 340/776–0635, 800/537–6246 ⊕ www.mclaughlinanderson.com.

RESTAURANTS
The beauty of St. Thomas and its sister islands has attracted a cadre of professionally trained chefs who know their way around fresh fish and local fruits. You can dine on everything from terrific

cheap local dishes such as goat water (a spicy stew) and fungi (a cornmeal polentalike side dish) to imports such as hot pastrami sandwiches and raspberries in crème fraîche.

Restaurants are spread all over the island, although fewer are found in the west and northwest sections. Most restaurants out of town are easily accessible by taxi and have ample parking. If you dine in Charlotte Amalie, take a taxi. Parking close to restaurants can be difficult to find.

WHAT IT COSTS in U.S. Dollars

$	$$	$$$	$$$$
RESTAURANTS			
under $13	$13–$20	$21–$30	over $30
HOTELS			
under $276	$276–$375	$376–$475	over $475

SAFETY

To be safe, keep your hotel or vacation villa door locked at all times, stick to well-lighted streets at night, and use the same kind of street sense that you would in any unfamiliar territory. Don't wander the streets of Charlotte Amalie alone at night. If you plan to carry things around, rent a car—not an open-air vehicle—and lock possessions in the trunk. Keep your rental car locked wherever you park. Don't leave cameras, purses, and other valuables lying on the beach while you snorkel for an hour (or even for a minute), no matter how many people are nearby.

SIGHTS

To explore outside Charlotte Amalie, rent a car or hire a taxi. Your rental car should come with a good map and perhaps a GPS unit; if not, pick up the pocket-size Road Map St. Thomas–St. John at a tourist information center. Roads are marked with route numbers, but they're confusing and seem to switch numbers suddenly. Roads are also identified by signs bearing the St. Thomas–St. John Hotel and Tourism Association's mascot, Tommy the Starfish. More than 100 of these color-coded signs line the island's main routes. Orange signs trace the route from the airport to Red Hook; green signs identify the road from town to Magens Bay; Tommy's face on a yellow background points from Mafolie to Crown Bay through the north side; red signs lead from Smith Bay to Four Corners via Skyline Drive; and blue signs mark the route from the cruise-ship dock at Havensight to Red Hook. These color-coded routes are not marked on most visitor maps, however. Allow yourself a day to explore, especially if you want to stop to take pictures or to enjoy a light bite or refreshing swim. Most gas stations are in town or on the island's more populated eastern side, so fill up before heading to the north side. And remember to drive on the left!

NIGHTLIFE

On any given night, especially in season, you can find steel-pan orchestras, rock and roll, piano music, jazz, broken-bottle dancing (actual dancing atop broken glass), disco, and karaoke. Pick up a free copy of the bright-yellow Virgin Islands This Week magazine when you arrive (it can be found at the airport, in stores, and in hotel lobbies). The back pages list who's playing where. The Friday edition of the Virgin Islands Daily News carries complete listings for the upcoming weekend.

SHOPPING

St. Thomas lives up to its billing as a duty-free shopping destination. Even if shopping isn't your idea of how to spend a vacation, you still may want to slip in on a quiet day (check the cruise-ship listings—Monday and Sunday are usually the least crowded) to browse. Among the best buys are liquor, linens, china, crystal (most stores will ship), and jewelry. The amount of jewelry available makes this one of the few items for which comparison shopping is worth the effort. Local crafts include shell jewelry, carved calabash bowls, straw brooms, woven baskets, and dolls. Creations by local doll maker Sally George—like her school-uniformed West Indian children and Mocko Jumbie dolls—have been little goodwill ambassadors, bought by visitors around the world. Spice mixes, hot sauces, and tropical jams and jellies are other native products.

On St. Thomas, stores on Main Street in Charlotte Amalie are open weekdays and Saturday 9 to 5. The hours of the shops in the Havensight Mall (next to the cruise-ship dock) and the Crown Bay Commercial Center (next to the Crown Bay cruise-ship dock) are the same, though occasionally some stay open until 9 on Friday, depending on how many cruise ships are anchored nearby. You may also find some shops open on Sunday if cruise ships are in port. Hotel shops are usually open evenings as well.

There's no sales tax in the USVI, and you can take advantage of the $1,600 duty-free allowance per family member (remember to save your receipts). Although you can find the occasional salesclerk who will make a deal, bartering isn't the norm.

VISITOR INFORMATION
CONTACTS U.S. Virgin Islands Hotel and Tourism Association. ☎ *340/774–6835* ⊕ *usvihta.com.* **USVI Department of Tourism.** ✉ *74B & 75 Kronprindsens Gade, Charlotte Amalie ✛ Downtown, behind the old USO building and public restrooms* ☎ *340/774–8784, 800/372–8784* ⊕ *www.visitusvi.com.*

Charlotte Amalie

Look beyond the pricey shops, T-shirt vendors, and bustling crowds for a glimpse of the island's history. The city served as the capital of Denmark's outpost in the Caribbean until 1917, an

aspect of the island often lost in the glitz of the shopping district.

Emancipation Gardens, right next to the fort, is a good place to start a walking tour. Tackle the hilly part of town first: head north up Government Hill to the historic buildings that house government offices and have incredible views. Several regal churches line the route that runs west back to the town proper and the old-time market. Virtually all the alleyways that intersect Main Street lead to eateries that serve frosty drinks, sandwiches, and West Indian fare. There are public restrooms in this area, too. Allow an hour for a quick view of the sights.

A note about the street names: in deference to the island's heritage, the streets downtown are labeled by their Danish names. Locals will use both the Danish name and the English name (such as Dronningens Gade and Norre Gade for Main Street), but most people refer to things by their location ("a block toward the Waterfront off Main Street" or "next to the Little Switzerland Shop"). You may find it more useful if you ask for directions by shop names or landmarks.

Sights

All Saints Episcopal Church
RELIGIOUS SITE | Built in 1848 from stone quarried on the island, the church has thick, arched window frames lined with the yellow brick that came to the islands as ballast aboard ships. Merchants left the brick on the waterfront when they filled their boats with molasses, sugar, mahogany, and rum for the return voyage. The church was built in celebration of the end of slavery in the USVI. ✉ *13 Commandant Gade, near the Emancipation Garden U.S. Post Office, Charlotte Amalie* ☎ *340/774–0217.*

Educators Park
MEMORIAL | A peaceful place amid the town's hustle and bustle, the park has memorials for three famous Virgin

Islanders: educator Edith Williams, J. Antonio Jarvis (a founder of the *Daily News*), and educator and author Rothschild Francis. The last gave many speeches here. ⊠ *Main St., across from Emancipation Garden post office, Charlotte Amalie.*

Edward Wilmoth Blyden IV Marine Terminal

MARINA | Locally called Tortola Wharf, this is where you can catch the *Native Son* and other ferries to the BVI. The restaurant upstairs is a good place to watch the Charlotte Amalie harbor traffic and sip an iced tea. Next door is the Charles F. Blair Jr. Seaplane Terminal, where Seaborne Airlines offers service to St. Croix, the BVI, and Puerto Rico. ⊠ *Veterans Dr., across from the Windward Passage Hotel, Charlotte Amalie* ☎ *340/774–1629* ⊕ *www.viport.com.*

Emancipation Garden

GARDEN | A bronze bust of a freed slave blowing a conch shell commemorates slavery's end in 1848—the garden was built to mark emancipation's 150th anniversary in 1998. The gazebo here is used for official ceremonies. Two other monuments show the island's Danish-American connection—a bust of Denmark's King Christian and a scaled-down model of the U.S. Liberty Bell. ⊠ *Between Tolbod Gade and Fort Christian, next to Vendor's Plaza, Charlotte Amalie.*

Fort Christian

MILITARY SITE | **FAMILY** | St. Thomas's oldest standing structure, this remarkable building was built between 1672 and 1680 and now has U.S. National Historic Landmark status. Over the years, it was used as a jail, governor's residence, town hall, courthouse, and church. In 2005, a multimillion-dollar renovation project started to stabilize the structure and halt centuries of deterioration. This project was completed in 2017 in time to commemorate the territory's centennial, or 100 years after the United States purchased the islands from Denmark in 1917. Inside, there is a museum;

guided tours start at 10 am and 1:45 pm. Outside, look for historic features, like the four renovated faces of the famous 19th-century clock tower. ⊠ *Waterfront Hwy., east of shopping district, Charlotte Amalie* ☎ *340/714–3678* ⊠ *$10* ⊙ *Closed weekends.*

Franklin D. Roosevelt Memorial Park

CITY PARK | **FAMILY** | The former Coconut Park was renamed in honor of Franklin D. Roosevelt in 1945. It's a great place to put your feet up and people-watch. Five granite pedestals represent the five branches of the military, bronze urns commemorate special events and can be lighted, and inscribed bronze plaques pay tribute to the territory's veterans who died defending the United States. There's also a children's playground. ⊠ *Intersection of Norre Gade and Rte. 35, adjacent to the Memorial Moravian Church, Charlotte Amalie* ☎ *340/774–5541* ⊕ *www.stthomashistoricaltrust.org.*

Frederick Evangelical Lutheran Church

RELIGIOUS SITE | This historic church has a massive mahogany altar, and its pews—each with its own door—were once rented to families of the congregation. Lutheranism is the state religion of Denmark, and when the territory was without a minister, the governor—who had his own elevated pew—filled in. ⊠ *7 Norre Gade, across from Emancipation Garden and the Grand Hotel, Charlotte Amalie* ☎ *340/776–1315.*

Gallery Camille Pissarro

MUSEUM | Housing an antiques shop and an art gallery, this was the birthplace and childhood home of the acclaimed 19th-century impressionist painter Camille Pissarro, who lived for most of his adult life in France. The art gallery on the second floor contains three original pages from Pissarro's sketchbook and two pastels by Pissarro's grandson, Claude. ⊠ *14 Dronningens Gade (Main St.), between Raadets Gade and Trompeter Gade, Charlotte Amalie.*

Charlotte Amalie

KEY
- ● Sights
- ● Restaurants
- ● Hotels

Fort Christian (1672–80), the oldest surviving structure in St. Thomas

Government House

GOVERNMENT BUILDING | Built in 1867, this neoclassical, white, brick-and-wood structure houses the offices of the governor of the Virgin Islands. Outside, the bright red Danish-style guard house is a perfect place for a photo. The view of the harbor is picture-postcard pretty from the First Lady's garden directly across the street. ■ **TIP→ The inside of the building is currently closed to visitors.** ✉ *Government Hill, 21–22 Kongens Gade, Charlotte Amalie* ⊹ *On the hill above the Frederick Lutheran Church* ☎ *340/774–0001* 🖃 *Free.*

Grand Galleria

HISTORIC SITE | This imposing building stands at the head of Main Street. Once the island's premier hotel, it has been converted into offices, shops, and a deli. ✉ *43-46 Norre Gade, at intersection of Tolbod Gade, adjacent to Emancipation Garden, Charlotte Amalie* ☎ *340/774–7282.*

Hassel Island

ISLAND | East of Water Island in Charlotte Amalie harbor, Hassel Island is part of the Virgin Islands National Park. On it are the ruins of a British military garrison (built during a brief British occupation of the USVI during the 1800s) and the remains of a marine railway (where ships were hoisted into dry dock for repairs). Daily guided kayak tours to the island are available from VI Ecotours. The St. Thomas Historical Trust leads three-hour walking tours throughout the year. ✉ *Charlotte Amalie harbor, Charlotte Amalie* ☎ *340/776–6201 Virgin Islands National Park main office* ⊕ *www.nps.gov/viis.*

Hebrew Congregation of St. Thomas

RELIGIOUS SITE | The synagogue's Hebrew name, *Beracha Veshalom Vegmiluth Hasidim,* translates as the Congregation of Blessing, Peace, and Loving Deeds. The small building's white pillars contrast with rough stone walls, as does the rich mahogany of the pews and altar. The sand on the floor symbolizes the exodus from Egypt. Since the synagogue first opened its doors in 1833, it has held a weekly service, making it the oldest synagogue building in continuous use under the American flag and the second-oldest (after the one on Curaçao) in the western hemisphere. Guided tours can be arranged. Brochures detailing the key structures and history are also available. Next door the Weibel Museum showcases Jewish history on St. Thomas. ⊠ *Synagogue Hill, 15 Crystal Gade, Charlotte Amalie ✛ From Main St., walk up Raadet's Gade (H. Stern is on the corner) to the top of the hill, turn left and synagogue is the 2nd bldg. on right* ☎ *340/774–4312* ⊕ *www.synagogue.vi.*

Legislature Building
GOVERNMENT BUILDING | Its lime green colonial-style exterior is the face of the vociferous political wrangling of the Virgin Islands Senate. Constructed originally by the Danish as a police barracks, the building was later used to billet U.S. Marines, and much later it housed a public school. You're welcome to sit in on sessions in the upstairs chambers. ⊠ *Waterfront Hwy. (aka Rte. 30), across from Fort Christian, Charlotte Amalie* ☎ *340/774–0880* ⊕ *www.legvi.org.*

Market Square
MARKET | Locals gather daily—especially by 4 am on Saturday mornings—at what was once a slave market in the 18th-century, to sell local fruits such as mangoes and papayas, root vegetables, and bunches of fresh herbs. Sidewalk vendors offer brightly colored fabrics, tie-dyed clothing, and handicrafts at good prices. A smaller number of vendors set up shop here all week long. ⊠ *Main St., at Strand Gade, Charlotte Amalie* ☎ *340/774–5182.*

Memorial Moravian Church
RELIGIOUS SITE | Built in 1884, this church was named to commemorate the 150th anniversary of the Moravian Church in the Virgin Islands. ⊠ *17 Norre Gade, next to Roosevelt Park, Charlotte Amalie* ☎ *340/776–0066.*

Big Event

April is a great time to visit St. Thomas, as the island comes alive for Carnival. The celebrations—steel-drum music, colorful costumes, and dancing in the streets—culminate the last weekend of the month.

99 Steps
NEIGHBORHOOD | This staircase "street," built by the Danes in the 1700s, leads to the residential area above Charlotte Amalie and to Blackbeard's Castle, a U.S. National Historic Landmark. If you count the stairs as you go up, you'll discover, as thousands have before you, that there are more than the name implies. ⊠ *Charlotte Amalie ✛ Look for steps heading north from Government Hill.*

Saints Peter and Paul Cathedral
RELIGIOUS SITE | This building was consecrated as a parish church in 1848, and serves as the seat of the territory's Roman Catholic diocese. The ceiling and walls are covered with 11 murals depicting biblical scenes; they were painted in 1899 by two Belgian artists, Father Leo Servais and Brother Ildephonsus. The marble altar and walls were added in the 1960s. Over a dozen statues of handcrafted saints represent the many nationalities of the congregants who worship here. ⊠ *22-AB Kronprindsens Gade, 1 block west of Market Sq., Charlotte Amalie* ☎ *340/774–0201* ⊕ *cathedralvi. com.*

St. Thomas Reformed Church
RELIGIOUS SITE | This church has an austere loveliness that's amazing considering all it's been through. Founded in 1744, it's been rebuilt twice after fires and hurricanes. The unembellished cream-color hall is quite peaceful. The only other color is the forest green of the shutters and the carpet. Call ahead if you wish

to visit at a particular time, as the doors are sometimes locked. Services are held at 9 am each Sunday. ⊠ *5 Crystal Gade at Nye Gade, Charlotte Amalie ✛ 1½ blocks north of Main St.* ☎ *340/776–8255* ⊕ *www.stthomasreformedchurch.org.*

U.S. Post Office

GOVERNMENT BUILDING | While you buy stamps, contemplate the murals of waterfront scenes by *Saturday Evening Post* artist Stephen Dohanos. His art was commissioned as part of the Works Project Administration in the 1930s. ⊠ *Tolbod Gade and Main St., 5046 Norre Gade, next to Emancipation Garden, Charlotte Amalie* ☎ *340/774–3750.*

Vendors Plaza

MARKET | **FAMILY** | Here merchants sell everything from T-shirts to leather goods. Look for local art among the ever-changing selections at this busy market. ⊠ *Waterfront, west of Fort Christian, Charlotte Amalie.*

★ Water Island

ISLAND | **FAMILY** | This island, the fourth largest of the U.S. Virgin Islands, floats about a ¼ mile (½ km) out in Charlotte Amalie harbor. A ferry between Crown Bay Marina and the island ($10 round-trip) operates several times daily, Monday through Saturday from 7 to 6 and Sunday and holidays 8 to 6. From the ferry dock, it's a hike of less than half a mile to Honeymoon Beach (though you have to go up a big hill), where Brad Pitt and Cate Blanchett filmed a scene of the movie *The Curious Case of Benjamin Button.* Get lunch from a food truck, which pulls up daily. Monday night is Movie Night at Honeymoon Beach, a fun activity for the whole family after a day on the beach. ⊠ *Charlotte Amalie harbor, Water Island* ☎ *340/690–4159 for ferry info.*

Weibel Museum

MUSEUM | This museum next to the Synagogue of Beracha Veshalom showcases 300 years of Jewish history on St. Thomas. The small gift shop sells a commemorative silver coin celebrating the anniversary of the Hebrew congregation's establishment on the island in 1796. There are also tropically inspired items, such as menorahs painted to resemble palm trees. ⊠ *Synagogue Hill, 15 Crystal Gade, Charlotte Amalie ✛ From Main St., walk up Raadets Gade (H. Stern is on the corner) to the top of the hill; turn left and it's the 2nd bldg. on the right* ☎ *340/774–4312* ⊕ *synagogue. vi* ⌨ *Free.*

🍴 Restaurants

★ Amalia Café

$$$$ | **SPANISH** | A great place to take a break and get a bite while shopping, this open-air café tucked into the alleyway of Palm Passage serves authentic Spanish cuisine for lunch and dinner. Try tapas such as mussels in brandy sauce, escargots with mushrooms and herb butter, or Galician-style octopus and baby eels served in a sizzling garlic sauce. **Known for:** authentic paella; caramel flan. ⑤ *Average main: $32* ⊠ *Palm Passage, 24 Dronnigens Gade, facing the Waterfront, Charlotte Amalie* ☎ *340/714–7373* ⊕ *www.amaliacafe.com* ۞ *Closed Sun.*

Café Amici

$$ | **ITALIAN** | Within the historic stonework and cascading tropical blossoms of A.H. Riise Alley, this charming open-air eatery will pull you in by the nose and send you straight to the wood-burning brick-oven pizza. **Known for:** pizza, subs, and pasta; popular with the local business crowd; alfresco seating. ⑤ *Average main: $18* ⊠ *37 Main St., in the A.H. Riise Mall, Charlotte Amalie* ☎ *340/714–7704* ۞ *No dinner. Closed Sun.*

★ Gladys' Cafe

$$ | **CARIBBEAN** | This cozy alleyway restaurant is rich in atmosphere, with its mahogany bar and native stone walls, making dining a double delight. Try the local specialties like conch in butter sauce, jerk pork, or panfried yellowtail

In Search of Pirates

The line between fact and fiction is often fluid, and it ebbs and flows according to who is telling the tale. So it is with the swashbuckling seafarers of St. Thomas, such as Bluebeard, Blackbeard, and Sir Francis Drake. But you'll find the story—we don't promise that it's completely true—if you follow the pirate trail.

Start atop Bluebeard's Hill to the east of Charlotte Amalie. Today this is the site of Bluebeard's Castle hotel. According to legend, it was Bluebeard—in reality Eduard de Barbe-Bleue—who picked this prime location to build a stone watchtower from which he could keep an eye on approaching enemies. Bluebeard kept his most prized booty, the lovely Señorita Mercedes, prisoner in the tower. That is, of course, until Mercedes broke free and discovered his gold-filled treasure chests along with gushing love letters to several other young ladies. Mercedes invited all of Bluebeard's paramours to the tower to pillage his plunder.

High atop Blackbeard's Hill, rising north of Fort Christian and

Government House, is Blackbeard's Castle. No one knows if Blackbeard—better known as Edward Teach—ever visited this site, but historians agree that this infamous pirate did indeed sail the Caribbean Sea in the early 18th century.

Drive over the hill to find Drake's Seat. Named for the English privateer Sir Francis Drake, this popular scenic overlook is supposedly where Drake spied ships approaching from what are now the British Virgin Islands. Don't let anyone tell you that the wooden bench is where Drake sat, however. Scholars have a hard enough time trying to prove that Drake really stood on this spot.

Finally, head back into downtown Charlotte Amalie and to Royal Dane Mall. This winding trio of brick-and-stone-paved alleyways is home to a couple of bronze plaques inscribed with historical facts about the island. One of them tells about buried pirate treasure. Some doubt it's really here. Others never stop dreaming of the day they'll find it.

---

snapper. **Known for:** service with a smile; homemade hot sauce; great place to sample local West Indian cuisine. $ *Average main: $16* ✉ *Waterfront, 28A Dronningens Gade, Charlotte Amalie* ✛ *West side of Royal Dane Mall* ☎ *340/774–6604* ⊕ *www.gladyscafe.com* ⊘ *No dinner* ⌗ *Only Amex credit cards accepted.*

Greenhouse Bar and Restaurant

$$ | **AMERICAN** | **FAMILY** | Fun-lovers come to this waterfront restaurant to eat, listen to music, and play games. Even the most finicky eater should find something to please on the eight-page menu that offers burgers, salads, and pizza all day

long, along with peel-and-eat shrimp, Caribbean lobster tail, Alaskan king crab, and Black Angus filet mignon for dinner. **Known for:** family-friendly vibe; live music; eight-page menu with huge selection of American-style fare. $ *Average main: $18* ✉ *Waterfront Hwy. at Store Tvaer Gade, Charlotte Amalie* ☎ *340/774–7998* ⊕ *www.thegreenhouserestaurant.com.*

★ Jen's Island Café and Deli

$$ | **AMERICAN** | **FAMILY** | This hole-in-the-wall eatery is the closest thing you can find to a New York–style Jewish deli, serving staples like smoked salmon and hot pastrami on rye. The deli also offers

Where to Shop for Groceries

High food prices in Virgin Islands supermarkets are enough to dull anyone's appetite. According to a report by the U.S. Virgin Islands Department of Labor, food is around 30% more expensive than on the mainland.

Although you'll never match the prices back home, you can shop around for the best deals. If you're traveling with a group, it pays to stock up on the basics at warehouse-style stores like Pricesmart (membership required) and Cost-U-Less. Even the nonbulk food items here are sold at lower prices than in the supermarkets or convenience stores. Good buys include beverages, meats, produce, and spirits.

After this, head to supermarkets such as Plaza Extra, Pueblo, and Food Center. Although the prices aren't as good as at the big-box stores, the selection is better.

Finally, if you want to splurge on top-quality meats, exotic produce and spices, and imported cheeses and spirits, finish off your shopping at high-end shops such as Moe's Fresh Market.

The Fruit Bowl is the place for fresh produce. The prices and selection are unbeatable.

For really fresh tropical fruits, vegetables, and seasoning herbs, visit the farm stands near Ft. Mylner (daily), on the Charlotte Amalie waterfront (daily), at Market Square (daily), at Yacht Haven Grande (first and third Sunday of the month), and in Estate Bordeaux (second and fourth Sunday of every month).

local specials like fresh snapper served whole in a creole sauce. **Known for:** homemade desserts; deli-style sandwiches; no parking nearby. ⑤ *Average main: $16* ✉ *Grand Galleria, 43–46 Norre Gade, across from Emancipation Garden, Charlotte Amalie* ☎ *340/777–4611* ⊕ *www.jensdeli.com* ⊙ *Closed Sun. No dinner.*

Mafolie Restaurant

$$$$ | CARIBBEAN | Enjoy a romantic meal with an iconic bird's-eye view of the Charlotte Amalie harbor. For starters, there's kallaloo soup (shrimp and crab in a thick, creamy spinach broth) and entrées include chicken with mango and chili, and seafood jambalaya. **Known for:** sublime key lime pie; tropical flavors; sweeping views. ⑤ *Average main: $39* ✉ *7091 Estate Mafolie, off Rte. 35, Charlotte Amalie* ☎ *340/774–2790* ⊕ *mafolie. com.*

Texas Pit BBQ

$$ | BARBECUE | FAMILY | The smell of smoky barbecue ribs, beef brisket, and chicken wafts enticingly from these mobile stands, which set up daily around 4 pm. Austin native and longtime Virgin Islands resident Bill Collins perfected his signature sauce, which received a thumbs-up from the late culinary great James Beard. **Known for:** barbecue; coleslaw and potato salad; no seating (head to the beach for a picnic). ⑤ *Average main: $15* ✉ *Waterfront, across from Windward Passage Hotel, Charlotte Amalie* ☎ *340/776–9579* ▭ *No credit cards* ⊙ *No lunch. Closed Sun.* ⑤ *Average main: $15* ✉ *Wheatley Center, Charlotte Amalie* ☎ *340/714–5775* ▭ *No credit cards* ⊙ *Closed Sun. No lunch.* ⑤ *Average main: $15* ✉ *Red Hook Plaza, northern end of the parking lot, Red Hook* ☎ *340/774–0610* ⊙ *No lunch. Closed Sun.*

Virgilio's

$$$$ | **ITALIAN** | For the island's best northern Italian cuisine, don't miss this intimate, elegant hideaway that's on a quiet side street. Come here for more than 40 homemade pastas topped with superb sauces, like capellini with fresh tomatoes and garlic or peasant-style spaghetti in a rich tomato sauce with mushrooms and prosciutto. **Known for:** tender osso buco; rich creamy tiramisu; eclectic art and decor. ⑤ *Average main: $32* ✉ *18 Dronningens Gade, Charlotte Amalie* ☎ *340/776–4920* ⊕ *www.virgiliosvi.com* ⊗ *Closed Sun.*

Hotels

Accommodations in town and near town offer the benefits of being close to the airport, shopping, and a number of casual and fine-dining restaurants. The downside is that this is the most crowded and noisy area of the island. Crime can also be a problem. Don't go for a stroll at night in the heart of town. Use common sense, and take the same precautions you would in any major city. Properties along the hillsides are less likely to have crime problems; plus, they command a steady breeze from the cool trade winds. This is especially important if you're visiting in summer and early fall.

The Green Iguana

$ | **HOTEL** | Atop Blackbeard's Hill, this value-priced small hotel offers the perfect mix of gorgeous harbor views, proximity to shopping (five-minute walk), and secluded privacy provided by the surrounding showy trees and bushy hibiscus. **Pros:** personalized service; near the center of town; laundry on premises. **Cons:** need a car to get around; town may be noisy at night depending on seasonal events. ⑤ *Rooms from: $145* ✉ *1002 Blackbeard's Hill, Charlotte Amalie* ☎ *340/776–7654, 855/473–4733* ⊕ *www.thegreeniguana.com* ⇄ *9 rooms* ⑩ *No meals.*

★ Mafolie Hotel

$ | **B&B/INN** | The view and the value are the selling points of this hotel perched 800 feet above Charlotte Amalie's harbor. **Pros:** fantastic views; nice restaurant and bar; family run establishment. **Cons:** tiny pool; on a busy street; need a car to get around. ⑤ *Rooms from: $240* ✉ *7091 Estate Mafolie, off Rte. 35, Charlotte Amalie* ☎ *340/774–2790, 800/225–7035* ⊕ *www.mafolie.com* ⇄ *22 rooms* ⑩ *Free Breakfast.*

Villa Santana

$ | **HOTEL** | Built by exiled General Antonio López Santa Anna of Mexico, this 1857 landmark provides a panoramic view of the harbor and plenty of West Indian charm, which will make you feel as if you're living in a slice of Virgin Islands history. **Pros:** historic charm; plenty of privacy; modern amenities like good Wi-Fi. **Cons:** not on a beach; no restaurant; need a car to get around. ⑤ *Rooms from: $180* ✉ *2602 Bjerge Gade, 2D Denmark Hill, Charlotte Amalie* ☎ *340/776–1311* ⊕ *www.villasantana.com* ⇄ *6 rooms* ⑩ *No meals.*

Windward Passage Hotel

$ | **HOTEL** | Business travelers, tourists on their way to the British Virgin Islands, and laid-back vacationers who want the convenience of being able to walk to duty-free shopping, sights, and restaurants stay at this harbor-front hotel. **Pros:** walking distance to Charlotte Amalie; nice harbor views; across from BVI ferry terminal. **Cons:** basic rooms; on a busy street; no water sports, but dive shop is on property. ⑤ *Rooms from: $275* ✉ *Waterfront Hwy., Charlotte Amalie* ☎ *340/774–5200, 800/524–7389* ⊕ *www.windwardpassage.com* ⇄ *180 rooms* ⑩ *No meals.*

Nightlife

Greenhouse Bar and Restaurant

BARS/PUBS | Once this popular eatery puts away the salt-and-pepper shakers after

10 pm on the weekends, it becomes a rock-and-roll club with a DJ or live reggae bands bringing the weary to their feet. ✉ *Waterfront Hwy., at Storetvaer Gade, Charlotte Amalie* ☎ *340/774–7998* ⊕ *www.thegreenhouserestaurant.com.*

⊜ Shopping

The prime shopping area in Charlotte Amalie is between Post Office and Market squares; it consists of two parallel streets that run east–west (Waterfront Highway and Main Street) and the alleyways that connect them. Particularly attractive are the historic **A.H. Riise Alley, Royal Dane Mall, Palm Passage,** and pastel-painted **International Plaza.**

Vendors Plaza, on the waterfront side of Emancipation Gardens in Charlotte Amalie, is a central location for vendors selling handmade earrings, necklaces, and bracelets; straw baskets and handbags; T-shirts; fabrics; African artifacts; and local fruits. Look for the many brightly colored umbrellas.

ART GALLERIES
Camille Pissarro Art Gallery
ART GALLERIES | This second-floor gallery, at the birthplace of St. Thomas's famous artist, offers a fine collection of original paintings and prints by local and regional artists. ✉ *14 Main St., Charlotte Amalie* ☎ *340/774–4621.*

CAMERAS AND ELECTRONICS
Boolchand's
CAMERAS/ELECTRONICS | This store sells brand-name cameras, audio and video equipment, and binoculars. ✉ *Havensight Mall, Bldg. II, Suite C, Rte. 30, Havensight* ☎ *340/776–0302* ⊕ *www. boolchand.com.*

Royal Caribbean
CAMERAS/ELECTRONICS | Find a wide selection of cameras, camcorders, stereos, watches, and clocks at this store. There are also branches at the Crown Bay Center. ✉ *33 Main St.,*

Charlotte Amalie ☎ *340/776–4110* ⊕ *www.royalcaribbeanvi.com.*

CHINA AND CRYSTAL
The Crystal Shoppe at A.H. Riise
CERAMICS/GLASSWARE | This retailer specializes in all that glitters, from Swarovski and Waterford crystal to figurines by Hummel, Daum, and Royal Copenhagen, and china by Belleek, Kosta Boda, and several Limoges factories. There's also a large selection of Lladró figurines. ✉ *37 Main St., at Riise's Alley, Charlotte Amalie* ☎ *340/777–2222, 800/323–7232* ⊕ *www. ahriise.com.*

Little Switzerland
CERAMICS/GLASSWARE | This popular Caribbean chain carries crystal from Baccarat, Waterford, and Orrefors; and china from Kosta Boda, Rosenthal, and Wedgwood. There's also an assortment of Swarovski cut-crystal animals, gemstone globes, and many other affordable collectibles. It also does a booming mail-order business. A branch located at the Crown Bay Center is open when a cruise ship is in port. There is also a branch at the Havensight Mall and the Ritz Carlton, St. Thomas. ✉ *5 Dronningens Gade, across from Emancipation Garden, Charlotte Amalie* ☎ *340/776–2010* ⊕ *www.little-switzerland.com.*

CLOTHING
Fresh Produce Sportswear
CLOTHING | FAMILY | This clothing store doesn't sell lime-green mangoes, peachy-pink guavas, or sunny-yellow bananas, but you will find these fun, casual colors on its clothing for children and adults. This is one of 30 stores nationwide to stock all of the California-created, tropical-feel line of women's separates. The dresses, shirts, slacks, and skirts are in small to plus sizes, and bags and hats and other accessories are also available. ✉ *Riise's Alley, 5189 Dronningens Gade, across from the Rolex store, Charlotte Amalie* ☎ *340/774–0807* ⊕ *www.fresh-produceclothes.com.*

Charlotte Amalie is filled with back alleys and interesting shops.

Local Color
CLOTHING | FAMILY | This St. Thomas chain has clothes for men, women, and children among its brand names, which include Jams World, Fresh Produce, and Urban Safari. You can also find St. John artist Sloop Jones's colorful, hand-painted island designs on cool dresses, T-shirts, and sweaters. The tropically oriented accessories include big-brimmed straw hats, bold-color bags, and casual jewelry. There's another location at the Havensight Mall. ⊠ *Rte. 30, at Buccaneer Mall, Charlotte Amalie ✛ Across from Port of Sale Mall* ☎ *340/776–5860* ⊕ *www. localcolorvi.com.*

Tommy Hilfiger
CLOTHING | This outlet for the popular designer specializes in classic American jeans and sportswear, as well as trendy bags, belts, ties, socks, caps, and wallets. ⊠ *Long Bay, Yacht Haven Grande Marina, Charlotte Amalie* ☎ *340/777–1189* ⊕ *www.tommy.com.*

FOODSTUFFS
Belgian Chocolate Factory
FOOD/CANDY | FAMILY | This store makes its beautiful chocolates before your eyes. Specialties include triple-chocolate rum truffles. You can find imported chocolates here as well. Both the homemade and imported delectables come in decorative boxes, so they make great gifts. ⊠ *Hibiscus Alley, 5093 Dronningens Gade, Suite 3, Charlotte Amalie* ☎ *340/777–5247.*

Pueblo Supermarket
FOOD/CANDY | This Caribbean chain carries stateside brands of most products—but at higher prices because of shipping costs to the islands. ⊠ *Subbase, ½ mile (¾ km) east of Crown Bay Marina, Charlotte Amalie* ☎ *340/774–4200.*

HANDICRAFTS
Made in the U.S. Virgin Islands
CRAFTS | This pop-up shop is open from Thanksgiving until early January each year and is located in a historic building across from Fort Christian. Inside, you'll find a treasure trove for bona fide made-in-the-Virgin Islands arts, crafts, and local

food products that make the perfect gifts. There are soaps, hot sauces, hand-tied palm brooms, native dolls, books by local authors, T-shirts, jewelry, and much more. Signs next to displays tell you about the respective artists. ⊠ *23 Dronningens Gade, across from Fort Christian, Charlotte Amalie* ☎ *340/714–1700.*

JEWELRY
★ Cardow Jewelers

JEWELRY/ACCESSORIES | You can get gold in several lengths, widths, sizes, and styles, along with jewelry made of diamonds, emeralds, and other precious gems from this small chain's main store. You're guaranteed 40% to 60% savings off U.S. retail prices, or your money will be refunded within 30 days of purchase. There's also a line of classy commemorative Virgin Islands watches made on-site. Branches located at the Cyril E. King Airport; Ritz-Carlton, St. Thomas; and Crown Bay Center. ⊠ *5195 Dronningens Gate, across from Emancipation Garden, Charlotte Amalie* ☎ *340/776–1140* ⊕ *www.cardow.com.*

Diamonds International

JEWELRY/ACCESSORIES | At this large chain with several outlets on St. Thomas, just choose a diamond, emerald, or tanzanite gem and a mounting, and you can have your dream ring set in an hour. Famous for having the largest inventory of diamonds on the island, this shop welcomes trade-ins, has a U.S. service center, and includes diamond earrings with every purchase. Branches located at Crown Bay Center and Havensight Mall. ⊠ *31 Main St., Charlotte Amalie* ☎ *340/774–3707* ⊕ *www.diamondsinternational.com.*

Jewels

JEWELRY/ACCESSORIES | This jewelry store sells name-brand jewelry and watches in abundance. Designer jewelry lines include David Yurman, Bulgari, Chopard, and Penny Preville. The selection of watches includes Jaeger Le Coultre, Tag Heuer, Breitling, Movado, and Gucci.

There is also a branch at the Crown Bay Center. ⊠ *Main St., at Riise's Alley, Charlotte Amalie* ☎ *248/809–5560* ⊕ *www.littleswitzerland.com.*

Rolex Watches at A. H. Riise

JEWELRY/ACCESSORIES | A.H. Riise is the official Rolex retailer of the Virgin Islands, and this shop offers one of the largest selections of these fine timepieces in the Caribbean. An After Sales Service Center helps you keep your Rolex ticking for a lifetime. ⊠ *37 Main St., at Riise's Alley, Charlotte Amalie* ☎ *340/777–6789* ⊕ *www.ahriise.com.*

Trident Jewels and Time

JEWELRY/ACCESSORIES | Fine gems and exquisite timepieces are the draw at this second-generation family-owned boutique. You'll find loose diamonds, sapphires, emeralds, and tanzanite as well as name-brand watches such as Ulysse Nardin, Harry Winston, Franck Muller, Bovet, Jaquet Droz, Bell & Ross, U-Boat, and Graham. ⊠ *9 Main St., Charlotte Amalie* ☎ *340/776–7152* ⊕ *www.tridentjewels.com.*

LEATHER GOODS
★ Zora's

SHOES/LUGGAGE/LEATHER GOODS | This store specializes in fine, made-to-order leather sandals. There's also a selection of locally made backpacks, purses, and briefcases in durable, brightly colored canvas. ⊠ *34 Norre Gade, across from Roosevelt Park, Charlotte Amalie* ☎ *340/774–2559.*

LINENS
The Fabric Store

HOUSEHOLD ITEMS/FURNITURE | Silks and fancy fabrics share space with colorful batiks, cotton prints, ribbons, and accessories in this small shop off the beaten path. ⊠ *1519 Prindsen Gade, Charlotte Amalie* ✛ *2 blocks north of Roosevelt Memorial Park, and halfway down street to the east* ☎ *340/774–1751.*

Mr. Tablecloth

HOUSEHOLD ITEMS/FURNITURE | This store has prices to please, and the friendly staff here will help you choose from the floor-to-ceiling selection of linens, which include Tuscan lace tablecloths and Irish linen pillowcases. ✉ *6–7 Main St., Charlotte Amalie* ☎ *340/774–4343* ⊕ *mrtablecloth-vi.com.*

LIQUOR AND TOBACCO

A. H. Riise Liquors and Tobacco

TOBACCO | This giant duty-free liquor outlet carries a large selection of tobacco (including imported cigars), as well as cordials, wines, and rare vintage Armagnacs, cognacs, ports, and Madeiras. It also stocks fruits in brandy and barware from England. Enjoy rum samples at the tasting bar. ✉ *37 Main St., at Riise's Alley, Charlotte Amalie* ☎ *340/777–2222* ⊕ *www.ahriise.com.*

East End

Although the eastern end has many major resorts and spectacular beaches, don't be surprised if a cow, a herd of goats, or even a deer crosses your path as you drive through the relatively flat, dry terrain. You can pick up sandwiches from a deli in the Red Hook area if you want a picnic lunch.

 Sights

★ Coral World Ocean Park

ZOO | FAMILY | This interactive aquarium and water-sports center lets you experience a variety of sea life and other animals. At the 2-acre dolphin habitat, you can swim with the graceful creatures. There are also several outdoor pools where you can pet baby sharks, feed stingrays, touch starfish, and view endangered sea turtles. During the Sea Trek Helmet Dive, you walk along an underwater trail wearing a helmet that provides a continuous supply of air. You can also try Snuba, a cross between snorkeling and scuba diving. Swim with a sea lion for the chance to play ball or get a big, wet, whiskered kiss. The park also

has an offshore underwater observatory, an 80,000-gallon coral reef exhibit (one of the largest in the world), and a nature trail with native ducks and tortoises. Daily feedings take place at most exhibits. ✉ *6450 Estate Smith Bay, Estate Smith Bay* ✛ *Coki Point Rd. north of Rte. 38* ☎ *340/775–1555* ⊕ *www.coralworldvi.com* ✉ *$23.50.*

Red Hook

MARINA | The IGY American Yacht Harbor marina here has fishing and sailing charter boats, a dive shop, and powerboat-rental agencies. There are also several bars and restaurants, including the Caribbean Saloon, The Tap & Still, Island Time Pub, Raw Sushi & Sake Bar, and Duffy's Love Shack. Other services include a Mail Service, veterinarian, doctors office, drug store, and grocery store. Ferries depart from Red Hook en route to St. John and the British Virgin Islands. ✉ *Red Hook, Intersection of Rtes. 38 and 32, Red Hook.*

 Beaches

★ Coki Beach

BEACH—SIGHT | FAMILY | Funky beach huts selling local foods such as pates (fried turnovers with a spicy ground-beef filling), quaint vendor kiosks, and a brigade of hair braiders and taxi men make this beach overlooking picturesque Thatch Cay feel like a carnival. But this is the best place on the island to snorkel and scuba dive. Fish—including grunts, snappers, and wrasses—are like an effervescent cloud you can wave your hand through. **Amenities:** food and drink; lifeguards; parking; showers; toilets; water sports. **Best for:** partiers; snorkeling. ✉ *Rte. 388, Estate Smith Bay* ✛ *Next to Coral World Ocean Park.*

Lindquist Beach

BEACH—SIGHT | FAMILY | This public beach has a serene sense of wilderness that isn't found on the more crowded beaches. A lifeguard is on duty between

8 am and 5 pm and picnic tables and restrooms are available. Try snorkeling over the offshore reef. **Amenities:** lifeguards; parking; toilets. **Best for:** swimming; snorkeling. ⊠ *Rte. 38, Estate Smith Bay* ⚓ *At end of a paved road, adjacent to a paved parking lot* ☎ *340/777–6300* 💻 *$5.*

Sapphire Beach

BEACH—SIGHT | FAMILY | A steady breeze makes this beach a windsurfer's paradise. The swimming is great, as is the snorkeling, especially at the reef near Pettyklip Point. Beach volleyball is big on the weekends as is the Sunday live music beach jam. Sapphire Beach Resort and Marina has a snack shop, a bar, and water-sports rentals. **Amenities:** parking; toilets. **Best for:** snorkeling; swimming; windsurfing. ⊠ *Rte. 38, Sapphire Bay* ⚓ *½ mile (1 km) north of Red Hook.*

Secret Harbour

BEACH—SIGHT | Placid waters make it easy to stroke your way out to a swim platform offshore from the Secret Harbour Beach Resort & Villas. Nearby reefs give snorkelers a natural show. There's a bar and restaurant, as well as a dive shop. **Amenities:** food and drink; parking; toilets; water sports. **Best for:** snorkeling; sunset; swimming. ⊠ *Rte. 322, Nazareth* ⚓ *Take 1st right off Rte. 322.*

Vessup Beach

BEACH—SIGHT | This wild, undeveloped beach is lined with seagrape trees and century plants. It's close to Red Hook harbor, so you can watch the ferries depart. The calm waters are excellent for swimming. It's popular with locals on weekends. **Amenities:** parking; water sports. **Best for:** swimming. ⊠ *Off Rte. 322, Nazareth.*

Restaurants

Caribbean Saloon

$$$ | AMERICAN | Sports on wide-screen TVs and live music on weekends are two added attractions at this hip sports bar

that's in the center of the action in Red Hook. The menu ranges from finger-licking barbecue ribs to more sophisticated fare, such as the signature filet mignon wrapped in bacon and smothered in melted Gorgonzola cheese. **Known for:** fresh catch of the day; late-night menu; live music on the weekends. ⓢ *Average main: $28* ⊠ *American Yacht Harbor, Bldg. B, Rte. 32, Red Hook* ☎ *340/775–7060* ⊕ *www.caribbeansaloon.com.*

Duffy's Love Shack

$$ | ECLECTIC | If the floating bubbles don't attract you to this zany eatery billed as the "ultimate tropical drink shack," the lime-green shutters, loud rock music, and fun-loving waitstaff just might. The menu has a selection of burgers, tacos, burritos, and salads, and bartenders shake up such exotic concoctions as the Love Shack Volcano—a 50-ounce flaming extravaganza. **Known for:** grilled fish tacos; conch fritters; tropical cocktails. ⓢ *Average main: $16* ⊠ *Red Hook Shopping Center, Rte. 32 and 6500 Red Hook Plaza, Red Hook* ⚓ *In the parking lot* ☎ *340/779–2080* ⊕ *www.duffysloveshack.com.*

Mirador by Chef Benny

$$$ | INTERNATIONAL | Arrive before sunset for the magnificent view and handcrafted cocktails at the Pineapple Bar, but stay for the Latin meets American mix of dinner selections. Chef Benny is from Puerto Rico and he cooks the food he grew up with—garlic tostones, chicken breast with garlic and truffle *mofonguitos,* and braised pork *masitas*—which is showcased during his Thursday special, a

Puerto Rican–style buffet; save room for the Coquito Rum Cake. **Known for:** Puerto Rican–style buffets on Thursday; fantastic views across the Atlantic Ocean; romantic setting. ⑤ *Average main: $28* ✉ *Point Pleasant Resort, 6600 Estate Smith Bay, Estate Smith Bay* ☎ *340/775–7200 Ext. 3* ⊕ *miradorbychefbenny.com* ☽ *No lunch.*

★ Old Stone Farmhouse

$$$$ | **ECLECTIC** | At this beautifully restored plantation house, guests can dine on sophisticated small plates such as a caprese burrata or simple entrées such as seared jumbo scallops or a center-cut fillet. Personalized attention makes dining here a delight, as does the incredible decor—think 18th-century stone walls meets modern-day elegance, with fine silver and china set on white-tablecloth-topped hardwood tables. **Known for:** excellent service; elegant setting; well-prepared dishes. ⑤ *Average main: $38* ✉ *Rte. 42, Lovenlund* ✛ *1 mile (1½ km) west of entrance to Mahogany Run Golf Course* ☎ *340/777–6277* ☽ *Closed Mon. and Tues.*

★ Pizza Pi

$$ | **PIZZA** | **FAMILY** | Sail up in a boat, paddle by in a kayak, or drive out in a dinghy to pick up freshly made New York–style pizza from this "floating" food truck. This 37-foot motor sailor is an authentic brick-oven pizzeria, serving pizzas topped with locally grown basil and fresh lobster. **Known for:** one-of-a-kind location; delicious pizza; excursion stop. ⑤ *Average main: $16* ✉ *Christmas Cove, Great St. James Island* ✛ *Across from Cowpet Bay, on the east end of St. Thomas* ☎ *340/643–4674* ⊕ *www.pizza-pi.com.*

XO Bistro

$$$ | **CONTEMPORARY** | Tucked into a Red Hook shopping center, this down-home eatery has a congenial atmosphere and well-prepared sandwiches, flatbreads, and entrées that make it popular with local professionals. Come early for a seat at the bar and get the scoop on local island news. **Known for:** more upscale food than surrounding restaurants; theme nights; friendly waitstaff with island knowledge. ⑤ *Average main: $29* ✉ *6501 Red Hook Plaza, Red Hook* ⊕ *www.xobistro.net.*

Hotels

You can find most of the large, luxurious beachfront resorts on St. Thomas's East End. The downside is that these properties are about a 30-minute drive from town and a 45-minute drive from the airport (substantially longer during peak hours). On the upside, these properties tend to be self-contained; plus, there are a number of good restaurants, shops, and water-sports operators in the area. Once you've settled in, you don't need a car to get around.

Pavilions and Pools

$$ | **RENTAL** | Perfect for those craving privacy, the villas here have full kitchens, lots of space, sunken garden showers, and a private swimming pool. **Pros:** intimate atmosphere; private pools; close to Red Hook and ferries to St. John and BVI. **Cons:** on a busy road; long walk to beach; each of the villas is privately owned, so conditions vary from unit to unit. ⑤ *Rooms from: $320* ✉ *6400 Estate Smith Bay, off Rte. 38, Estate Smith Bay* ☎ *340/775–6110, 800/524–2001* ⊕ *www.pavilionsandpools.com* 🛏 *25 villas* ⦿ *Free Breakfast.*

Point Pleasant Resort

$$$ | **RESORT** | Hilltop suites give you an eagle's-eye view of the East End and beyond, and those in a building adjacent to the reception area offer incredible sea views, but the sea-level junior suites, where the sounds of lapping waves lull you to sleep, are smaller. **Pros:** a resort shuttle; convenient kitchens; pleasant pools. **Cons:** steep climb from beach; need a car to get around; some rooms need refurbishing. ⑤ *Rooms from: $450* ✉ *6600 Estate Smith Bay, off Rte. 38, Estate Smith Bay* ☎ *340/775–7200,*

888/619–4010 ⊕ www.pointpleasantre-
sort.com ⌘ 128 suites ⫯Ol No meals.

Ritz-Carlton, St. Thomas

$$$$ | **RESORT** | **FAMILY** | Everything
sparkles at the island's most luxurious
resort, from the in-room furnishings and
amenities to the infinity pool, white-sand,
eco-friendly Blue Flag–designated beach,
and turquoise sea beyond. **Pros:** gorgeous views; great water-sports facilities;
beautiful beach; airport shuttle. **Cons:** $80
per person per day resort fee; food and
drink can lack flair and are expensive ($19
hamburger, $12 piña colada); half-hour or
more drive to town and airport. ⑤ *Rooms
from: $740* ⊠ *6900 Estate Great Bay, off
Rte. 317, Estate Great Bay* ☎ *340/775–
3333, 800/241–3333* ⊕ *www.ritzcarlton.
com* ⌘ *180 rooms* ⫯Ol *No meals.*

Secret Harbour Beach Resort

$$ | **RENTAL** | There's not a bad view
from these low-rise studio, one-, and
two-bedroom condos, which are either
beachfront or perched on a hill overlooking an inviting cove. **Pros:** beautiful beach
and great snorkeling; good restaurant;
secluded location. **Cons:** some rooms
are small; car needed to get around;
condo owners are territorial about beach
chairs. ⑤ *Rooms from: $340* ⊠ *Rte.
317, 6280 Estate Nazareth, Nazareth*
☎ *340/775–6550, 800/524–2250* ⊕ *www.
secretharbourvi.com* ⌘ *49 suites* ⫯Ol *Free
Breakfast.*

Two Sandals by the Sea

$ | **B&B/INN** | This cozy bed-and-break-
fast feels like a home away from home
because of its casual ambience, pictur-
esque setting overlooking Red Hook Harbor, and the friendliness of the owners.
Pros: quaint and clean; close to beaches;
breakfast included in price. **Cons:** fellow
visitors in close proximity; need a car to
get around, especially to major sights
and town; no pool. ⑤ *Rooms from: $160*
⊠ *On Ridge Rd., 6264 Estate Nazareth,
Nazareth* ☎ *340/998–2395* ⊕ *www.
twosandals.com* ⌘ *6 rooms* ⫯Ol *Free
Breakfast.*

Wyndham Margaritaville Vacation Club

$$ | **RESORT** | The laid-back, flip-flop vibe is
alive and well here at this Jimmy Buffett–
themed beachfront resort, along with
all the comforts and conveniences you'd
expect from upscale tropical accommodations. **Pros:** beachfront property;
restaurant on-site; quiet setting. **Cons:**
need a car to get around; small beach.
⑤ *Rooms from: $325* ⊠ *6080 Estate
Smith Bay, Estate Smith Bay* ✈ *Next to
Coki Beach and Coral World Ocean Park*
☎ *340/775–8300* ⊕ *www.margaritavil-
levacationclub.com* ⌘ *80 rooms* ⫯Ol *No
meals.*

Nightlife

Duffy's Love Shack

BARS/PUBS | At this island favorite, funky
cocktails, a loud sound system, and dancing under the stars are the big draws for
locals and visitors alike. ⊠ *Red Hook Plaza, Rte. 32, Red Hook* ☎ *340/779–2080*
⊕ *www.duffysloveshack.com.*

Shopping

Red Hook has **American Yacht Harbor,** a
waterfront shopping area with a dive
shop, a tackle store, clothing and jewelry
boutiques, a bar, and a few restaurants.

Don't forget **St. John.** A ferry ride (an hour
from Charlotte Amalie or 20 minutes
from Red Hook) will take you to the
charming shops of **Mongoose Junction**
and **Wharfside Village,** which specialize in
unusual, often island-made articles.

CLOTHING

Caribbean Surf Co.

CLOTHING | **FAMILY** | There's something for
every beachgoer, surfers and sunbathers
alike, at this local, family-owned surf
store. Brand-name Billabong, Oakley, and
Reef swimwear, sunglasses, and sandals
are available for adults and children.
There are additional locations in Havensight Mall and Charlotte Amalie's Main
Street. Surfboards and surf gear are only

available at this location and in Havensight. ✉ *6500 Red Hook Plaza, Suite 205, Red Hook* ☎ *340/774–3583.*

FOODSTUFFS
Food Center
FOOD/CANDY | This supermarket sells fresh produce, meats, and seafood. There's also an on-site bakery and deli with hot and cold prepared foods, which are the big draw here, especially for those renting villas, condos, or charter boats in the East End area. ✉ *Rte. 32, 1 mile (2 km) west of Red Hook, Estate Frydenhoj* ☎ *340/777–8806* ⊕ *www.foodcentervi. com.*

Moe's Fresh Market
FOOD/CANDY | This gourmet market near the ferry to St. John has the best deli cheeses, prepared-to-order subs, and selection of organic foods, coffees, and wines on the island. Two other locations are at Yacht Haven Grande near the cruise ship dock in Havensight and at the corner of Waterfront Drive and Espanole Strade in Charlotte Amalie. ✉ *Rte. 32, 6502 Smith Bay Rd., Red Hook* ☎ *340/693–0254* ⊕ *moesvi.com.*

JEWELRY
Little Switzerland
JEWELRY/ACCESSORIES | Designer jewelry available in this major chain includes David Yurman, Bulgari, Chopard, and Penny Preville. The selection of watches is also extensive. ✉ *Ritz-Carlton, St. Thomas, Rte. 322, Nazareth* ☎ *248/809–5560* ⊕ *www.littleswitzerland.com.*

South Shore

Sights

French Heritage Museum
MUSEUM | The museum houses fishing nets, accordions, tambourines, mahogany furniture, photographs, and other artifacts illustrating the lives of the island's French descendants during the 18th through 20th centuries. Admission is free, but donations are accepted. ✉ *Rue de St. Anne and rue de St. Barthélemy, next to Joseph Aubain Ballpark, Frenchtown* ☎ *340/714–2583* ⊕ *www.frenchheritagemuseum.com* 💲 *Free, donations accepted.*

Frenchtown
COMMERCIAL CENTER | Popular for its bars and restaurants, Frenchtown is also the home of descendants of immigrants from St. Barthélemy (St. Barth). You can watch them pull up their brightly painted boats and display their equally colorful catch of the day along the waterfront. If you chat with them, you can hear speech patterns slightly different from those of other St. Thomians. Get a feel for the residential district of Frenchtown by walking west to some of the town's winding streets, where tiny wooden houses have been passed down from generation to generation. ✉ *Turn south off Waterfront Hwy. (Rte. 30) at post office, Frenchtown.*

★ Skyride to Paradise Point
VIEWPOINT | FAMILY | Fly skyward in a seven-minute gondola ride to Paradise Point, an overlook with breathtaking views of Charlotte Amalie, the harbor, and the neighboring islands of St. Croix to the south and Vieques and Culebra to the west. You'll find several shops, a bar (the specialty here is the Bushwacker, a creamy frozen alcoholic libation), and a restaurant. You can also skip the $21 gondola ride and take a taxi to the top for $7 per person from the Havensight Dock. ✉ *Rte. 30, across from Havensight Mall, Havensight* ☎ *340/774–9809* ⊕ *www. paradisepointvi.com* 💲 *$21.*

★ Virgin Islands Children's Museum
MUSEUM | FAMILY | Giant bubble makers, a rainbow-colored gear table, and a larger-than-life abacus are just a few of the interactive exhibits at this indoor, family-friendly, play-and-learn museum. Science was never so fun! ✉ *Buccaneer Mall, Havensight* ✛ *Across from the cruise ship dock* ☎ *340/643–0366*

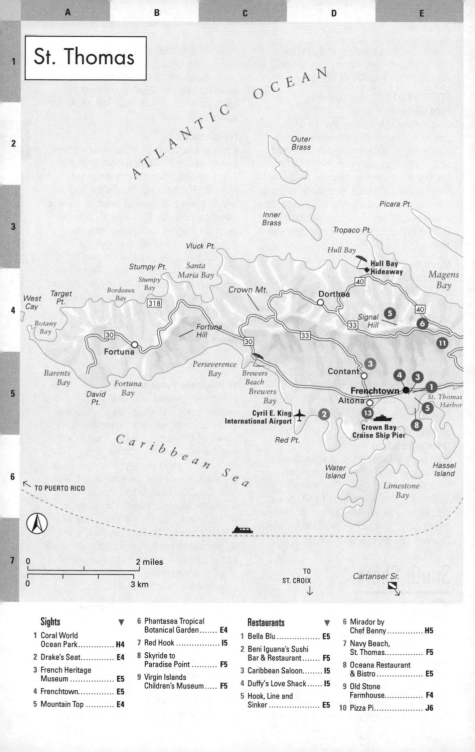

St. Thomas

ATLANTIC OCEAN

Caribbean Sea

Outer Brass

Inner Brass

Picara Pt.

Tropaco Pt.

Hull Bay

Hull Bay Hideaway

Magens Bay

Vluck Pt.

Stumpy Pt.

Santa Maria Bay

Stumpy Bay

Bordeaux Bay

Crown Mt.

Dorthea

Signal Hill

West Cay

Target Pt.

318

40

40

5

6

11

Botany Bay

30

Fortuna Hill

Fortuna

Perseverence Bay

Brewers Beach

Brewers Bay

30

33

33

Contant

3

4

3

Frenchtown

Altona

1

St. Thomas Harbor

5

Barents Bay

David Pt.

Fortuna Bay

Cyril E. King International Airport

2

13

8

Crown Bay Cruise Ship Pier

Red Pt.

Water Island

Hassel Island

Limestone Bay

TO PUERTO RICO

| 0 | | 2 miles |
| 0 | | 3 km |

TO ST. CROIX ↓

Cartanser Sr.

Sights ▼		Restaurants ▼	
1 Coral World Ocean Park **H4**	6 Phantasea Tropical Botanical Garden **E4**	1 Bella Blu **E5**	6 Mirador by Chef Benny **H5**
2 Drake's Seat **E4**	7 Red Hook **I5**	2 Beni Iguana's Sushi Bar & Restaurant **F5**	7 Navy Beach, St. Thomas **F5**
3 French Heritage Museum **E5**	8 Skyride to Paradise Point **F5**	3 Caribbean Saloon **I5**	8 Oceana Restaurant & Bistro **E5**
4 Frenchtown **E5**	9 Virgin Islands Children's Museum **F5**	4 Duffy's Love Shack **I5**	9 Old Stone Farmhouse **F4**
5 Mountain Top **E4**		5 Hook, Line and Sinker **E5**	10 Pizza Pi **J6**

F	**G**	**H**	**I**	**J**

KEY
- **1** *Sights*
- **1** *Restaurants*
- **1** *Hotels*
- *Cruise Ship Terminal*
- *Beaches*
- *Dive Sites*
- *Ferry*

UNITED STATES VIRGIN ISLANDS

ST. THOMAS

Tortola

ST. JOHN

Distance from St. Thomas to St. Croix approx. 40 miles

ST. CROIX

Hans Lollick

Lovelund Bay

Mandal Pt.

The General Rogers

Thatch Cay

St. James Bay

Grass Cay and Congo Cay

Magens Bay

9

42

Mandal

Tutu Bay

Coki Beach

10 **1**

6

6

Lindquist Beach

Charlotte Amalie see detail map

7

40

Frydendal

38

38

Cabes Pt.

Sapphire Beach

5

TO ST. JOHN →

2

Tutu

32

5

Redhook Bay

2

9

14 **3**

7

Vessup Beach

Cow and Calf Rocks

8

12

4

4

Red Hook

9

7

Great Bay

Great St. James Island

Paradise Pt.

Nadir

30

Secret Harbour

8

10

1

Jersey Bay

Little St. James Island

Coculus Pt.

Long Pt.

TO ST. JOHN →

Frenchcap

11 Sib's on the Mountain **E4**

12 Smoking Rooster BBQ **F5**

13 Tickles Dockside Pub **D5**

14 XO Bistro................. **I5**

Hotels ▼

1 Bolongo Bay Beach Resort............ **G6**

2 Emerald Beach Resort............ **D5**

3 Island View Guesthouse............. **D4**

4 Marriott's Frenchman's Cove **F6**

5 Pavilions and Pools **I5**

6 Point Pleasant Resort **H5**

7 Ritz-Carlton, St. Thomas................ **I6**

8 Secret Harbour Beach Resort............. **I6**

9 Two Sandals by the Sea **I6**

10 Wyndham Margaritaville Vacation Club **H5**

⊕ *www.vichildrensmuseum.org* ⊠ *$8*
⊙ *Closed Mon.*

Beaches

Brewers Beach

BEACH—SIGHT | Watch jets land at the
Cyril E. King Airport as you dip into the
usually calm seas. Rocks at either end
of the shoreline, patches of grass poking
randomly through the sand, and shady
tamarind trees 30 feet from the water
give this beach a wild, natural feel. Civi-
lization has arrived, in the form of one or
two mobile food vans parked on the nearby road. Buy a fried-chicken leg and john-
nycake or burgers and chips to munch on
at the picnic tables. **Amenities:** food and
drink; lifeguards; parking; toilets. **Best for:**
sunset; swimming. ⊠ *Rte. 30, west of
University of the Virgin Islands.*

Restaurants

Beni Iguana's Sushi Bar & Restaurant

$$ | **JAPANESE** | Edible art is an apt
description of the sushi and sashimi
feast that draws visitors and locals alike.
The favorite here is steamed mussels in
a house-made creamy sesame dress-
ing dubbed "iguana sauce," which is,
happily, not made from the spiny reptile
that roams the island's hillsides and
roadways. **Known for:** vegetarian options;
fresh seafood; red snapper roll. ⑤ *Average main: $16* ⊠ *Havensight Mall,
West Indian Dock Rd., Bldg. IX, facing
the cruise ship dock, Charlotte Amalie*
☎ *340/777–8744* ⊕ *beniiguanassushibar.
com* ⊙ *Closed Sun.*

Navy Beach, St. Thomas

$$$ | **SEAFOOD** | With its colorful maritime
flags, blue-and-white decor, and mil-
lion-dollar views of megayachts docked
just yards away, this open-air eatery has
a seafood-centric menu to match its
nautical theme. Small plates include tuna
crudo, lump crab cakes, and shrimp ceviche, while entrée-size offerings feature
soy-glazed red snapper and island-spiced

blackened mahimahi. **Known for:** excellent
views; creative house cocktails; seafood.
⑤ *Average main: $28* ⊠ *Long Bay, 5403
Yacht Haven Grande, Charlotte Amalie*
⊕ *Adjacent to the property's central lawn*
☎ *340/714–3566* ⊕ *www.navybeach.
com/st-thomasvi/* ⊙ *Closed Mon.*

★ Oceana Restaurant & Bistro

$$$$ | **ECLECTIC** | In the old Russian consu-
late house at the tip of the Frenchtown
peninsula, this restaurant offers superb
views along with an eclectic array of
dishes expertly prepared by longtime
Virgin Islands chef Patricia LaCourte
and her staff. Choose from the more
casual bistro-style menu, which features
taste-and-share charcuterie and artisanal
cheese plates and entrées like flatbreads
and burgers, or splurge on the more formal dinner selections like butter-poached
local lobster and filet mignon. **Known for:**
seaside view; indulgent dishes; location
near Frenchtown bars. ⑤ *Average main:
$62* ⊠ *Villa Olga, 8A Honduras, French-
town* ⊕ *Turn off Rte. 30 into Frenchtown,
at intersection of post office. Take 1st
right, with ballfield on left, then take next
left and immediate next left; follow this
road ½ mile to the end* ☎ *340/774–4262*
⊕ *www.oceanavi.com* ⊙ *No dinner Sun.*

Smoking Rooster BBQ

$$ | **BARBECUE** | House-smoked hand-
rubbed meats with a side of rum draws
locals and visitors alike. Order the
Sampler Platter for a taste of everything:
choice of two meats like pulled pork and
beef brisket, two sides such as potato
mac salad (a mishmash of two favorites
with a flavor all its own) and brisket
beans, plus pickled veggies and biscuits
with honey butter. **Known for:** barbecue
with house-made dry rubs; small-batch
tap-only craft beer; house-pickled veggie
sides. ⑤ *Average main: $18* ⊠ *Havensight
Mall, Charlotte Amalie* ☎ *340/714–7373*
⊕ *www.thesmokingrooster.com.*

Hotels

The south shore of St. Thomas connects to the east end of the island via a beautiful road that rambles along the hillside, with frequent peeks between the hills for views of the ocean, and, on a clear day, of St. Croix some 40 miles (60 km) to the south. The resorts here are on their own beaches. They offer several opportunities for water sports, as well as land-based activities, fine dining, and evening entertainment.

Bolongo Bay Beach Resort

$$$ | RESORT | All the rooms at this family-run resort tucked along a palm-lined beach have balconies with ocean views; down the beach are nine condos with full kitchens. **Pros:** family-run property; on the beach; water sports abound. **Cons:** a bit run-down; on a busy road; need a car to get around. $ *Rooms from: $420* ⊠ *Rte. 30, Bolongo* ☎ *340/775–1800, 800/524–4746* ⊕ *www.bolongobay.com* 🛏 *74 rooms* ⦿ *No meals.*

Marriott's Frenchman's Cove

$$$$ | RESORT | Not to be confused with neighboring Frenchman's Reef Hotel, this beachfront villa-style timeshare property offers the glitz of a resort with the comfort and amenities of a private club. **Pros:** infinity pool with water slide; ferry service to Charlotte Amalie; secluded beach. **Cons:** limited parking for those with rental cars; only one restaurant on property; adjoining hotel property is closed, thus no current access to walking distance shops, restaurants, and an additional beach. $ *Rooms from: $570* ⊠ *7338 Estate Bakkeroe, Estate Bakkero* ☎ *340/693-4800* ⊕ *www.marriott.com* 🛏 *221 rooms* ⦿ *No meals.*

Nightlife

Iggies' Oasis

BARS/PUBS | FAMILY | Bolongo Bay's poolside bar and restaurant offers live music on the weekends. ⊠ *Bolongo Beach Club & Villas, Rte. 30, Bolongo* ☎ *340/775–1800* ⊕ *www.iggiesbeachbar. com.*

📣 Performing Arts

★ Pistarkle Theater

THEATER | FAMILY | This theater in the Tillett Gardens complex is air-conditioned and has more than 100 seats; it hosts a half-dozen productions annually, plus a children's summer drama camp. ⊠ *Tillett Gardens, Rte. 38, across from Tutu Park Shopping Mall, Tutu* ☎ *340/775–7877* ⊕ *pistarkletheater.com.*

👜 Shopping

West of Charlotte Amalie, the pink-stucco **Nisky Center,** on Harwood Highway about ½ mile (¾ km) east of the airport, is more of a hometown shopping center than a tourist area.

At the Crown Bay cruise-ship pier, the **Crown Bay Center,** off the Harwood Highway in Subbase about ½ mile (¾ km) west of Frenchtown, has quite a few shops, but they only tend to be open on days when a cruise ship is docked at the Crown Bay Cruise Ship Pier.

Havensight Mall, next to the cruise-ship dock, may not be as charming as downtown Charlotte Amalie, but it does have more than 60 shops. It also has an excellent bookstore, a bank, a pharmacy, a gourmet grocery, and smaller branches of many downtown stores. The shops at **Port of $ale,** adjoining Havensight Mall (its buildings are pink instead of brown), sell discount goods. Next door to Port of $ale is the **Yacht Haven Grande** complex, a stunning megayacht marina with beautiful, safe walkways and many upscale shops.

East of Charlotte Amalie on Route 38, **Tillett Gardens** is an oasis of artistic endeavor across from the Tutu Park Shopping Mall. The late Jim and Rhoda Tillett converted this Danish farm into

3

St. Thomas SOUTH SHORE

an artists' retreat in 1959. Today you can watch artisans produce silk-screen fabrics, candles, pottery, and other handicrafts. Something special is often happening in the gardens as well: the Classics in the Gardens program is a classical music series presented under the stars, Arts Alive is a semiannual arts-and-crafts fair held in November and May, and the Pistarckle Theater holds its performances here from November through April.

Tutu Park Shopping Mall, across from Tillett Gardens, is the island's one and only enclosed mall. More than 50 stores and a food court are anchored by Kmart and Plaza Extra grocery store. Archaeologists have discovered evidence that Arawak Indians once lived near the grounds.

ART GALLERIES
Mango Tango
ART GALLERIES | This gallery sells and displays works by popular local artists— originals, prints, and note cards. There's a one-person or multiple-person show at least one weekend a month. ⊠ *4003 Raphune Hill, off Rte. 38, Raphune Hill, above the Paint Depot, ½ mile (1 km) east of Charlotte Amalie, Raphune* ☎ *340/777–3060* ⊕ *www.mangotangoart. com.*

CAMERAS AND ELECTRONICS
Boolchand's
CAMERAS/ELECTRONICS | This store sells brand-name cameras, audio and video equipment, and binoculars. ⊠ *Havensight Mall, Rte. 30, Bldg. II, Suite C, Havensight* ☎ *340/776–0302* ⊕ *www. boolchand.com.*

CHINA AND CRYSTAL
Caribbean Gems
CERAMICS/GLASSWARE | Find the best of Scandinavia here, including Royal Copenhagen, Georg Jensen, Kosta Boda, and Orrefors. There's also a large selection of jewels like white diamonds, rainbow sapphires, and Caribbean topaz. ⊠ *Havensight Mall, Bldg. III, Rte. 30, Havensight*

⚓ *The last store closest to cruise ship dock* ☎ *340/714–2162.*

CLOTHING
White House/Black Market
CLOTHING | This boutique sells sophisticated clothing for women. You'll find just the right party or evening-wear look in dresses, tops, and bottoms made out of everything from sequins to shimmering and satiny fabrics. Check out the perpetual sale rack in the back for the best deals. ⊠ *5316 Yacht Haven Grande, Suite 116, Charlotte Amalie* ☎ *340/776–5566* ⊕ *www.whitehouseblackmarket.com.*

FOODSTUFFS
Cost-U-Less
FOOD/CANDY | This is the Caribbean equivalent of Costco and Sam's Club and it sells everything from soup to nuts—in giant sizes and case lots—without a membership fee. The meat-and-seafood department, however, has family-size portions. There's a well-stocked fresh-produce section and a case filled with rotisserie chicken and baked goods. ⊠ *Rte. 38, ¼ mile (½ km) west of Rte. 39 intersection, Estate Annas Retreat* ☎ *340/777–3588* ⊕ *www.costuless.com.*

★ Fruit Bowl
FOOD/CANDY | This grocery store is the best place on the island to go for fresh fruits and vegetables. There are many ethnic, vegetarian, and health-food items as well as a fresh meat area, seafood department, and extensive salad and hot food bar. ⊠ *Wheatley Center, Intersection of Rtes. 38 and 313, Charlotte Amalie* ☎ *340/774–8565* ⊕ *www.thefruitbowlvi. com.*

Plaza Extra
FOOD/CANDY | This large, U.S.–style supermarket sells everything you need from produce to meat, including fresh seafood, a deli, and a bakery. You can find Caribbean ingredients and there's a liquor department, too. ⊠ *Tutu Park Shopping Mall, Rte. 38, Tutu* ☎ *340/775–5646* ⊕ *www.plazaextratutu.com.*

PriceSmart

FOOD/CANDY | FAMILY | This giant emporium carries everything from electronics to housewares in its members-only warehouse-size store. The meat, poultry, and seafood departments are especially popular. A small café in front sells pizzas, hot dogs, and the cheapest bottled water on the island—just $1 a pop. ⌧ *4400 Estate Charlotte Amalie, Rte. 38 west of Fort Mylner, Tutu* ☎ *340/777–3430* ⊕ *www. pricesmart.com.*

JEWELRY

Cardow Jewelers

JEWELRY/ACCESSORIES | This store is a chain—with gold in several lengths, widths, sizes, and styles—along with diamonds, emeralds, and other precious gems. You're guaranteed 40% to 60% savings off U.S. retail prices or your money will be refunded within 30 days of purchase. ⌧ *Crown Bay Center, Rte. 305, Crown Bay* ☎ *340/776–2038* ⊕ *www. cardow.com.*

Diamonds International

JEWELRY/ACCESSORIES | At this major chain shop with several outlets on St. Thomas, just choose a diamond, emerald, or tanzanite gem and a mounting, and you can have your dream ring set in an hour. Famous for having the largest inventory of diamonds on the island, this shop welcomes trade-ins, has a U.S. service center, and offers free diamond earrings with every purchase. ⌧ *Havensight Mall, Rte. 30, Bldg. II, Havensight* ☎ *340/776–0040* ⊕ *www.diamondsinternational. com.*

LIQUOR AND TOBACCO

Duty Free St. Thomas

TOBACCO | This giant duty-free liquor outlet offers a large selection of tobacco (including imported cigars), as well as cordials, wines, and rare vintage Armagnacs, cognacs, ports, and Madeiras. It also stocks fruits in brandy and barware from England. Enjoy rum samples at the tasting bar. Prices are among the best in St. Thomas. ⌧ *Havensight Mall, Rte. 30, Bldg. II, Havensight* ☎ *340/776–2303, 800/315–1600.*

Tobacco Discounters

TOBACCO | This duty-free outlet carries a full line of discounted brand-name cigarettes, cigars, and tobacco accessories. ⌧ *9100 Port of $ale Mall, Rte. 30, next to Havensight Mall, Havensight* ☎ *340/774–2256.*

West End

The west end of the island is lusher and quieter—with fewer houses and less traffic. Here there are roller-coaster routes (made all the scarier because the roads have no shoulders) as well as incredible vistas. Leave time in the afternoon for a swim and enjoy a slice of pizza at Magens Bay before leaving. A day in the country will reveal the tropical pleasures that have enticed more than one visitor to become a resident.

Sights

Drake's Seat

VIEWPOINT | Sir Francis Drake was supposed to have kept watch over his fleet from this vantage point, looking for enemy ships. The panorama is especially breathtaking (and romantic) at dusk, and if you plan to arrive late in the day, you'll miss the hordes of day-trippers on taxi tours who stop here to take pictures. ⌧ *Rte. 40, Mafolie* ✛ *Located ¼ mile (½ km) west of the intersection of Rtes. 40 and 35.*

Mountain Top

VIEWPOINT | FAMILY | Head out to the observation deck—more than 1,500 feet above sea level—to get a bird's-eye view that stretches from Puerto Rico's out-island of Culebra in the west all the way to the British Virgin Islands in the east. There's also a restaurant, restrooms, and duty-free shops that sell everything from Caribbean art to nautical antiques, ship models, and touristy T-shirts. Kids will like talking to the parrots—and hearing them answer back. ⊠ *Estate St. Peter* ✛ *Head north off Rte. 33, look for signs* ☏ *340/774–2400* ⊕ *www.mountaintopvi. com* ⊠ *Free.*

Phantasea Tropical Botanical Garden

GARDEN | Orchids, palms, cactus, and bromeliads are a few of the stunning plants that bloom along the self-guided hiking trails. These gardens are the essence of peace and quiet; they are located high on the island's lush north side. There are critters here too: peacocks, hummingbirds, and hermit crabs, to name a few. ⊠ *Bishop Dr. (intersection of Rtes. 334 and 33)* ✛ *On the road to Mountain Top* ☏ *340/774–2916* ⊕ *www.stthomasbotanicalgarden.com* ⊠ *$10.*

 Beaches

Hull Bay

BEACH—SIGHT | Watch surfers ride the waves here from December to March, when huge swells roll in from north Atlantic storms. The rest of the year, tranquility prevails at this picturesque neighborhood beach. Enjoy hot pizza, barbecue ribs, and a game of darts at the Hull Bay Hideaway Bar & Restaurant, home of the annual Bastille Day Kingfish Tournament held each July. **Amenities:** food and drink; parking; water sports. **Best for:** swimming; snorkeling; partiers. ⊠ *Hull Bay, Rte. 37, at end of road on north side, Estate Hull Bay.*

★ Magens Bay

BEACH—SIGHT | **FAMILY** | Deeded to the island as a public park, this heart-shape stretch of white sand is considered one of the most beautiful in the world. The bottom of the bay is flat and sandy, so this is a place for sunning and swimming rather than snorkeling. On weekends and holidays the sounds of music from groups partying under the sheds fill the air. There's a bar, snack shack, and beachwear boutique; bathhouses

with restrooms, changing rooms, and saltwater showers are close by. Sunfish, kayaks, and paddleboards are the most popular rentals at the water-sports kiosk. **Amenities:** food and drink; lifeguards; parking (fee); showers; toilets; water sports. **Best for:** partiers; swimming; walking. ⊠ *Magens Bay, Rte. 35, at end of road on north side of island* ☏ *340/777–6300* ⊕ *www.magensbayauthority.com* ⊠ *Adults $5, parking $2.*

🍴 Restaurants

Bella Blu

$$$ | **AUSTRIAN** | The Austrian-inspired menu at this quaint café includes five varieties of schnitzel and boasts a Caribbean flair with fresh-fish dishes like the house specialty of mahimahi in a lemon-butter sauce. Fork into omelets, waffles, Benedicts, or panini during weekend brunch from 10 am to 3 pm. **Known for:** hearty weekend brunch; local art; quaint setting on the waterfront in Frenchtown. ⑤ *Average main: $28* ⊠ *Frenchtown Mall, 24-A Honduras St., Frenchtown* ✛ *Across from the ballpark* ☏ *340/774–4349* ⊕ *www.bellabludining. com.*

Hook, Line and Sinker

$$$ | **SEAFOOD** | **FAMILY** | Anchored on the breezy Frenchtown waterfront and close to the pastel-painted boats of the local fishing fleet, this harbor-view eatery serves high-quality fish dishes like almond-crusted yellowtail snapper. Spicy jerk-seasoned swordfish and grilled tuna topped with a yummy mango-rum sauce are also good bets. **Known for:** creative seafood dishes; Sunday brunch; located 10 feet from the water. ⑤ *Average main: $24* ⊠ *Frenchtown Mall, 62 Honduras St., Frenchtown* ✛ *At the head of the French- town Marina docks* ☏ *340/776–9708* ⊕ *hlsvi.com.*

Sib's on the Mountain

$$ | **AMERICAN** | **FAMILY** | With live music and football on TV, Sib's is the perfect

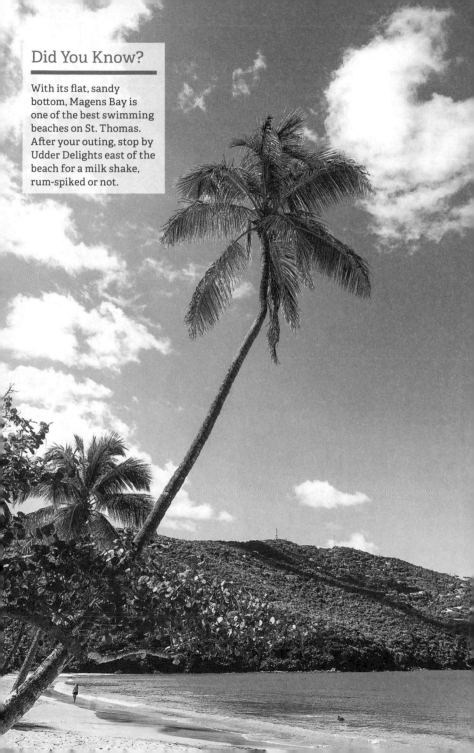

Did You Know?

With its flat, sandy bottom, Magens Bay is one of the best swimming beaches on St. Thomas. After your outing, stop by Udder Delights east of the beach for a milk shake, rum-spiked or not.

Mocko Jumbie Magic

Mocko Jumbies, the island's other-worldly stilt walkers, trace their roots back to West Africa. The steps of the stilt walkers held religious significance in West Africa, but today's West Indian version is more secular—bending backward to gravity-defying lengths and high kicking to the pulsating beat of drums, bells, and whistles.

Today satins and sequins have replaced costumes made of grasses, shells, and feathers. Festive headpieces—braids of feathers, glittering crowns, tall hats, and even spiky horns—attract plenty of attention from onlookers. A mask completes the outfit, assuring that the dancer's identity is concealed from spectators, thus maintaining the magic of the Mocko Jumbie.

Beyond Carnival celebrations, the Mocko Jumbie is so popular that it's a mainstay at many hotels. Mocko Jumbie dancers also perform at store openings, when cruise ships dock, or even at weekend beach jams. Old-fashioned or newfangled, Mocko Jumbies will always be loved best for driving away "jumbie spirits," as they say in the islands.

place for a casual dinner after a day at the beach. In addition to burgers, barbecue ribs and chicken, and beer, there's also a breakfast café outside with island-roasted coffees, including the signature "Bushwackercappuccino." **Known for:** casual American-style foods; historic locals hangout; gaming machines. ⑤ *Average main: $14* ✉ *Rte. 35, Mafolie* ☎ *340/774–8967* ⊕ *sibsonthemountain.com.*

Tickles Dockside Pub

$$ | **AMERICAN** | **FAMILY** | Nautical types and locals come here for casual fare with homey appeal: chicken-fried steak, meat loaf with mashed potatoes, and baby back ribs. Hearty breakfasts feature eggs and pancakes, and lunch is an array of burgers, salads, sandwiches, and soups. **Known for:** marina views; hearty food; Sunday brunch. ⑤ *Average main: $18* ✉ *8168 Crown Bay Marina, Suite 308, off Rte. 304, Contant* ☎ *340/777–8792* ⊕ *ticklesdocksidepub.com.*

Hotels

A few properties are in the hills overlooking Charlotte Amalie to the west or near Frenchtown, which is otherwise primarily residential.

Emerald Beach Resort

$ | **HOTEL** | You get beachfront ambience at this reasonably priced mini resort tucked beneath the palm trees, but the trade-off is that it's directly across from a noisy airport runway. **Pros:** beachfront location; good value; great Sunday brunch. **Cons:** airport noise until 10 pm; on a busy road; limited water sports. ⑤ *Rooms from: $240* ✉ *8070 Lindbergh Bay, Lindbergh Bay* ☎ *340/777–8800, 800/780–7234* ⊕ *www.emeraldbeach.com* ⌁ *90 rooms* ⑩ *Free Breakfast.*

Island View Guesthouse

$ | **B&B/INN** | Perched 545 feet up the face of Crown Mountain, this small, homey inn has hands-on owners who can book tours or offer tips about the best sightseeing spots. **Pros:** spectacular views; friendly atmosphere; good value. **Cons:** small pool; need a car to get around. ⑤ *Rooms from: $140* ✉ *Rte. 332,*

Contant ☎ *340/774–4270, 800/524–2023* 🛏 *12 rooms* 🍴 *Free Breakfast.*

Activities

AIR TOURS
Caribbean Buzz Helicopters
TOUR—SPORTS | Near to the UVI field, Caribbean Buzz Helicopters offers a minimum 30-minute tour that includes St. Thomas, St. John, the west end of Tortola, Jost Van Dyke, and all the cays in between. It's a nice ride if you can afford the splurge (tours are from $750 for up to three people), but in truth, you can see most of the aerial sights from Paradise Point or Mountain Top, and there's no place you can't reach easily by car or boat. ✉ *Jet Port, 8202 Lindbergh Bay, Charlotte Amalie* ☎ *340/775–7335* ⊕ *www.caribbean-buzz.com.*

BOATING AND SAILING
Calm seas, crystal waters, and nearby islands (perfect for picnicking, snorkeling, and exploring) make St. Thomas a favorite jumping-off spot for day- or weeklong sails or powerboat adventures. With more than 100 vessels from which to choose, St. Thomas is the charter-boat center of the U.S. Virgin Islands. You can go through a broker to book a sailing vessel with a crew or contact a charter company directly. Crewed charters start at approximately $3,800 per person per week, while bareboat charters can start at as little as $2,600 per person for a 50- to 55-foot sailboat (but this doesn't include provisioning, fuel, and optional add-ons like water-toy rentals), which can comfortably accommodate up to six people. If you want to rent your own boat, hire a captain. Most local captains are excellent tour guides.

Single-day charters are also a possibility. You can hire smaller boats for the day, including the services of a captain if you wish to have someone take you on a guided snorkel trip around the islands.

Island Yachts
BOATING | The sailboats from Island Yachts are available for charter with or without crews. ✉ *6100 Red Hook Quarter, 18B, Red Hook* ☎ *340/775–6666, 800/524–2019* ⊕ *www.iyc.vi.*

★ Magic Moments
BOATING | *Luxury* is the word at Magic Moments, where crews aboard the 45-foot Sea Rays offer pampered island-hopping snorkeling cruises for between $1,650 and $2,450 for up to six people. Nice touches include a wine-and-lobster lunch and icy-cold eucalyptus-infused washcloths for freshening up. ✉ *American Yacht Harbor, 6501 Red Hook Plaza, Suite 201, Docks B and C, Red Hook* ☎ *340/775–5066* ⊕ *www.yachtmagicmoments.com.*

Nauti Nymph
BOATING | Fountain 29-foot center console powerboats are available from this company. Rates, which start at $750 a day, include snorkeling gear, water skis, and outriggers, but not fuel. Half-day rates available. You can hire a captain for $150 more per day. ✉ *American Yacht Harbor Marina, 6501 Red Hook Plaza, Suite 201, Docks B and C, Red Hook* ☎ *540/775–5066, 800/734–7345* ⊕ *www.nautinymph.com.*

Stewart Yacht Charters
BOATING | Run by longtime sailor Ellen Stewart, this company is skilled at matching clients with yachts and crews for weeklong charter holidays. ✉ *6501 Red Hook Plaza, Suite 20, Red Hook* ☎ *340/775–1358, 800/432–6118.*

VIP Yacht Charters
BOATING | Powerboats from 49 to 59 feet, including a selection of stable trawlers, are available for bareboat charter. Professional captains available on request, for an extra charge. ✉ *Compass Point Marina, 6300 Estate Frydenhoj, south of Rte. 32, Suite 27, Estate Frydenhoj* ☎ *340/774–9224, 866/847–9224* ⊕ *www.vipyachts.com.*

DIVING AND SNORKELING

Popular dive sites include such wrecks as the *Cartanser Sr.,* a beautifully encrusted World War II cargo ship sitting in 35 feet of water, and the *General Rogers,* a Coast Guard cutter resting at 65 feet. Here you can find a gigantic resident barracuda. Reef dives offer hidden caves and archways at **Cow and Calf Rocks,** coral-covered pinnacles at **Frenchcap,** and tunnels where you can explore undersea from the Caribbean to the Atlantic at **Thatch Cay, Grass Cay,** and **Congo Cay.** Many resorts and charter yachts offer dive packages. A one-tank dive starts at $120; two-tank dives are $140 and up. Call the USVI Department of Tourism to obtain a free eight-page guide to Virgin Islands dive sites. There are plenty of snorkeling possibilities, too.

Admiralty Dive Center

SCUBA DIVING | Boat dives, rental equipment, and a retail store are available from this dive center. You can also get multiple-tank packages if you want to dive over several days. ⊠ *Frenchtown Marina, Charlotte Amalie* ✛ *Next to Hook, Line and Sinker Restaurant* ☎ *340/777–9802, 888/900–3483* ⊕ *www.admiraltydive. com.*

B.O.S.S. Underwater Adventure

SCUBA DIVING | As an alternative to traditional diving, try an underwater motor scooter called B.O.S.S., or Breathing Observation Submersible Scooter. A 3½-hour tour, including snorkel equipment, rum punch, and towels, is $140 per person. ⊠ *Crown Bay Marina, Rte. 304, Charlotte Amalie* ☎ *340/777–3549* ⊕ *www.bossusvi.com.*

Coki Dive Center

SCUBA DIVING | **FAMILY** | Snorkeling and dive tours in the fish-filled reefs off Coki Beach are available from this PADI 5 Star outfit, as are classes, including one on underwater photography. It's run by the avid diver Peter Jackson. ⊠ *Rte. 388 at Coki Point, Frydendal* ☎ *340/775–4220* ⊕ *www.cokidive.com.*

Snuba of St. Thomas

SCUBA DIVING | **FAMILY** | In Snuba, a snorkeling and scuba-diving hybrid, a 20-foot air hose connects you to the surface. The cost is $85. Children must be age eight or older to participate. ⊠ *Rte. 388 at Coki Point, Estate Smith Bay* ☎ *340/693–8063* ⊕ *www.visnuba.com.*

St. Thomas Diving Club

SCUBA DIVING | This PADI 5 Star center offers boat dives to the reefs around Buck Island and nearby offshore wrecks, as well as multiday dive packages. ⊠ *Bolongo Bay Beach Resort, Rte. 30, Bolongo* ☎ *340/776–2381* ⊕ *www.stthomasdivingclub.com.*

FISHING

Fishing here is synonymous with blue marlin angling—especially from June through October. Four 1,000-pound-plus blues, including three world records, have been caught on the famous North Drop, about 20 miles (32 km) north of St. Thomas. A day charter for marlin with up to six anglers costs from $1,750 to $2,000 for the day. If you're not into marlin fishing, try hooking sailfish in winter, dolphin (the fish, not the mammal) in spring, and wahoo in fall. Inshore trips for four hours range from $750 to $950. To find the trip that will best suit you, walk down the docks at either American Yacht Harbor or Sapphire Beach Marina in the late afternoon and chat with the captains and crews.

Abigail III

FISHING | Captain Red Bailey's *Abigail III* specializes in marlin fishing. It operates out of the Sapphire Condominium Resort's marina. ⊠ *Estate Smith Bay, Rte. 38, ¼ mile (½ km) northwest of Red Hook, Sapphire Bay* ☎ *340/775–6024* ⊕ *www.visportfish.com.*

★ Double Header Sportfishing

FISHING | **FAMILY** | This company offers trips out to the North Drop on its 40-foot sportfisher and half-day reef and bay trips aboard its two speedy 37-foot

center consoles. ⌂ *Sapphire Bay Marina, Rte. 38, Sapphire Bay* ☏ *340/777–7317* ⊕ *www.doubleheadersportfishing.net.*

Marlin Prince

FISHING | Captain Eddie Morrison, one of the most experienced charter operators in St. Thomas, specializes in fly-fishing for blue marlin from his 45-foot Viking boat. ⌂ *American Yacht Harbor, 6100 Red Hook Quarters No. 2, slip A-16, Red Hook* ☏ *340/693–5929* ⊕ *www.marlinprince. com.*

GUIDED TOURS

VI Taxi Association St. Thomas City-Island Tour

TOUR—SPORTS | The VI Taxi Association gives a two-hour tour for two people in an open-air safari bus or enclosed van. Aimed at cruise-ship passengers, this $29 tour includes stops at Drake's Seat and Mountain Top. Other tours include a three-hour trip to Coki Beach with a shopping stop in downtown Charlotte Amalie for $35 per person; a three-hour trip to the Coral World Ocean Park for $45 per person; and a five-hour beach tour to St. John for $75 per person. For $60 for two, you can hire a taxi for a customized three-hour drive around the island. Make sure to see Mountain Top, as the view is wonderful. ☏ *340/774–4550* ⊕ *vitaxiassociation.com.*

SEA EXCURSIONS

Landlubbers and seafarers alike will enjoy the wind in their hair and salt spray in the air while exploring the waters surrounding St. Thomas. Several businesses can book you on a snorkel-and-sail to a deserted cay for a half day that starts at $90 per person or a full day that begins at $140 per person. An excursion over to the British Virgin Islands starts at $145 per person, not including customs fees. A luxury daylong motor-yacht cruise complete with gourmet lunch is $450 or more per person.

★ Adventure Center

BOATING | **FAMILY** | For a soup-to-nuts choice of sea tours including a stand-up paddleboard safari, full- and half-day sails, sunset cruises, fishing trips, powerboat rentals, and kayak tours, contact the Adventure Center. ⌂ *Marriott Frenchman's Cove Vacation Club, Rte. 315, Estate Bakkero* ☏ *340/473–5708* ⊕ *www. adventurecenters.net.*

SEA KAYAKING

★ Virgin Islands Ecotours

KAYAKING | **FAMILY** | Fish dart, birds sing, and iguanas lounge on the limbs of dense mangrove trees deep within a marine sanctuary on St. Thomas's southeast shore. With Virgin Islands Ecotours you can learn about the islands' natural history in a guided kayak-snorkel tour to Patricia Cay or via an inflatable boat tour to Cas Cay for snorkeling and hiking. Both are 2½ hours long. VI Ecotours also offers three- and five-hour guided kayak tours to St. Thomas's Mangrove Lagoon, Hassel Island, Henley Cay, and St. John's Honeymoon Bay. All trips include free snorkel instruction with snacks on three-hour trips and lunch on five-hour trips. The historic Hassel Island tour includes a visit to some of the historic forts and military structures on the island, a short hike to a breathtaking vista, and a swim off a deserted beach. In addition to kayaks, there's also a one-hour tour in the Mangrove Lagoon on stand-up paddleboards. ⌂ *Mangrove Lagoon, Rte. 32, 2 miles (3 km) east of the intersection of Rtes. 32 and 30, Nadir* ☏ *340/779–2155, 877/845–2925* ⊕ *www.viecotours.com* ⌑ *From $69 to $139 per person; 1-hr SUP tour $39.*

STAND-UP PADDLEBOARDING

St. Thomas Scuba & Snorkel Adventures

WATER SPORTS | There's a large variety of stand-up paddleboards to rent, something that can suit every family member. The waters off Hull Bay Beach are usually calm, protected by offshore reefs, and ideal for a paddle. ⌂ *Hull Bay Hideaway* *bar and restaurant, 10-1 Hull Bay, Estate Hull Bay ☎ 340/474–9332 ⊕ www. stthomasadventures.com ✉ $60 per day for board; additional $50 for lesson and guide.*

TENNIS

Ritz-Carlton, St. Thomas

TENNIS | Two courts are available at the Ritz-Carlton, where nonguests can take lessons. ⊠ *6900 Great Bay, end of Rte. 317, Nazareth* ☎ *340/775–3333* ⊕ *www. ritzcarlton.com* ✉ *$120 per hour and $60 per half hour.*

Subbase

TENNIS | There are two public tennis courts, open on a first-come, first-served basis at no cost. Lights are on until 10 pm. ⊠ *Rte. 306, next to Water and Power Authority, Charlotte Amalie.*

Chapter 4

ST. JOHN

4

Updated by
Carol Bareuther

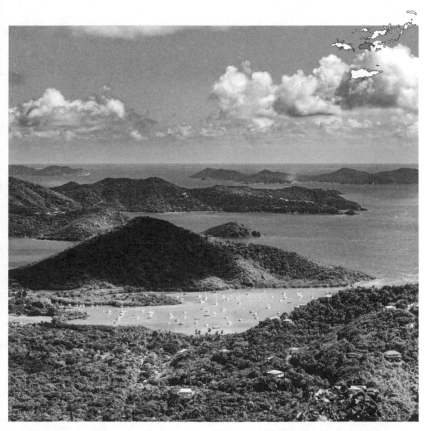

👁 Sights	🍴 Restaurants	🛏 Hotels	🛍 Shopping	🍸 Nightlife
★★★★★	★★★★★	★★★☆☆	★★☆☆☆	★★★☆☆

WELCOME TO ST. JOHN

TOP REASONS TO GO

★ **Beach-hopping:** Fill your cooler with cold drinks, grab the snorkeling gear, and stash your beach chair in the back of your car for a day spent at the beaches along St. John's North Shore Road.

★ **Hiking Reef Bay:** Opt for a trip with a ranger in Virgin Islands National Park. A safari bus takes you to the trailhead, and a boat brings you back.

★ **Snorkeling at Trunk Bay:** Trunk Bay is St. John's most popular snorkeling spot, and for good reason: a snorkeling trail teaches you about the local marine life.

★ **Relaxing in a villa:** There are about 1,000 vacation villas across the island in all sizes, prices, and locations; most will give you all the comforts of home.

★ **Exploring Cruz Bay:** Spend a half day poking around Cruz Bay's varied stores, shopping for that perfect gift for the folks back home.

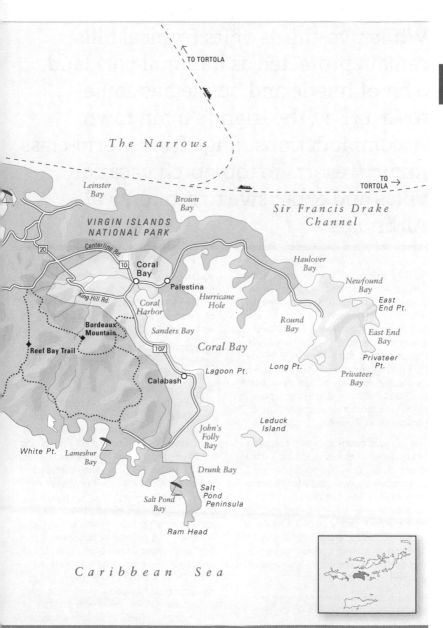

TO TORTOLA

The Narrows

Leinster Bay

Brown Bay

Sir Francis Drake Channel

TO TORTOLA →

VIRGIN ISLANDS
NATIONAL PARK

Centerline Rd.

20

10 **Coral Bay**

Palestina

Haulover Bay

Newfound Bay

King Hill Rd.

Coral Harbor

Hurricane Hole

East End Pt.

Bordeaux Mountain

Sanders Bay

Round Bay

East End Bay

107

Coral Bay

Privateer Pt.

Reef Bay Trail

Long Pt.

Privateer Bay

Calabash

Lagoon Pt.

Leduck Island

White Pt.

Lameshur Bay

John's Folly Bay

Drunk Bay

Salt Pond Bay

Salt Pond Peninsula

Ram Head

Caribbean Sea

Only 3 miles (5 km) from St. Thomas but still a world apart, St. John is the least developed of the U.S. Virgin Islands. While two-thirds of its tropical hills remain protected as national parkland, a bit of hustle and bustle has come to Cruz Bay, the island's main town. Accommodations range from world-class luxury resorts to top-notch vacation villas and expensive to economical Airbnbs.

St. John's heart is Virgin Islands National Park, a treasure that takes up a full two-thirds of St. John's 20 square miles (53 square km). The park was spearheaded by Laurance S. Rockefeller and Frank Stick and was finally handed over to the Department of the Interior in 1956. The park helps keep the island's interior in its pristine and undisturbed state, but if you go at midday you'll probably have to share your stretch of beach with others, particularly at Trunk Bay.

The island is booming, and it can get a tad crowded at the ever-popular Trunk Bay Beach during the busy winter season; parking woes plague the island's main town of Cruz Bay, but you won't find traffic jams or pollution. It's easy to escape from the fray: just head off on a hike or go early or late to the beach. The sun won't be as strong, and you may have that perfect crescent of white sand all to yourself.

St. John doesn't have a major agrarian past like her sister island, St. Croix, but if you're hiking in the dry season, you can probably stumble upon the stone ruins of old plantations. The less adventuresome can visit the repaired ruins at the park's Annaberg Plantation.

In 1675 Jorgen Iverson claimed the unsettled island for Denmark. By 1733 there were more than 1,000 slaves working more than 100 plantations. In that year the island was hit by a drought, hurricanes, and a plague of insects that destroyed the summer crops. With famine a real threat and the planters keeping them under tight rein, the slaves revolted on November 23, 1733. They captured the fort at Coral Bay, took control of the island, and held on to it for six months. During this period, about 20% of the island's total population was killed. The rebellion was eventually put down in part by French troops from Martinique. Slavery continued until 1848, when slaves in St. Croix marched on Frederiksted to demand their freedom from the Danish government. This time it was granted. After emancipation, St. John's inhabitants mostly made a living on small farms. Life continued in much the same way until the national park opened in 1956 and tourism became an industry.

Of the three U.S. Virgin Islands, St. John, which has 5,000 residents, has the strongest sense of community, which is primarily rooted in a desire to protect the island's natural beauty. Despite the growth, there are still many pockets of tranquility. Here you can truly escape the pressures of modern life for a day, a week—perhaps forever.

Getting Here and Around

AIR

St. John does not have an airport, so you will need to fly into St. Thomas and then take a ferry over.

BUS

Modern Vitran buses on St. John run from the Cruz Bay ferry dock through Coral Bay to the far eastern end of the island at Salt Pond, making numerous stops in between. The fare is $1 to any point, but the service is slow and not always reliable.

CAR

You will almost certainly need a car if you are staying in a villa or in Coral Bay, but you might be able to get by with taxis if you are staying elsewhere. The terrain in St. John is very hilly, the roads are winding, and the blind curves numerous. Major roads are well paved, but once you get off a specific route, dirt roads filled with potholes are common. For such driving, a four-wheel-drive vehicle is your best bet. Be aware that you can't bring all rental cars over to St. John from St. Thomas. Even more important, the barge service is very busy, so you can't always get a space.

St. John has only two gas stations, both at the Cruz Bay end of the island, so make sure you're not near empty when you set out for Coral Bay.

■TIP→ **Parking in Cruz Bay is difficult, but if you can't find a spot, there's plenty of room at the lot near the public tennis courts. Your best bet is to rent a car from a company that allows you to park in its lot.** Make sure you ask before you sign on the dotted line if you plan to spend time in Cruz Bay.

CAR RENTALS

All the car-rental companies in St. John are locally owned, and most are just a short walk from the ferry dock in Cruz Bay. Those located a bit farther away will pick you up.

CONTACTS Best. ⊠ *Near library, Cruz Bay* ☎ *340/693–8177.* **Cool Breeze.** ⊠ *1 block east of the passenger ferry dock, Cruz Bay* ☎ *340/776–6588* ⊕ *www.cool-breezecarrental.com.* **Courtesy.** ⊠ *Near St. Ursula's Church, Cruz Bay* ☎ *340/776–6650* ⊕ *www.courtesycarrental.com.* **Denzil Clyne.** ⊠ *North Shore Rd., across from creek, Cruz Bay* ☎ *340/776–6715.* **O'Connor Car Rental.** ⊠ *Rte. 104, near the roundabout, Cruz Bay* ☎ *340/776–6343* ⊕ *www.oconnorcarrental.com.* **St. John Car Rental.** ⊠ *Bay St., near Wharfside Village, Cruz Bay* ☎ *340/776–6103* ⊕ *www. stjohncarrental.com.*

FERRY

There's frequent daily service from both Red Hook and Charlotte Amalie on St. Thomas to Cruz Bay (the more frequent ferry is the one from Red Hook). There's also frequent service from Cruz Bay to Tortola and less frequent service to the other British Virgin Islands, including Jost Van Dyke (some via Tortola). Virgin Islands ferry schedules are published on the website of the Virgin Islands Vacation Guide and Community. The actual schedules change, so you should check with the ferry companies to determine the current schedules. Remember that a passport is now required to travel between the USVI and BVI by ferry.

CONTACTS Virgin Islands Vacation Guide and Community. ⊕ *www.vinow.com.*

TAXI

Taxis meet ferries arriving in Cruz Bay. Most drivers use vans or open-air safari buses. You can find them congregated at the dock and at hotel parking lots. You can also hail them anywhere on the road. Almost all trips will be shared, and prices are per person. Paradise Taxi will pick you up if you call, but most drivers don't provide that service. If you need one to pick you up at your rental villa, ask the villa manager to call or arrange a ride in advance.

CONTACTS Paradise Taxi. ✉ *Waterfront, Cruz Bay* ☎ *340/714–7913.*

Essentials

BANKS

St. John has one full-service bank plus several bank ATMs. First Bank provides full services at its location one block up from the ferry dock. Banco Popular has a convenient ATM one block from the ferry dock.

BEACHES

St. John is blessed with many beaches, and all of them fall into the good, great, and don't-tell-anyone-else-about-this-place categories. Those along the north shore are all within the national park. Some are more developed than others—and many are crowded on weekends, holidays, and in high season—but by and large they're still pristine. Beaches along the south and eastern shores are quiet and isolated.

HOTELS

St. John doesn't have many beachfront hotels, but that's a small price to pay for all the pristine sand. The island's one major resort—Westin St. John Resort & Villas—is on the beach. Most villas are in the residential south-shore area, a 15-minute drive from the north-shore beaches. If you head east you come to the laid-back community of Coral Bay, where there are growing numbers of villas and cottages. If you're looking for village charm, there are a few inns in Cruz Bay. Your choice of accommodations also includes condominiums and cottages near town; ecoresorts; and luxurious villas, often with a pool or a hot tub (sometimes both) and a stunning view.

St. John attracts so many different kinds of travelers because accommodations come in all price ranges. Folks on a budget can find inexpensive digs via Airbnb and VRBO. Cruz Bay has a few moderately priced guesthouses and no-frills vacation villas. Those with fatter wallets will have no trouble finding a room at the island's resort or luxury vacation villas. St. John also has several resort-style condo complexes. Many of the island's condos are just minutes from the hustle and bustle of Cruz Bay, but you can find more scattered around the island. You need a car, since most lodgings are in the hills and very few are at the beach.

Hotel reviews have been shortened. For full information go to Fodors.com.

Carefree Getaways

This company manages vacation villas, private homes, cottages, and condos on the island's eastern and western sides. ✉ *Cruz Bay* ☎ *340/779–4070, 888/643–6002* ⊕ *www.carefreegetaways.com.*

Caribbean Villas of St. John, USVI

Caribbean Villas handles condo rentals for Battery Hill, Bougainvillea Villa, Cruz Views, Lavender Hill, and Grande Bay Resort, as well as for many private villas. ☎ *340/776–6152, 800/338–0987* ⊕ *www.caribbeanvilla.com.*

Caribe Havens

Specializing in the budget market, Caribe Havens has properties primarily in the Cruz Bay area. ✉ *Cruz Bay* ☎ *340/776–6518* ⊕ *www.caribehavens.com.*

Catered to Vacation Homes

Specializing in luxury villas, this company has listings mainly in the middle of the island and on the western side.

✉ *Marketplace Suite 206, 5206 Enighed, Cruz Bay* ☎ *340/776–6641, 800/424–6641* ⊕ *www.cateredto.com.*

Cloud 9 Villas

Two beautiful villas for rent, one near Cruz Bay and the other in Coral Bay. ☎ *503/819–5385* ⊕ *www.cloud9villas. com.*

Island Getaways

Options from Island Getaways are mainly villas in the Rendezvous, Chocolate Hole, and Coral Bay areas. ☎ *340/693–7676, 888/693–7676* ⊕ *www.islandgetaway-sinc.com.*

Seaview Homes

As the name implies, this company's specialty is houses with views of the ocean: they are in the Chocolate Hole, Great Cruz Bay, and Fish Bay areas. ☎ *340/776–6805* ⊕ *www.seaviewhomes. com.*

St. John Ultimate Villas

St. John Ultimate Villas manages villas across the island. ☎ *340/776–4703, 888/851–7588* ⊕ *www.stjohnultimatevil-las.com.*

Star Villas

Star has cozy villas just outside Cruz Bay. ☎ *340/626–5118* ⊕ *www.starvillas.com.*

Vacation Vistas

This company's villas are mainly in the Chocolate Hole, Great Cruz Bay, and Rendezvous areas. ☎ *340/776–6462, 888/334–5222* ⊕ *www.vacationvistas. com.*

Windspree

Windspree's stock is mainly in and around Coral Bay. ✉ *7924 Emmaus, Coral Bay* ☎ *340/201–3002* ⊕ *www.windspree. com.*

RESTAURANTS

The cuisine on St. John seems to get better every year, with culinary school–trained chefs vying to see who can come up with the most imaginative dishes. There are restaurants to suit every taste

and budget—from some of the more elegant establishments in Cruz Bay (where the only dress code is "no bathing suits") to the casual beach bars of Coral Bay. For quick lunches, try the West Indian food stands and food trucks in Cruz Bay Park and across from the post office. Some restaurants close for vacation in September and even October. If you have your heart set on a special place, call ahead to make sure it's open during these months. In the December to April peak season, reservations are often required.

With the exception of the grown-on-the-island greens, which you can find in salads at a wide variety of local restaurants, and an occasional catch of local fish, almost all the food served here is imported from the mainland. This means that you may find prices on restaurant menus and supermarket shelves on the high side, since the shipping costs are passed along to the consumer.

WHAT IT COSTS in U.S. Dollars

	$	$$	$$$	$$$$
RESTAURANTS				
	under $13	$13–$20	$21–$30	over $30
HOTELS				
	under $276	$276–$375	$376–$475	over $475

NIGHTLIFE

St. John isn't the place to go for glitter and all-night partying. Still, after-hours Cruz Bay can be a lively little town in which to dine, drink, and dance. Notices posted on the bulletin board outside the Connections telephone center—up the street from the ferry dock—or listings in the island's newspaper (*Tradewinds*) will keep you apprised of local events.

SAFETY

Although crime is not as prevalent on St. John as it is on St. Thomas and St. Croix, it does exist. Keep your hotel or vacation villa door locked at all times, even during the day if you are, say, out by the pool. Stick to well-lighted streets at night, and use the same kind of street sense that you would in any unfamiliar territory. It's not a good idea to walk around Cruz Bay late at night. If you don't have a car, plan on taking a taxi, which you should arrange in advance.

TOUR OPTIONS

On St. John taxi drivers provide tours of the island, making stops at various sites, including Trunk Bay and Annaberg Plantation, for about $25 per person. Rangers at the V.I. National Park Visitors Center give several guided tours on- and offshore (some requiring reservations).

CONTACTS V.I. National Park Visitors Center. ⊠ *North Shore Rd., at creek, Cruz Bay* ☎ *340/776–6201* ⊕ *www.nps.gov/ viis.*

VISITOR INFORMATION

CONTACTS USVI Division of Tourism. ⊠ *Henry Samuel St., next to post office, Cruz Bay* ☎ *340/776–6450* ⊕ *www.visitusvi.com.* **Virgin Islands Hotel & Tourism Association.** ☎ *340/774–6835* ⊕ *usvihta. com.*

Cruz Bay and Environs

Sights

St. John's main town may be compact (it consists of only several blocks), but it's definitely a hub: the ferries from St. Thomas and the British Virgin Islands pull in here, and it's where you can get a taxi or rent a car to travel around the island. There are plenty of shops in which to browse, a number of watering holes where you can stop for a breather, many restaurants, and a grassy square with benches where you can sit back and take everything in. Look for the current edition of the handy, amusing "St. John Map" featuring Max the Mongoose.

Elaine Ione Sprauve Library

LIBRARY | On the hill just above Cruz Bay is the Enighed Estate greathouse, built in 1757. *Enighed* is Danish for "concord" (unity or peace). The house and its outbuildings (a sugar factory and horse-driven mill) were destroyed by fire and hurricanes, and the house sat in ruins until 1982. Don't miss the collection of books, paintings, newspaper clippings, and photographs that document the island's history. ⊠ *Rte. 104, Cruz Bay* ⊹ *Make a right past St. Ursula's Church* ☎ *340/776–6359* ⊠ *Free.*

★ Virgin Islands National Park

NATIONAL/STATE PARK | Covering more than 60% of St. John, Virgin Islands National Park preserves the island's natural environments. If you're interested in bird-watching, snorkeling, camping, history, or just strolling in beautiful environs, then Virgin Islands National Park is the place for you. At Francis Bay there's a boardwalk through the mangroves, where birds may be plentiful; Salt Pond Bay offers pleasant snorkeling; and plantation history can be explored at Annaberg Sugar Mill ruins.

There are more than 20 trails on the north and south shores, with guided hikes along the most popular routes. A full-day trip to Reef Bay is a must; it's an easy hike through lush and dry forest, past the ruins of an old plantation, and to a sugar factory adjacent to the beach. It can be a bit arduous for young kids, however. The nonprofit Friends of the Virgin Islands National Park runs a $60 per person ranger-guided tour to Reef Bay that includes a safari bus ride to the trailhead and a boat ride back to the visitor center. The schedule changes from season to season; call for times and to make reservations, which are essential. To pick up a useful guide to St. John's hiking trails, see various large maps of the island, and find out about current Park Service programs—including guided walks and cultural demonstrations—stop

4

St. John CRUZ BAY AND ENVIRONS

Cruz Bay

KEY
- ① Sights
- ① Restaurants
- ① Quick Bites
- ① Hotels
- ⚓ Ferry

0.5 mi
0.5 km

Sights ▶
1 Elaine Ione Sprauve Library G2
2 Virgin Islands National Park F1

Restaurants ▶
1 Café Roma F1
2 Greengo's Caribbean Cantina G1
3 High Tide Bar & Seafood Grill E2
4 Lime Inn E2
5 Morgan's Mango F1
6 North Shore Deli G1
7 Sam and Jack's Deli H3
8 Sun Dog Café G1
9 The Tap Room Brew Pub G1
10 Uncle Joe's Barbecue ... F1
11 Zozo's H2O B1

Quick Bites ▶
1 St. John Scoops G1

Hotels ▶
1 Coconut Coast Villas C3
2 Estate Lindholm F1
3 Gallows Point Resort ... B2
4 Garden by the Sea Bed and Breakfast C3
5 Grande Bay Resort C2
6 Inn at Tamarind Court ... G2
7 St. John Inn G3
8 Sea Shore Allure D3
9 Westin St. John Resort and Villas H3

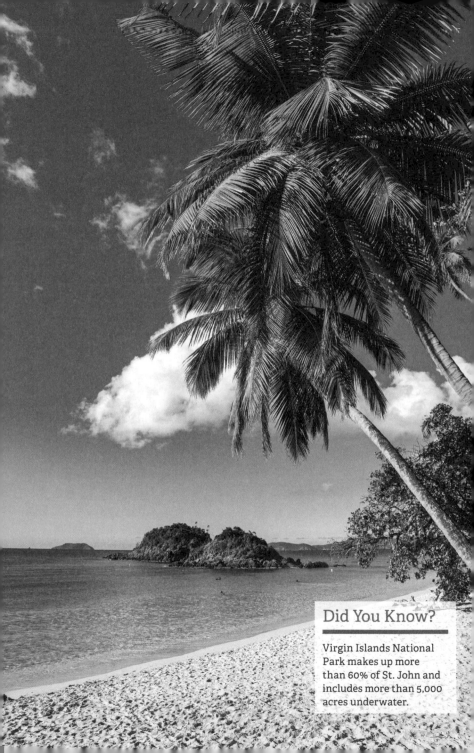

Did You Know?

Virgin Islands National Park makes up more than 60% of St. John and includes more than 5,000 acres underwater.

by the park visitor center at the western tip of the park in Cruz Bay on North Shore Road. ⊠ *North Shore Rd., near creek, Cruz Bay* ☎ *340/776–6201* ⊕ *www.nps. gov/viis.*

🍴 Restaurants

Café Roma

$$$ | **ITALIAN** | **FAMILY** | This second-floor restaurant in the heart of Cruz Bay is *the* place for traditional Italian cuisine: lasagna, spaghetti and meatballs, and seafood manicotti. Small pizzas are available at the table, but larger ones are for takeout or at the bar. **Known for:** authentic Italian cuisine; lively atmosphere; rum-spiked bread pudding. ⑤ *Average main: $26* ⊠ *Vesta Gade, Cruz Bay* ☎ *340/776–6524* ⊕ *www.stjohn-caferoma.com* ⊙ *No lunch.*

Greengo's Caribbean Cantina

$$ | **MEXICAN** | This is the place to go for Mexican food on St. John. You'll find nacho starters, tacos, burritos, and enchiladas as well as a half dozen margarita variations to wash it all down. **Known for:** fresh tortillas; infused tequila; cool murals. ⑤ *Average main: $16* ⊠ *Mongoose Junction shopping center, North Shore Rd., Cruz Bay* ☎ *340/777–8226* ⊕ *www.greengoscantina.com.*

High Tide Bar & Seafood Grill

$$$ | **ECLECTIC** | **FAMILY** | This casual spot right at Cruz Bay Beach serves everything from hamburgers and mahimahi sandwiches to surf and turf and Caribbean lobster. At happy hour, order a Painkiller and watch the sunset over the bay. **Known for:** family-friendly atmosphere; beachfront setting; good happy hour. ⑤ *Average main: $29* ⊠ *Wharfside Village, Strand St., Cruz Bay* ☎ *340/714–6169* ⊕ *www.hightidevi.com.*

Lime Inn

$$$ | **ECLECTIC** | The vacationers and mainland transplants who call St. John home like to flock to this alfresco spot for the congenial hospitality and good food, including all-you-can-eat shrimp on Wednesday night. Fresh lobster is the specialty, and the menu also includes shrimp-and-steak dishes and rotating chicken and pasta specials. **Known for:** fresh lobster; local hangout; Lime Out, a floating taco bar off the east end of the island. ⑤ *Average main: $30* ⊠ *Lemon Tree Mall, King St., Cruz Bay* ☎ *340/776–6425* ⊕ *thelimeinn.com* ⊙ *No lunch weekends.*

Morgan's Mango

$$$ | **CARIBBEAN** | A visit to this alfresco eatery requires you to climb a long flight of stairs, but the food is well worth the effort. Although fish is the specialty—try the voodoo snapper topped with a fruity salsa—the chef also creates a vegetarian platter with black beans, fried plantains, and a mound of sweet potatoes. **Known for:** fresh fish; vegetarian dishes. ⑤ *Average main: $25* ⊠ *Across from V.I. National Park Visitors Center, North Shore Rd., Cruz Bay* ☎ *340/693–8141* ⊕ *www. morgansmango.com* ⊙ *No lunch.*

North Shore Deli

$ | **ECLECTIC** | At this air-conditioned (but no-frills) sandwich shop you place your order at the counter and wait for it to be delivered to your table or for takeout. The classic Reuben is a favorite, but other sandwiches, like the turkey pesto and vegan flatbread, also get rave reviews. **Known for:** hearty sandwiches; tropical fruit smoothies; grab-and-go menu makes great beach or hiking picnic fixings. ⑤ *Average main: $10* ⊠ *Mongoose Junction Shopping Center, North Shore Rd., Cruz Bay* ☎ *340/777–3061* ⊕ *www. northshoredelistjohn.com* ▭ *No credit cards* ⊙ *No dinner.*

★ Sam and Jack's Deli

$$ | **DELI** | The sandwiches are scrumptious, but this deli also dishes up wonderful meals to-go that just need heating. There are a few seats inside, but most folks opt to eat at the tables in front of the deli. **Known for:** picnic-ready meals; truffle-and-wild-mushroom ravioli;

villa and yacht provisioning available. Ⓢ *Average main: $14* ✉ *Marketplace Shopping Center, 3rd fl., Rte. 104, Cruz Bay* ☎ *340/714–3354* ⊕ *www.samandjacksdeli.com.*

★ Sun Dog Café

$$ | **ECLECTIC** | There's an unusual assortment of dishes at this charming alfresco restaurant, which you'll find tucked into a courtyard in the upper reaches of the Mongoose Junction shopping center. The Jamaican jerk chicken salad and the black-bean quesadilla are good choices. **Known for:** eclectic menu; white pizza with artichoke hearts; live music on the weekends. Ⓢ *Average main: $16* ✉ *Mongoose Junction Shopping Center, North Shore Rd., Cruz Bay* ☎ *340/693–8340* ⊕ *www.sundogcafe.com.*

The Tap Room Brew Pub

$$ | **AMERICAN** | More than a dozen house-brewed beers on tap, including the signature Tropical Mango Pale Ale, make dining at St. John Brewers' tap room special. The rich wood decor is the perfect place for a soft Bavarian-style pretzel, burgers, and build-your-own-pizzas. **Known for:** on-site microbrewery; lively atmosphere; local hangout. Ⓢ *Average main: $16* ✉ *Mongoose Junction Shopping Center, Rte. 104, Cruz Bay* ☎ *340/715–7775* ⊕ *stjohnbrewers.com.*

Uncle Joe's Barbecue

$$ | **BARBECUE** | **FAMILY** | Juicy ribs and tasty chicken legs dripping with house barbecue sauce make for one of St. John's best dining deals. An ear of corn, rice, and a generous scoop of macaroni salad, potato salad, or coleslaw round out the plate. **Known for:** casual sidewalk dining; good value. Ⓢ *Average main: $15* ✉ *North Shore Rd., across from post office, Cruz Bay* ☎ *340/693–8806.*

★ Zozo's H20

$$$$ | **ECLECTIC** | Creative takes on old standards coupled with lovely presentations draw crowds to this restaurant on Lovango Cay, a short ferry ride away from Cruz Bay. Start with appetizers like lump crab poke with heirloom tomatoes and watermelon radish, then move on to the burger with house-made pickles or the extraordinary seared tuna served over spicy buckwheat soba noodles. **Known for:** breathtaking sunset views; fine-dining atmosphere; location on an offshore island. Ⓢ *Average main: $38* ✉ *Lovango Cay, Estate Caneel Bay* ☎ *860/450–6649* ⊕ *www.zozoslovango.com.*

Coffee and Quick Bites

St. John Scoops

$ | **FAST FOOD** | While you can get the usual chocolate and vanilla ice cream as well as smoothies at this tiny spot, owner Colette Rethage also dishes up frozen treats blended with alcoholic beverages. Try the champagne sorbet, espresso martini, peach margarita, or that tropical favorite, the rum-laced Painkiller. **Known for:** boozy ice cream; house-made waffle cones; more than 20 flavors. Ⓢ *Average main: $6* ✉ *Mongoose Junction shopping center, North Shore Rd., Cruz Bay* ⊕ *www.StJohnScoops.com.*

🛏 Hotels

Coconut Coast Villas

$$ | **RENTAL** | This small condominium complex with studio, two-, and three-bedroom apartments is a 10-minute walk from Cruz Bay, but it's insulated from the town's noise in a sleepy suburban neighborhood. **Pros:** good snorkeling; full kitchens; walk to Cruz Bay. **Cons:** small beach; some uphill walks; nearby utility plant can be noisy. Ⓢ *Rooms from: $329* ✉ *Near pond, Turner Bay, Cruz Bay* ☎ *340/693–9100, 800/858–7989* ⊕ *www.coconutcoast.com* ⤴ *9 units* ❑ *No meals.*

Estate Lindholm

$$$ | **B&B/INN** | Built among old stone ruins on a lushly planted hill overlooking Cruz Bay, Estate Lindholm has an enchanting setting—you'll feel as if you're out of the fray, but still near enough to run into town when you want. **Pros:** lush landscaping; gracious host; pleasant decor. **Cons:** can be noisy; some uphill walks; on a busy road. $ *Rooms from: $395 ☒ 63B Estate Lindholm, Caneel Hill, Cruz Bay* ☎ *340/776–6121, 800/322–6335* ⊕ *www.estatelindholm. com* ⇱ *17 rooms* �“❘ *Free Breakfast.*

★ Gallows Point Resort

$$$$ | **RENTAL** | You're a short walk from restaurants and shops at this waterfront location just outside Cruz Bay, but once you step into your condo, the hustle and bustle are left behind. **Pros:** walk to shopping; excellent restaurant; comfortably furnished rooms. **Cons:** some rooms can be noisy; mediocre beach; insufficient parking. $ *Rooms from: $595 ☒ 3AAA Estate Enighed, Cruz Bay* ☎ *340/776–6434, 800/323–7229* ⊕ *gallowspointresort.com* ⇱ *60 units* ❘❙❘ *No meals.*

Garden by the Sea Bed and Breakfast

$ | **B&B/INN** | Located in a middle-class residential neighborhood, this adults-only, cozy bed-and-breakfast is an easy walk from Cruz Bay and it's perfect for folks who enjoy peace and quiet: there are no phones or TVs in the rooms. **Pros:** homey atmosphere; great breakfasts; breathtaking view from deck; near a bird-filled salt pond. **Cons:** noise from nearby power substation; some uphill walks; basic amenities. $ *Rooms from: $195 ☒ Near pond, Enighed* ☎ *340/779–4731* ⊕ *gardenbythesea.com* ▱ *No credit cards* ⇱ *3 rooms* ❘❙❘ *Free Breakfast.*

Grande Bay Resort

$$$$ | **RENTAL** | Located just a few minutes' walk from Cruz Bay's restaurants and shops, this modern condominium complex puts you close to the town's hustle and bustle. **Pros:** close to restaurants and shops; modern decor; walking distance to the ferry. **Cons:** need car or taxi to reach island attractions and the best beaches; beach across the street is minimal. $ *Rooms from: $515 ☒ Bay St., Cruz Bay* ☎ *340/693–4668, 888/383–9019* ⊕ *grandebayresort.com* ⇱ *64 condos* ❘❙❘ *No meals.*

Inn at Tamarind Court

$ | **B&B/INN** | Good for travelers on a budget, the Inn at Tamarind Court has rooms with rather pedestrian decor, but they're clean, and you can't beat the location, a five-minute walk from the heart of Cruz Bay's action. **Pros:** walk to restaurants and shops; good breakfasts; convivial atmosphere. **Cons:** on a busy road; bland decor; need a car to get around. $ *Rooms from: $202 ☒ Rte. 104, Cruz Bay* ☎ *340/776–6378, 800/221–1637* ⊕ *www.innattamarindcourt.com* ⇱ *14 rooms* ❘❙❘ *Free Breakfast.*

St. John Inn

$$ | **B&B/INN** | A stay here gives you a bit of style at what passes for budget prices in St. John. **Pros:** walk to restaurants and shops; convivial atmosphere; pretty pool. **Cons:** need a car to get around; noisy location; insufficient parking. $ *Rooms from: $305 ☒ 277 Estate Enighed, Cruz Bay* ☎ *340/693–8688* ⊕ *www.stjohninn. com* ⇱ *10 units* ❘❙❘ *Free Breakfast.*

Sea Shore Allure

$$$$ | **RENTAL** | Located at the water's edge in a residential neighborhood, Sea Shore Allure combines attractive and modern decor with an easy, and safe, walk to Cruz Bay's restaurants and shops. **Pros:** lovely decor; waterfront location; close to town. **Cons:** need car or taxi to get to beach; road passes through modest but safe local neighborhood. $ *Rooms from: $540 ☒ Fish Ferry Rd., Great Cruz Bay, Enighed* ☎ *340/779–2800, 855/779–2800* ⊕ *www.seashoreallure.com* ⇱ *8 units* ❘❙❘ *No meals.*

Westin St. John Resort and Villas

$$$$ | **RESORT** | **FAMILY** | The island's largest resort provides a nice beachfront location and enough activities to keep you busy. **Pros:** restaurants on property; pretty pool area; many activities. **Cons:** mediocre beach; long walk to some parts of the resort; need car to get around. $ *Rooms from: $929 ☒ Rte. 104, Estate Chocolate Hole and Great Cruz Bay* ☎ *340/693–8000, 888/627–7206* ⊕ *www.*

Local St. John Celebrations

Although the U.S. Virgin Islands mark all of the same federal holidays as the mainland, they have a few of their own. Transfer Day, on March 31, commemorates Denmark's sale of the territory to the United States in 1917. Emancipation Day, on July 3, marks the date slavery was abolished in the Danish West Indies in 1848. Liberty Day, on November 1, honors David Hamilton Jackson, who secured freedom of the press and assembly from King Christian X of Denmark.

While you're on St. John, don't hesitate to attend local events like the annual Memorial Day and Veterans Day celebrations and Fourth of July Festival Parade in Cruz Bay, complete with costumed troupes, steel pan bands, and stilt-walking Mocko Jumbies. These small parades give a poignant glimpse into island life. The St. Patrick's Day Parade is another blink-and-you'll-miss-it event. It's fun to join the islanders who come out decked in green. The annual Friends of Virgin Islands National Park meeting in January is another place to mix and mingle with the locals.

westinresortstjohn.com ⬗ *96 rooms, 200 villas* ⍥ *No meals.*

⛓ Nightlife

Tap Room

BREWPUBS/BEER GARDENS | A rotating selection of distinctive brews makes the Tap Room popular with locals and visitors. Entertainment includes live music a few times a month at night and weekday brewery tours on the hour between noon and 3 pm. ✉ *Mongoose Junction Shopping Center, Cruz Bay* ☎ *340/715–7775* ⊕ *www.stjohnbrewers.com.*

Woody's Seafood Saloon

BARS/PUBS | Folks like to gather here, a short walk from the ferry dock, where the sidewalk tables provide a close-up view of Cruz Bay action. There's live entertainment on weekends. ✉ *Cruz Bay* ✛ *2 blocks east of the ferry dock* ☎ *340/779–4625* ⊕ *www.woodysseafood.com.*

👜 Shopping

Luxury goods and handicrafts can be found on St. John. Most shops carry a little of this and a bit of that, so it pays to poke around. The main Cruz Bay shopping district runs from **Wharfside Village,** just around the corner from the ferry dock, to **Mongoose Junction,** an inviting shopping center on North Shore Road. (The name of this upscale shopping mall, by the way, is a holdover from a time when those furry island creatures gathered at a nearby garbage bin.) Out on Route 104, the **Marketplace** has the island's only pharmacy. It also has a good selection of kid's beach toys. On St. John, store hours run from 9 or 10 to 5 or 6. Wharfside Village and Mongoose Junction shops in Cruz Bay are often open into the evening.

ART GALLERIES

★ **Bajo el Sol**

ART GALLERIES | This gallery sells pieces from a roster of the island's best artists. You can shop for oils, pastels, watercolors, and turned-wood pieces as well as ceramic and metal works. Check out the gallery's First Friday events where you can meet and mingle with the artists. ⊠ *Mongoose Junction Shopping Center, North Shore Rd., Cruz Bay* ☎ *340/693–7070* ⊕ *bajo-el-sol-gallery.business.site.*

Caravan Gallery
GIFTS/SOUVENIRS | Caravan sells affordable jewelry, unique gifts, and artifacts that its owner, Radha Speer, has traveled the world to find. The more you look, the more you see—Caribbean larimar jewelry, unusual sterling pieces, and tribal art cover the walls and tables, making this a great place to browse. ⊠ *Mongoose Junction Shopping Center, North Shore Rd., Cruz Bay* ☎ *340/779–4566* ⊕ *www.caravangallery.com.*

Coconut Coast Studios
ART GALLERIES | This waterside shop, a five-minute walk from the center of Cruz Bay, showcases the work of Elaine Estern. She specializes in undersea scenes. ⊠ *Frank Bay, Cruz Bay* ☎ *340/776–6944* ⊕ *www.coconutcoast-studios.com.*

BOOKS
★ Friends of the Park Store
ART GALLERIES | Find books and locally made beachwear, such as flip-flops made of coconut husks and recycled rubber, at this store run by the nonprofit group that raises money for Virgin Islands National Park. It's a great spot to buy educational materials for kids and books about the island. It's also the place to make reservations for a guided hike along Reef Bay Trail. ⊠ *Mongoose Junction Shopping Center, North Shore Rd., Cruz Bay* ☎ *340/779–4940* ⊕ *www.friendsvinp.org.*

National Park Headquarters Bookstore
BOOKS/STATIONERY | The bookshop at Virgin Islands National Park Visitor Center sells several good histories of St. John, including *St. John Back Time* by Ruth Hull Low and Rafael Lito Valls and, for intrepid explorers, longtime resident Pam Gaffin's *Feet, Fins and Four-Wheel Drive.* ⊠ *Visitor Center, North Shore Rd., Cruz Bay* ☎ *340/776–6201* ⊕ *www.nps.gov/viis.*

CLOTHING
Big Planet Adventure Outfitters
CLOTHING | You knew when you arrived that someplace on St. John would cater to the outdoors enthusiasts who hike up and down the island's trails. This store sells flip-flops and Reef footwear, along with colorful and durable cotton clothing and accessories by Billabong. The store also sells children's clothes. ⊠ *Mongoose Junction Shopping Center, North Shore Rd., Cruz Bay* ☎ *340/776–6638* ⊕ *www.big-planet.com.*

FOOD
If you're renting a villa, condo, or cottage and doing your own cooking, there are several good places to shop for food, particularly in Cruz Bay; just be aware that prices are much higher than those at home.

Dolphin Market
FOOD/CANDY | This small store in Cruz Bay is a good source for fresh produce, deli items, and all the basics. Two smaller branches are in Chocolate Hole, near Great Cruz Bay, and in Coral Bay. ⊠ *Boulon Center, Rte. 10, Cruz Bay* ☎ *340/776–5328* ⊕ *www.dolphinmarkets.com.*

Starfish Market
FOOD/CANDY | The island's largest store usually has the best selection of meat, fish, and produce. ⊠ *The Marketplace, Rte. 104, Cruz Bay* ☎ *340/779–4949* ⊕ *www.starfishmarket.com.*

GIFTS
★ Bamboula
CLOTHING | This multicultural boutique carries unusual housewares, rugs, bedspreads, accessories, and men's and women's clothes and shoes that owner Jo Sterling has found on her world travels. ⊠ *Mongoose Junction Shopping Center, North Shore Rd., Cruz Bay* ☎ *340/693–8699* ⊕ *www.bamboulastjohn.com.*

Donald Schnell Studio

GIFTS/SOUVENIRS | You'll find distinctive clay pieces, unusual handblown glass, wind chimes, kaleidoscopes, fanciful fountains, and pottery bowls here. Your purchases can be shipped worldwide. ✉ *Amore Center, 27 Southside Rd., near roundabout, Enighed* ☎ *340/776–6420* ⊕ *donaldschnell.com/the-studio.*

Gallows Point Gift & Gourmet

GIFTS/SOUVENIRS | The store at Gallows Point Resort has a bit of this and a bit of that. Shop for Caribbean books, picture frames decorated with shells, and T-shirts with tropical motifs. Residents and visitors also drop by for a cup of coffee. ✉ *Gallows Point Resort, Bay St., Cruz Bay* ☎ *340/693–7730* ⊕ *gallowspointresort.com.*

Pink Papaya

GIFTS/SOUVENIRS | Head to this shop and art gallery for the work of longtime Virgin Islands resident Lisa Etre. There's also a huge collection of one-of-a-kind gifts, including bright tableware, trays, and tropical jewelry. ✉ *Lemon Tree Mall, King St., Cruz Bay* ☎ *340/693–8535* ⊕ *www.pinkpapaya.com.*

JEWELRY
Freebird Creations

JEWELRY/ACCESSORIES | This is your on-island destination for special handcrafted jewelry—earrings, bracelets, pendants, chains—as well as a good selection of water-resistant watches. ✉ *Dockside Mall, next to ferry dock, Cruz Bay* ☎ *340/693–8625* ⊕ *www.freebirdcreations.com.*

Little Switzerland

JEWELRY/ACCESSORIES | A branch of the St. Thomas store, Little Switzerland carries diamonds and other jewels in attractive yellow- and white-gold settings, as well as strings of creamy pearls, watches, and other designer jewelry. ✉ *Mongoose Junction Shopping Center, North Shore Rd., Cruz Bay* ☎ *248/809–5560, ext. 10040* ⊕ *www.littleswitzerland.com.*

R&I PATTON goldsmithing

JEWELRY/ACCESSORIES | This store is owned by Rudy and Irene Patton, who design most of the lovely silver and gold jewelry on display. The rest comes from various designer friends. Sea fans (those large, lacy plants that sway with the ocean's currents) in filigreed silver, starfish and hibiscus pendants in silver or gold, and gold sand-dollar-shape charms and earrings are choice selections. ✉ *Mongoose Junction Shopping Center, North Shore Rd., Cruz Bay* ☎ *340/776–6548* ⊕ *www.pattongold.com.*

North Shore

◉ Sights

★ Annaberg Plantation

HISTORIC SITE | In the 18th century, sugar plantations dotted the steep hills of this island. Slaves and free Danes and Dutchmen toiled to harvest the cane that was used to create sugar, molasses, and rum for export. Built in the 1780s, the partially restored plantation at Leinster Bay was once an important sugar mill. Although there are no official visiting hours, the National Park Service has regular tours, and some well-informed taxi drivers will show you around. Occasionally you may see a living-history demonstration—someone making johnnycakes or weaving baskets. For information on tours and cultural events, contact the Virgin Islands National Park Visitors Center. ✉ *Leinster Bay Rd., Annaberg* ☎ *340/776–6201* ⊕ *www.nps.gov/viis* 🎫 *$5.*

Peace Hill

HISTORIC SITE | It's worth stopping here, just past the Hawksnest Bay overlook, for great views of St. John, St. Thomas, and the BVI. On the flat promontory is an old sugar mill. ✉ *Off Rte. 20, Estate Denis Bay.*

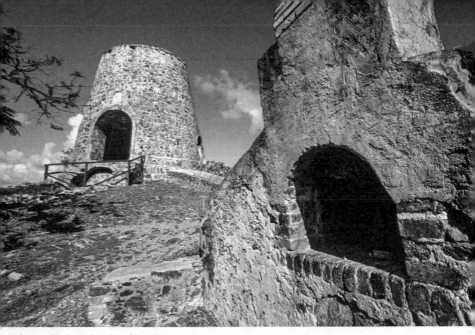

Sugar mill ruins at Annaberg Plantation

 Beaches

Cinnamon Bay Beach

BEACH—SIGHT | This long, sandy beach faces beautiful cays. There's excellent snorkeling off the point to the right; look for the big angelfish and large schools of purple triggerfish. Afternoons on Cinnamon Bay can be windy—a boon for windsurfers but an annoyance for sunbathers—so arrive early to beat the gusts. The Cinnamon Bay hiking trail begins across the road from the beach parking lot; ruins mark the trailhead. There are actually two paths here: a level nature trail (with signs to identify flora) that loops through the woods and passes an old Danish cemetery, and a steep trail that starts where the road bends past the ruins and heads straight up to Route 10. **Amenities:** parking; toilets. **Best for:** snorkeling; swimming; walking; windsurfing. ⊠ *North Shore Rd., Rte. 20, Cinnamon Bay* ✚ *About 4 miles (6 km) east of Cruz Bay* ⊕ *www.nps.gov/viis.*

Francis Bay Beach

BEACH—SIGHT | Because there's little shade, this beach gets toasty warm in the afternoon when the sun comes around to the west, but the rest of the day it's a delightful stretch of white sand. The only facilities are a few picnic tables tucked among the trees and a portable restroom, but folks come here to watch the birds that live in the swampy area behind the beach. There's a boardwalk here for bird-watching. The park offers bird-watching hikes here on Friday morning; sign up at the visitor center in Cruz Bay. To get here, turn left at the Annaberg intersection. **Amenities:** parking; toilets. **Best for:** snorkeling; swimming; walking. ⊠ *North Shore Rd., Rte. 20, Francis Bay* ✚ *¼ mile (½ km) from Annaberg intersection* ⊕ *www.nps.gov/viis.*

Hawksnest Beach

BEACH—SIGHT | Seagrapes and waving palm trees line this narrow beach, and there are portable toilets, cooking grills, and a covered shed for picnicking. A patchy reef just offshore means

St. John

A B C D E

1

↑
TO
JOST VAN DYKE

2

Mary Point

Windward Passage

Whistling Cay

Francis Bay Beach

Francis Bay

Maho Bay Beach

3

Trunk Bay Beach

Cinnamon Bay Beach

Henley Cay

4

Hawksnest Beach

20

North Shore Rd.

♦ Cinnamon Bay Campground

20

Caneel Bay

3

4

← TO
ST. THOMAS

Camelberg Peak

5

Stephen's Cay

⚓

Cruz Bay
see detail
map

VIRGIN ISLANDS
NATIONAL PARK

5

104

Great Cruz Bay

Blasbalg Pt.

Reef Bay

6

Chocolate Hole

Rendezvous Bay

Fish Bay

Dever's Bay

Bovocoap Pt.

Dittlif Pt.

White Pt.

7

0 ————— 1 miles
0 ————— 1 km

Caribbean Sea

Sights ▼	Restaurants ▼
1 Annaberg Plantation ... **F2**	1 Caribbean Oasis **G4**
2 Bordeaux Mountain **F5**	2 Miss Lucy's Restaurant............... **G5**
3 Catherineberg Ruins ... **C4**	
4 Peace Hill................ **B3**	3 Rhumb Lines............. **G3**
5 Reef Bay Trail **E4**	4 Skinny Legs.............. **G4**

F   G   H   I   J

TO TORTOLA

KEY

1 Sights
1 Restaurants
Beaches
Dive Sites
Ferry
Trail

1

The Narrows

TO TORTOLA →

2

Leinster
Bay

1

Brown
Bay

Sir Francis Drake
Channel

VIRGIN ISLANDS
NATIONAL PARK

3

Centerline Rd.

Haulover
Bay

Newfound
Bay

10

Coral
Bay

3

King Hill Rd.

4

Palestina

Hurricane
Hole

East
End Pt.

1

Coral
Harbor

EAST END

East End
Bay

4

Sanders Bay

Round
Bay

2

107

Coral Bay

Long Pt.

Privateer
Pt.

5

Calabash

Lagoon Pt.

Privateer
Bay

2

John's
Folly
Bay

Leduck
Island

6

Lameshur
Bay Beach

Drunk Bay

Salt
Pond
Peninsula

UNITED STATES VIRGIN ISLANDS

Tortola

ST. THOMAS

ST. JOHN

Salt Pond
Bay Beach

Distance from St. Thomas to
St. Croix approx. 40 miles

Ram Head

ST. CROIX

7

snorkeling is an easy swim away, but the best underwater views are reserved for ambitious snorkelers who head farther to the east along the bay's fringes. Watch out for boat traffic—a channel guides dinghies to the beach, but the occasional boater strays into the swim area. It's the closest drivable beach to Cruz Bay, so it's often crowded with locals and visitors. **Amenities:** parking; toilets. **Best for:** snorkeling; swimming. ⊠ *North Shore Rd., Rte. 20, Estate Hawksnest* ⊹ *About 2 miles (3 km) east of Cruz Bay* ⊕ *www.nps.gov/viis.*

Maho Bay Beach

BEACH—SIGHT | Maho Bay Beach is a gorgeous strip of sand that sits right along the North Shore Road. It's a popular place, particularly on weekends, when locals come out in droves to party at the picnic tables at the south end of the beach. Snorkeling along the rocky edges is good, but the center is mostly sea grass. If you're lucky, you'll cross paths with turtles. There are portable toilets, and a food truck parked across from the beach. **Amenities:** parking. **Best for:** snorkeling; swimming. ⊠ *North Shore Rd., Rte. 20, Estate Maho Bay* ⊕ *www.nps.gov/viis.*

★ Trunk Bay Beach

BEACH—SIGHT | St. John's most photographed beach is also the preferred spot for beginning snorkelers because of its underwater trail. (Cruise-ship passengers interested in snorkeling for a day flock here, so if you're looking for seclusion, arrive early or later in the day.) Crowded or not, this stunning beach is one of the island's most beautiful. There are changing rooms with showers, bathrooms, a food truck, picnic tables, a gift shop, phones, lockers, and snorkeling-equipment rentals. The parking lot often overflows, but you can park along the road as long as the tires are off the pavement. **Amenities:** lifeguards; parking; toilets. **Best for:** snorkeling; swimming; windsurfing. ⊠ *North Shore Rd., Rte. 20, Estate Trunk Bay* ⊹ *About 2½ miles (4 km) east of Cruz Bay* ⊕ *www.nps.gov/viis* 🚲 *$5.*

Mid Island

Sights

Bordeaux Mountain

MOUNTAIN—SIGHT | St. John's highest peak rises to 1,277 feet. Route 10 passes near enough to the top to offer breathtaking vistas. Don't stray into the road here—cars whiz by at a good clip along this section. Instead, drive nearly to the end of the dirt road that heads off to Picture Point and the trailhead of the hike downhill to Lameshur. Get a trail map from the park service before you start. It's a relatively easy 2 miles (3 km) down, but the hike back up is strenuous due to the steep incline. ⊠ *Rte. 10, Bordeaux.*

Catherineberg Ruins

HISTORIC SITE | At this fine example of an 18th-century sugar and rum factory, there's a storage vault beneath the windmill. Across the road, look for the round mill, which was later used to hold water. In the 1733 slave revolt Catherineberg served as headquarters for the Amina warriors, a tribe of Africans that had been captured into slavery. ⊠ *Catherineberg Rd., off Rte. 10.*

★ Reef Bay Trail

ARCHAEOLOGICAL SITE | This is one of the most interesting hikes on St. John, but unless you're a rugged individualist who wants a physical challenge (and that describes a lot of people who stay on St. John), you can probably get the most out of the trip if you join a hike led by a park service ranger. A ranger can identify the trees and plants on the hike down, fill you in on the history of the Reef Bay Plantation, and tell you about the petroglyphs on the rocks at the bottom of the trail. A side trail takes you to the plantation's greathouse, a gutted but mostly intact structure with vestiges of its former beauty. Take the safari bus from the park's visitor center. A boat takes you from the beach at Reef Bay back to the visitor center, saving you the uphill climb.

Waves crash against the rocky coastline near Lameshur Bay.

It's a good idea to make reservations for this trip, especially during the winter season. They can be made at the Friends of the Park store, in Mongoose Junction. ✉ *Rte. 10, Reef Bay* ☎ *340/779–4940 for reservations* ⊕ *www.nps.gov/viis* 🎫 *$40 includes a safari bus ride to the trailhead, a guided tour, and a boat ride back to the visitor center.*

Coral Bay and Environs

Beaches

Lameshur Bay Beach

BEACH—SIGHT | This seagrape-fringed beach is toward the end of a partially paved rut-strewn road (don't attempt without a four-wheel-drive vehicle) on the southeast coast. The reward for your long drive is good snorkeling and a chance to spy on some pelicans. The beach has a couple of picnic tables, rusting barbecue grills, and a portable restroom. The ruins of the old plantation are a five-minute walk down the road past the beach. The

area has good hiking trails, including a trek (nearly 2 miles [3 km]) up Bordeaux Mountain before an easy walk to Yawzi Point. **Amenities:** parking; (portable) toilets. **Best for:** snorkeling; swimming; walking. ✉ *Off Rte. 107, Lameshur Bay* ✛ *About 1½ miles (2½ km) from Salt Pond* ⊕ *www.nps.gov/viis.*

Salt Pond Bay Beach

BEACH—SIGHT | If you're adventurous, this rocky beach on the scenic southeastern coast—next to rugged Drunk Bay—is worth exploring. It's a short hike down a hill from the parking lot, and the only facilities are a portable toilet and a few picnic tables scattered about. Tide pools are filled with all sorts of marine creatures, and the snorkeling is good, particularly along the bay's edges. A short walk takes you to a pond where salt crystals collect around the edges. Hike farther uphill past cactus gardens to Ram Head for see-forever views. Leave nothing valuable in your car, as thefts are common. **Amenities:** parking; portable toilets. **Best for:** snorkeling; swimming;

St. John Archaeology

Archaeologists continue to unravel St. John's past through excavations at Trunk Bay and Cinnamon Bay, both prime tourist destinations within Virgin Islands National Park.

Work began back in the early 1990s, when the park wanted to build new bathhouses at the popular Trunk Bay. In preparation for that project, the archaeologists began to dig, turning up artifacts and the remains of structures that date to AD 900. The site was once a village occupied by the Taíno, a peaceful group that lived in the area for many centuries. A similar but not quite as ancient village was discovered at Cinnamon Bay.

By the time the Taíno got to Cinnamon Bay—they lived in the area from about AD 1000 to 1500—their society had developed to include chiefs, commoners, workers, and slaves. The location of the national park's Cinnamon Bay campground was once a Taíno temple that belonged to a king or chief. When archaeologists began digging in 1998,

they uncovered several dozen *zemis*, which are small clay gods used in ceremonial activities, as well as beads, pots, and many other artifacts.

Near the end of the Cinnamon Bay dig archaeologists turned up another less ancient but still important discovery. A burned layer indicated that a plantation slave village had also stood near Cinnamon Bay campground; it was torched during the 1733 revolt because its inhabitants had been loyal to the planters. Since the 1970s, bones from slaves buried in the area have been uncovered at the water's edge by beach erosion.

Today, you can see archaeology students working from the old lifeguard station at Trunk Bay. Throughout the year, the nonprofit Friends of the National Park offers programs and seminars to the public that share the latest on the digs into the island's past. Check the organization's website, ⊕ *www.friendsvinp.org*, for details.

walking. ✉ *Rte. 107, about 3 miles (5 km) south of Coral Bay, Concordia* ⊕ *www. nps.gov/viis.*

 Restaurants

Caribbean Oasis
$$ | **AMERICAN** | What looks like a ramshackle hut serves some of the best southern food on the island. Meat loaf, fried chicken, macaroni and cheese, collard greens, and pecan pie are all on the menu. **Known for:** down-home cooking; laid-back tropical vibe; great, unpretentious food. ⑤ *Average main: $15* ✉ *Estate Carolina, 10-41, Rte. 107, Coral Bay* ☎ *340/774-1030* ⊕ *oasisstjohn.com* ⊘ *Closed Sun. and Mon.*

Miss Lucy's Restaurant
$$$ | **CARIBBEAN** | Sitting seaside at remote Friis Bay, Miss Lucy's dishes up Caribbean food with a contemporary flair. Dishes such as tender conch fritters, a spicy West Indian stew called callaloo, and fried fish make up most of the menu, but you also find a generous paella filled with seafood, sausage, and chicken on the menu. **Known for:** Sunday brunch; full-moon parties; outdoor dining. ⑤ *Average main: $28* ✉ *Rte. 107, Friis Bay* ☎ *340/693-5244* ⊘ *Closed Mon. No dinner Sun.*

Rhumb Lines
$$$ | **ASIAN FUSION** | Pacific Rim meets Caribbean cooking in the cozy dining room of this open-air eatery, with

bamboo furnishings and local flora providing a tropical backdrop. Thai crab cakes, Cuban mojo pork, and sesame-encrusted Szechuan tuna are excellent choices. **Known for:** pupu platters; lively vibe; live music on weekends. $ *Average main: $29* ⊠ *3 Estate Emmaus, Rte. 10, Coral Bay* ☎ *340/776–0303* ⊕ *www.rhumblinesstjohn.com.*

★ Skinny Legs

$ | **AMERICAN** | Sailors who live aboard boats anchored offshore and an eclectic coterie of residents and visitors gather for lunch and dinner at this funky spot in the middle of a boatyard and shopping complex. It's a great place for burgers, fish sandwiches, and whatever sports are on the satellite TV. **Known for:** people-watching; pub food; local flavor. $ *Average main: $12* ⊠ *Rte. 10, Coral Bay* ☎ *340/779–4982* ⊕ *www.skinnylegs. com.*

🍸 Nightlife

Aqua Bistro

MUSIC CLUBS | This seafood restaurant is known for its fresh catch of talented local and off-island musicians who play at happy hour and into the evenings, especially on the weekends. ⊠ *Rte. 107, In the Cocolobo Complex, Coral Bay* ☎ *340/776–5336* ⊕ *www.aquabistrostjohn.com.*

★ Skinny Legs

BARS/PUBS | Landlubbers and old salts listen to music and swap stories at this popular casual restaurant and bar on the far side of the island. ⊠ *Rte. 10, Coral Bay* ☎ *340/779–4982* ⊕ *www.skinnylegs. com.*

🛍 Shopping

At the island's East End, there are a few stores—selling clothes, jewelry, and artwork—here and there from the village of **Coral Bay** to the small complex at **Shipwreck Landing.**

CLOTHING
Jolly Dog

CLOTHING | Head here for the stuff you forgot to pack. Sarongs in cotton and rayon, beach towels with tropical motifs, and hats and T-shirts sporting the "Jolly Dog" logo fill the shelves. ⊠ *Isola Shoppes Complex, next to Coral Bay Caribbean Oasis, Rte. 107, Coral Bay* ☎ *802/489–2901* ⊕ *www.thejollydog.com.*

Sloop Jones

CLOTHING | This store's worth the trip all the way out to the island's East End to shop for made-on-the-premises clothing and pillows, in fabrics splashed with tropical colors. The clothes are made from cotton, gauze, and modal, and are supremely comfortable. Sloop also holds painting workshops. ⊠ *Off Rte. 10, East End* ☎ *340/779–4001* ⊕ *www.sloopjones. com.*

FOOD
Calabash Market

FOOD/CANDY | If you're renting a villa on the island's southeast end or headed to Salt Pond or Lameshur Bay for the day, provision at this minimarket. The selection is quite good, and villa renters will find enough choices for simple meals and snacking. ⊠ *Rte. 107, Calabash Boom* ☎ *340/775–7172.*

Love City Market

FOOD/CANDY | The store may not look like much from the road, but it's one of the very few places to shop in Coral Bay and has a surprising selection. ⊠ *Off Rte. 107, Coral Bay* ☎ *340/693–5790.*

GIFTS
Mumbo Jumbo

CLOTHING | With what may be the best prices in St. John, Mumbo Jumbo carries tropical clothing, stuffed sea creatures, local hot sauces, and other gifty items in a cozy little shop. ⊠ *Skinny Legs Shopping Complex, Rte. 10, Coral Bay* ☎ *340/779–4277.*

JEWELRY

ZEMI Island Designs

JEWELRY/ACCESSORIES | The necklaces, bracelets, and rings sold at Zemi (the native Taíno term for spirit symbol) feature petroglyph designs as well as more contemporary hook bracelets, wreck coins, and gemstones. Its sister store, Jolly Dog, is next door. ⊠ *Isola Shoppes, Rte. 107, Coral Bay* ☎ *340/776–8355* ⊕ *www.zemistj.com.*

 # Activities

BOATING AND SAILING

If you're staying at a hotel, your activities desk will usually be able to help you arrange a sailing excursion aboard a nearby boat. Most day sails leaving Cruz Bay head out along St. John's north coast. Those that depart from Coral Bay might drop anchor at some remote cay off the island's east end or even in the nearby British Virgin Islands. Your trip usually includes lunch, beverages, and at least one snorkeling stop. Keep in mind that inclement weather could interfere with your plans, though most boats will still go out if rain isn't too heavy.

Ocean Runner

BOATING | For a speedier trip to the cays and remote beaches off St. John, you can rent a powerboat with a captain from Ocean Runner. The company has everything from a 47-foot Sea Ray for up to 12 people for $2,800 to 15-foot runabouts for up to 4 people for $320 per day. Gas and oil will run you $100 to $300 a day extra, depending on how far you're going. ⊠ *Wharfside Village, Waterfront, Cruz Bay* ☎ *340/693–8809* ⊕ *www.oceanrunnerusvi.com.*

St. John Concierge Service

BOATING | The capable staff can find a charter sail or powerboat that fits your style and budget. The company also books fishing and scuba trips. ⊠ *Henry Samuel St., across from post office, Cruz Bay* ☎ *340/514–5262* ⊕ *www. stjohnconciergeservice.com.*

DIVING AND SNORKELING

Although just about every beach has nice snorkeling—Trunk Bay, Cinnamon Bay, and Waterlemon Cay at Leinster Bay get the most praise—you need a boat to head out to the more remote snorkeling locations and the best scuba spots.

Sign on with any of the island's watersports operators to get to spots farther from St. John. If you use the one at your hotel, just stroll down to the dock to hop aboard. Their boats will take you to hot spots between St. John and St. Thomas, including the tunnels at **Thatch Cay,** the ledges at **Congo Cay,** and the wreck of the *General Rogers*. Dive off St. John at **Stephens Cay,** a short boat ride out of Cruz Bay, where fish swim around the reefs as you float downward. At **Devers Bay,** on St. John's south shore, fish dart about in colorful schools. **Carval Rock,** shaped like an old-time ship, has gorgeous rock formations, coral gardens, and lots of fish. It can be too rough here in winter, though. Count on paying $120 for a one-tank dive and $145 for a two-tank dive. Rates include equipment and a tour. If you've never dived before, try an introductory course called a resort course. Or if certification is in your vacation plans, the island's dive shops can help you get your card.

Cruz Bay Watersports

SCUBA DIVING | Cruz Bay Watersports offers regular reef, wreck, and night dives and USVI and BVI snorkel tours. ⊠ *The Westin St. John, 300 Chocolate Hole, Cruz Bay* ⊹ *Located on the property of the Westin St. John* ☎ *844/359–5457* ⊕ *www.cruzbaywatersports.com.*

Low Key Watersports

SCUBA DIVING | Low Key Watersports offers two-tank dives and specialty courses. It's a PADI 5 Star training facility. ⊠ *1 Bay St., Cruz Bay* ☎ *340/693–8999* ⊕ *www.divelowkey.com.*

Continued on page 124

BELOW THE WAVES By Lynda Lohr

Colorful reefs and wrecks rife with corals and tropical fish make the islands as interesting underwater as above. Brilliantly colored reef fish vie for your attention with corals in wondrous shapes. Scuba diving gets you up close and personal with the world below the waves.

Bright blue tangs and darting blue-headed wrasses. Corals in wondrous shapes—some look like brains, others like elk antlers. Colorful, bulbous sponges. All these and more can be spotted along the myriad reefs of the U.S. and British Virgin Islands. You might see a pink conch making its way along the ocean bottom in areas with seagrass beds. If you're really lucky, a turtle may swim into view, or a lobster may poke its antennae out of a hole in the reef or rocks. If you do a night dive, you might run into an octopus. But you may be surprised at how much you can see by simply hovering just below the surface, with nothing more than a mask and snorkel. It's a bird's-eye view, but an excellent one. Whether scuba diving or snorkeling, take along an underwater camera to capture memories of your exciting adventure. You can buy disposable ones at most dive shops or bring one from home.

DIVE AND SNORKELING SITES IN BRITISH VIRGIN ISLANDS

TORTOLA

Although a major base for dive operations in the BVI (due to its proximity to so many exceptional dive sites), Tortola itself doesn't have as much to offer divers. However, there are still some noteworthy destinations. The massive **Brewer's Bay Pinnacles** grow 70 feet high to within 30 feet of the surface; the rock mazes are only for advanced divers because of strong currents and they are not always acces-

sible. Abundant reefs close to shore make **Brewer's Bay** popular with snorkelers, as are **Frenchman's Cay** and **Long Bay Beef Island. Diamond Reef**, between Great Camanoe and Scrub Island, is a small wall about 200 yards long. **Shark Point**, off the northeast coast of Scrub Island, does have resident sharks. Though isolated in open ocean, the wreck of the *Chikuzen,* a Japanese refrigerator ship, is a popular site.

THE ISLANDS OF THE SIR FRANCIS DRAKE CHANNEL

Southeast of Tortola lie a string of islands with some of the BVI's finest dive sites, some world famous. The wreck of the royal mail ship *Rhone* is between Peter and Salt islands and is, perhaps, the most famous dive site in the BVI. **Wreck Alley,** consisting of three sunken modern ships, is between Salt and Cooper islands. At **Alice in Wonderland**, south of Ginger Island, giant,

mushroom-shaped corals shelter reef fish, moray eels, and crustaceans. **Alice's Backside**, off the northwestern tip of Ginger Island, is usually smooth enough for snorkeling and shallow enough so that beginner divers can get a good look at the myriad sealife and sponges.

KEY

Dive Sites
Snorkel
Ferry

2 miles

2 km

Bones Right

Loblolly Bay

Flash of Beauty Channel

The Settlement

Flamingo Pond

Red Pond

Lower Bay

Budrock Pond

ANEGADA
(15 miles north of Necker Is.)

Wreck of the *Rokus*

White Bay

3 miles

3 km

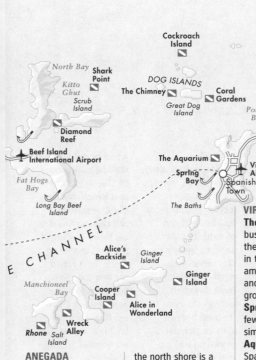

Necker Island

Eustatia Island

Long Bay

Berchers Bay

Cockroach Island

DOG ISLANDS

North Bay

Shark Point

Kitto Ghut

Scrub Island

The Chimney

Coral Gardens

Great Dog Island

Virgin Gorda Peak

North Sound

South Sound

Pond Bay

VIRGIN GORDA

Anegada Passage

Diamond Reef

Beef Island International Airport

Fat Hogs Bay

Handsome Bay

The Aquarium

Virgin Gorda Airport

Spring Bay

Spanish Town

Long Bay Beef Island

The Baths

E CHANNEL

Alice's Backside

Ginger Island

Ginger Island

Manchioneel Bay

Cooper Island

Alice in Wonderland

Rhone

Wreck Alley

Salt Island

ANEGADA

Surrounded by the third-largest barrier reef in the world, Anegada has great snorkeling from virtually any beach on the island. But there are also some notable dive sites as well. The **Flash of Beauty Channel** on the north shore is a great open-water dive, but only suitable for experienced divers. But even novices can enjoy diving at the **Wreck of the *Rokus***, a Greek cargo ship off the island's southern shore.

VIRGIN GORDA

The Baths, though busy, offers some of the best snorkeling in the Virgin Islands among giant boulders and the resulting grottoes. Nearby is **Spring Bay,** with fewer visitors and similar terrain. **The Aquarium,** close to Spanish Town and a good novice site, is so called because of the abundance of reef fish that swim around the submerged granite boulders that are similar to those of The Baths. Further west of Virgin Gorda, the Dog Islands have some in-

Virgin Gorda

teresting and popular sites, including **The Chimney,** a natural opening covered by sponges off Great Dog. South of Great Dog, **Coral Gardens** has a large coral reef with a submerged airplane wreck nearby. Fish are drawn to nearby **Cockroach Island.**

DIVE AND SNORKELING SITES IN U.S. VIRGIN ISLANDS

Big Hans
Lollick

Hans Lollik
Island

The
Brass
Islands

Inner
Brass

Picara Pt.

Santa
Maria
Bay

Hull
Bay

Magens
Bay

Lovenlund Bay

Thatch
Cay

Stumpy
Bay

Botany
Bay

Coki Beach

Dorothea

ST. THOMAS

Fortuna

Charlotte
Amalie

Water Bay

David
Pt.

Brewers
Bay

Cyril E. King
International
Airport

Nadir

Red
Hook

KEY

◣	Dive Sites
✓	Snorkel Sites
⛴	Ferry
🚢	Port of Call

← TO
PUERTO RICO

Water
Island

Frenchman
Bay

Bovoni
Bay

Long Pt.

TO ST. CROIX
(SEE INSET)
↓

Caribbean Sea

Cow and
Calf Rocks

ST. THOMAS

St. Thomas has at least 40 popular dive sites, most shallow. Favorite reef dives off St. Thomas include **Cow and Calf Rocks**, which barely break water off the southeast coast of St. Thomas; the coral-covered pinnacles of **Frenchcap** south of St. Thomas; and tunnels where you can explore undersea from the Caribbean to the Atlantic at **Thatch Cay** (where the Coast Guard cutter *General Rogers* rests at 65 feet). **Grass Cay** and **Mingo Cay** between St. Thomas and St. John are also popular dive sites. **Coki Beach** offers the best off-the-beach snorkeling in St. Thomas. Nearby Coral World offers a dive-helmet walk for the untrained, and Snuba of St. Thomas has tethered shallow dives for non-certified divers. **Magens Bay**, the most popular beach on St. Thomas, provides lovely snorkeling if you head along the edges. You're likely to see some colorful sponges, darting fish, and maybe even a turtle if you're lucky. This is a stop on every island tour.

ST. JOHN

St. John is particularly known for its myriad good snorkeling spots—certainly more than for its diving opportunities, though there are many dive sites within easy reach of Cruz Bay. **Trunk Bay** often receives the most attention because of its underwater snorkeling trail created by the National Park Service; signs let you know what you're seeing in terms of coral and other underwater features. And the beach is easy to reach since taxis leave on demand from Cruz Bay.

A patchy reef just offshore means good snorkeling at **Hawksnest Beach**. Additionally, **Cinnamon Bay** and **Leinster Bay** also get their fair share of praise as snorkeling spots. That's not to say that you can't find good dive sites near St. John. **Deaver's Bay** is a short boat ride around the point from Cruz Bay, where you can see angelfish, southern stingrays, and triggerfish feeding at 30 to 50 feet. **The Leaf** is a large coral reef off St. John's southern shore.

TORTOLA

Great Thatch Island

West End

Grass Cay

Mingo Cay

Mary Pt.

Leinster Bay

The Narrows

Cinnamon Bay

Trunk Bay

Hawksnest Beach

Cinnamon Bay

Haulover Bay

Honeymoon Beach

East End Pt.

Pillsbury Sound

Lind Point

Cruz Bay

ST. JOHN

Coral Harbor

Long Pt.

Privateer Pt.

Christmas Cove

Great St. James Island

Deaver's Bay

Reef Bay

The Leaf

Salt Pond

Flanagan Island

Little St. James Island

Salt Pond Bay

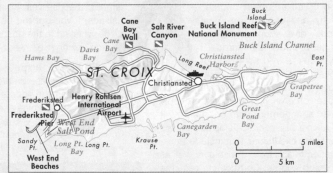

Cane Bay Wall

Salt River Canyon

Buck Island

Buck Island Reef National Monument

Cane Bay

Davis Bay

Buck Island Channel

Hams Bay

ST. CROIX

Long Reef

Christiansted Harbor

East Pt.

Christiansted

French Cap

Frederiksted

Frederiksted Pier

Henry Rohlsen International Airport

West End Salt Pond

Grapetree Bay

Great Pond Bay

Canegarden Bay

Sandy Pt.

Long Pt. Long Pt. Bay

Krause Pt.

West End Beaches

5 miles

5 km

ST. CROIX

The largest of the U.S. Virgin Islands is a favorite of both divers and snorkelers and offers something for everyone. Snorkelers are often fascinated by the marked snorkeling trail at **Buck Island Reef**, which is a short boat ride from the island's east end; it's a U.S. national monument. Divers are drawn to the north shore, especially the **Cane Bay Wall**, a spectacular drop-off that's reachable from the beach, though usually reached by boat. Another north-shore site is the **Salt River Canyon**, where you can float downward through a canyon filled with colorful fish and coral. On the island's west end, **Frederiksted Pier** is home to a colony of sea horses, creatures seldom seen in the waters of the Virgin Islands. Casual snorkelers would also enjoy snorkeling at the **West End Beaches**.

Coral near St. Croix

SCUBA DIVING

St. Croix

If you've never been diving, start with an introductory lesson—often called a "resort course"—run by any one of the Virgin Islands' dive shops. All meet stringent safety standards. If they didn't, they'd soon be out of business. If you're staying at a hotel, you can often find the dive shop on-site; otherwise, your hotel probably has an arrangement with one nearby. If you're on a cruise, cruise-ship companies offer shore excursions that include transportation to and from the ship as well as the resort course. Certification requires much more study and practice, but it is required to rent air tanks, get air refills, and join others on guided dives virtually anywhere in the world.

The number one rule of diving is safety. The basic rules for safe diving are simple, and fools ignore them at their own peril. Serious diving accidents are becoming increasingly rare these days, thanks to the high level of diver training. However, they do still occur occasionally. Surfacing too rapidly without exhaling—or going too deep for too long—can result in an air embolism or a case of the bends.

Schneider Regional Medical Center in St. Thomas has a decompression chamber that serves all the Virgin Islands. If you get the bends, you'll be whisked to the hospital for this necessary treatment.

Fauna is another concern. Though sharks, barracuda, and moray eels are on the most-feared list, more often it's sea urchins and fire coral that cause pain when you accidentally bump them. Part of any scuba-training program is a review of sea life and the

Divers learn how to jump in from a boat

St.Croix

importance of respecting the new world you're exploring. Dive professionals recognize the value of protecting fragile reefs and ecosystems in tropical waters, and instructors emphasize look-don't-touch diving (the unofficial motto is: take only pictures, leave only bubbles). Government control and protection of dive sites is increasing, especially in such heavily used areas as the Virgin Islands.

While you can scuba dive off a beach—and you can find shops renting scuba equipment and providing airfills at the most popular beaches—a trip aboard a dive boat provides a more extensive glimpse into this wonderful undersea world. Since the dive shops can provide all equipment, there's no need to lug heavy weights and a bulky BC in your luggage. For the most comfort, you might want to bring your own regulator if you have one. The dive-boat captains and guides know the best dive locations, can find alternatives when the seas are rough, and will help you deal with heavy tanks and cumbersome equipment. Trips are easy to organize. Dive shops on all islands make frequent excursions to a wide variety of diving spots, and your hotel, villa manager, or cruise-ship staff will help you make arrangements.

If you fly too soon after diving, you're at risk for decompression sickness, which occurs when nitrogen trapped in your bloodstream doesn't escape. This creates a painful and sometimes fatal condition called the bends, not a sickness you want to develop while you're winging your way home after a fun-filled beach vacation. Opinions vary, but as a rule of thumb, wait at least 12 hours after a single dive to fly. However, if you've made multiple dives or dived several days in a row, you should wait at least 18 hours. If you've made dives that required decompression stops, you should also wait at least 24 hours before flying. To be safe, consult with your physician.

The Virgin Islands offer a plethora of dive sites, and you'll be taken to some of the best if you sign on to a dive trip run by one of the many dive operations scattered around the islands.

DIVER TRAINING

(top) Underwater shot of tropical reef, (bottom) Diver silhouette, Cane Bay, St Croix

Good to know: Divers can become certified through PADI *(www.padi.com)*, NAUI *(www.naui.org)*, or SSI *(www.divessi. com)*. The requirements for all three are similar, and if you do the classroom instruction and pool training with a dive shop associated with one organization, the referral for the open water dives will be honored by most dive shops. Note that you should not fly for at least 24 hours after a dive, because residual nitrogen in the body can pose health risks upon decompression. While there are no rigid rules on diving after flying, make sure you're well-hydrated before hitting the water.

NOT CERTIFIED?

Not sure if you want to commit the time and money to become certified? Not a problem. Most dive shops and many resorts will offer a discover scuba day-long course. In the morning, the instructor will teach you the basics of scuba diving: how to clear your mask, how to come to the surface in the unlikely event you lose your air supply, etc. In the afternoon, instructors will take you out for a dive in relatively shallow water—less than 30 feet. Be sure to ask where the dive will take place. Jumping into the water off a shallow beach may not be as fun as actually going out to the coral. If you decide that diving is something you want to pursue, the open dive may count toward your certification.

■ TIP→ You can often book discover dives at the last minute. It may not be worth it to go out on a windy day when the currents are stronger. Also the underwater world looks a whole lot brighter on sunny days.

SNUBA

Beyond snorkeling or the requirements of scuba, you also have the option of "Snuba." The word is a trademarked portmanteau or combo of snorkel and scuba. Marketed as easy-to-learn family fun, Snuba lets you breathe underwater via tubes from an air-supplied vessel above, with no prior diving or snorkel experience required.

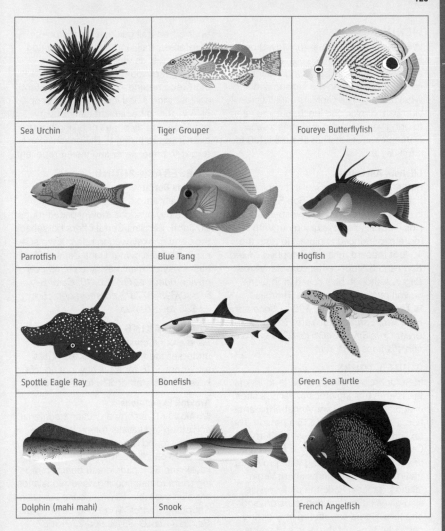

Sea Urchin

Tiger Grouper

Foureye Butterflyfish

Parrotfish

Blue Tang

Hogfish

Spottle Eagle Ray

Bonefish

Green Sea Turtle

Dolphin (mahi mahi)

Snook

French Angelfish

REEF CREATURES IN THE VIRGIN ISLANDS

From the striped sergeant majors to bright blue tangs, the reefs of the Virgin Islands are teeming with life, though not nearly as many as in eons past. Warming waters and pollution have taken their toll on both coral and fish species. But many reefs in the Virgin Islands still thrive; you'll also see sponges, crustaceans, perhaps a sea turtle or two, and bigger game fish like grouper and barracuda; sharks are seen but are rarely a problem for divers. Beware of fire corals, which are not really corals but rather a relative of the jellyfish and have a painful sting; if you brush up against a fire coral, spread vinegar on the wound as soon as possible to minimize the pain.

FISHING

Well-kept charter boats—approved by the U.S. Coast Guard—head out to the north and south drops or troll along the inshore reefs, depending on the season and what's biting. The captains usually provide bait, drinks, and lunch, but you need to bring your own hat and sunscreen. Fishing charters start at about $1,100 for a full-day trip.

Offshore Adventures

FISHING | **FAMILY** | An excellent choice for fishing charters, Captain Rob Richards is patient with beginners—especially kids—but also enjoys going out with more experienced anglers. He runs the 40-foot inboard tuna-tower-topped *Mixed Bag I* and 32-foot center-console *Mixed Bag II*. Although he's based in St. John, he will pick up parties in St. Thomas. ✉ *The Westin St. John, 300A Chocolate Hole Rd., Estate Chocolate Hole and Great Cruz Bay* ☎ *340/513–0389* ⊕ *www. sportfishingstjohn.com.*

GUIDED TOURS

In St. John, taxi drivers provide tours of the island, making stops at various sites, including Trunk Bay and Annaberg Plantation. Prices run around $15 a person. The taxi drivers congregate near the ferry in Cruz Bay. The dispatcher will find you a driver for your tour. Along with providing trail maps and brochures about Virgin Islands National Park, the park service also gives several guided tours on- and offshore. Some are offered only during particular times of the year, and some require reservations.

V.I. National Park Visitors Center

TOUR—SPORTS | ✉ *North Shore Rd., near creek, Cruz Bay* ☎ *340/776–6201* ⊕ *www. nps.gov/viis.*

HIKING

Although it's fun to go hiking with a Virgin Islands National Park guide, don't be afraid to head out on your own. To find a hike that suits your ability, stop by the park's visitor center in Cruz Bay and pick up the free trail guide; it details points of interest, trail lengths, and estimated hiking times, as well as any dangers you might encounter. Although the park staff recommends long pants to protect against thorns and insects, most people hike in shorts because it can get very hot. Wear sturdy shoes or hiking boots even if you're hiking to the beach. Don't forget to bring water and insect repellent.

HORSEBACK RIDING
Carolina Corral

HORSEBACK RIDING | Clip-clop along the island's byways for a slower-paced tour of St. John. Carolina Corral offers horseback trips and donkey wagon rides down scenic roads with owner Dana Barlett. She has a way with animals and calms even novice riders. ✉ *Off Rte. 10, Coral Bay* ☎ *340/693–5778* ⊕ *horsesstjohn.com* 🏷 *$85 for 2-hr ride.*

SEA KAYAKING

Poke around crystal bays and explore undersea life from a sea kayak. Rates run about $110 for a full day in a double kayak. Tours start at $75 for a half day.

Arawak Expeditions

KAYAKING | This company uses traditional and sit-on-top kayaks for exploring the waters around St. John. They also rent stand-up paddleboards (SUP). Multiday kayak and SUP paddle and beach camping tours to neighboring deserted islands are also available. ✉ *Mongoose Junction Shopping Center, North Shore Rd., Cruz Bay* ☎ *340/693–8312, 800/238–8687* ⊕ *www.arawakexp.com* 🏷 *Single sit-atop kayak rentals $50 per day, doubles $65; half-day SUP rentals $50, full day $75.*

Crabby's Watersports

BOATING | Explore Coral Bay Harbor and Hurricane Hole on the eastern end of the island in a sea kayak or on a stand-up paddleboard from Crabby's Watersports. Crabby's also rents snorkel gear, beach chairs, umbrellas, coolers, and floats. ✉ *Rte. 107, next to Cocoloba shopping*

Did You Know?

The 2.2-mile Reef Bay Trail is the most popular hike in Virgin Islands National Park. You can take a shuttle from the park office to the trailhead and then a boat back to the visitor center.

center, Coral Bay ☎ *340/626–1570*
⊕ *www.crabbyswatersports.com.*

Virgin Islands Ecotours

KAYAKING | Coral reefs, deserted offshore cays, lush seagrass beds filled with marine life, and even sea turtles are what you can see on VI Ecotours' two-, three-, and five-hour kayak tours off Caneel Bay and the northwest coast of St. John. ✉ *Honeymoon Beach, Rte. 20, Estate Caneel Bay* ☎ *340/779–2155, 877/684– 2441* ⊕ *www.viecotours.com.*

Chapter 5

ST. CROIX

Updated by
Robert Curley

 Sights
★★★★★

 Restaurants
★★★★★

 Hotels
★★★★☆

 Shopping
★★★★☆

 Nightlife
★★★☆☆

WELCOME TO ST. CROIX

TOP REASONS TO GO

★ **Sailing to Buck Island:** The beach at the western end of Buck Island is a great spot to relax after a snorkeling adventure or a hike up the hill to take in the stunning view.

★ **Diving the Wall:** Every dive boat in St. Croix makes a trip to the Cane Bay Wall, one of the Caribbean's best diving experiences, but you can also enjoy great shore diving from Cane Bay Beach.

★ **Exploring Fort Christiansvaern:** History buffs flock to Christiansted National Historic site. Head to the upper ramparts of Fort Christiansvaern to ponder how life was for early settlers.

★ **Reflecting on history:** Visiting Whim Plantation is a chance to learn about St. Croix's agrarian past. The estate has been lovingly restored.

★ **Strolling around Christiansted:** You can easily while away the better part of a day in Christiansted, St. Croix's main town.

TO ↑
ST. THOMAS

Cane Bay

Hams Bluff   North Star

Hams Bay   Davis Bay

63   Annaly

West End   Rain   76   Rd.
Beaches   Forest
Mahogany

Frederiksted   St. George
Hill

Centerline Rd.

Melvin H. Evans Hwy

66

Long Pt.
Bay   Long Pt.

80

Blue Mt.

Midland Rd.

72   75

69   Kingshill

70

Henry E. Rohlsen
Airport

0		2 miles
0		3 km

Caribbean Sea

Buck Island

Buck Island Reef
National Monument

Salt River Bay

**Salt River Bay
National Historical
Park**

Green
Cay

Long
Reef

Tamarind
Reef Beach

Pull
Pt.

Coakley
Bay

Cramer's
Park

Cottongarden
Pt.

*Northside
Rd.* **Estate**

Christiansted
Harbor

East End Rd.

82

Teague
Bay

Sugarloaf Hill

Little Princess
Golden Rock
Estate

Christiansted

Point Udall

Sunny Isles

Gallow's
Bay

Recovery
Hill

Prospect
Hill

South Side Rd.

60

Isaacs Bay
Grapetree Bay

Grassy Pt.

Robin
Bay

South Side Rd.

62

Milord
Pt.

*Great Pond
Bay*

Manchenil
Bay

*Krause
Pt.*

*Canegarden
Bay*

ATLANTIC OCEAN

The largest of the USVI, St. Croix is 40 miles (64 km) south of St. Thomas. Plantation ruins, reminders of the days when St. Croix was a big producer of sugar, dot the island. Its northwest is covered by a lush rain forest, its drier East End spotted with cacti. The restored Danish port of Christiansted and the more Victorian-looking Frederiksted are its main towns; Buck Island, off the island's northeast shore, attracts many day visitors.

Until 1917 Denmark owned St. Croix and her sister Virgin Islands, an aspect of the island's past that is reflected in street names in the main towns of Christiansted and Frederiksted, as well as the surnames of many island residents. Those early settlers from Denmark and other European nations left behind a slew of 18th- and 19th-century plantation ruins, all of them worked by slaves brought over on ships from Africa, their descendants, and white indentured servants lured to St. Croix to pay off their debt to society. Some of these ruins—such as the Christiansted National Historic site, Whim Plantation, the ruins at St. George Village Botanical Garden, and the ruins at Estate Mount Washington and Judith's Fancy—are open for easy exploration. Others are on private land, but a drive around the island passes the ruins of 100 plantations here and there on St. Croix's 84 square miles (218 square km). Their windmills, greathouses, and factories are all that's left of the 224 plantations that once grew abundant sugarcane, tobacco, and other agricultural products.

An economic downturn began in 1801, when the British occupied the island. The end of the slave trade in 1803, another British occupation from 1807 to 1815, droughts, the development of the sugar-beet industry in Europe, political upheaval, and a depression sent the island on a downward economic spiral.

Even though the slave trade ended in 1803, slavery continued here until 1848, when slaves in St. Croix marched on Frederiksted to demand their freedom from the Danish government. The freeing of all of the slaves, followed by labor riots, fires, hurricanes, and an earthquake during the last half of the 19th century, brought what was left of the island's economy to its knees. The start of Prohibition in 1922 called a halt to the island's rum industry, further crippling the economy. The situation remained dire so bad that President Herbert Hoover called the territory an "effective poorhouse" during a 1931 visit—until the rise of tourism in the late 1950s and 1960s. With tourism came economic improvements coupled with an influx of residents from other Caribbean islands and the mainland.

Today suburban subdivisions fill the fields where sugarcane once waved in the tropical breeze. Condominium complexes line the beaches along the north coast outside Christiansted. Homes that are more elaborate dot the rolling hillsides. Modern strip malls and shopping centers sit along major roads, and it's as easy to find a U.S. chain restaurant as it is Caribbean fare.

Although St. Croix sits firmly in the 21st century, with only a little effort you can easily step back into the island's past.

Getting Here and Around

AIR

While St. Croix is not as well served as St. Thomas when it comes to nonstop flights from the United States, you will still be able to fly nonstop from Atlanta (on Delta) or from Miami (on American Airlines). Spirit Airlines flies to St. Croix three times a week from Fort Lauderdale. You can also get connecting service through San Juan or St. Thomas via Cape Air, which offers code-share arrangements with all major airlines, so your luggage can transfer seamlessly. Seaborne Airlines flies between St. Thomas, St. Croix, and San Juan.

AIRPORTS Henry Rohlsen Airport. ⊠ *Estate Mannings Bay, Frederiksted* ☎ *340/778–1012* ⊕ *www.viport.com/hera.html.*

BUS

Privately owned taxi vans crisscross St. Croix regularly, providing reliable service between Frederiksted and Christiansted along Route 70. This inexpensive

($2.50 one way) mode of transportation is favored by locals, and though the many stops on the 20-mile (32-km) drive between the two main towns make the ride slow, it's never dull. Vitran public buses aren't the quickest way to get around the island, but they're comfortable and affordable. The fare is $1 between Christiansted and Frederiksted or to places in between.

CAR

You can certainly get by without a car, particularly if your hotel is close to Christiansted and offers a shuttle into town, but more than on most of the other Virgin Islands, having a car is a big advantage on St. Croix. With a wide variety of good restaurants and no large concentration of accommodations around either Christiansted or Frederiksted, a car can be very helpful regardless of where you are staying. Accommodations along the North Shore are even more isolated, making a car more of a necessity to travelers staying there. Even if you are staying in or near Christiansted, you might want to rent a car for a day or two so you can explore the island.

Although roads are not well signposted, there's a highway from the airport to the East End of the island that makes travel fairly easy. Street parking can be hard to find in Christiansted, but there are some paid lots. Just remember that you drive on the *left* even though cars are U.S.–made with steering wheels on the left.

CAR RENTALS

Avis is at Henry Rohlsen Airport and at the cruise pier in Frederiksted. Budget has branches at the airport and near the seaplane terminal in Christiansted. Hertz is at the airport. Judi of Croix delivers vehicles to your hotel. Olympic is outside Christiansted, but will pick up at hotels.

CONTACTS Avis. ⊠ *Henry E. Rohlsen Airport* ☎ *340/778–9636, 800/352–7900* ⊕ *www.avis.com.* **Budget.** ⊠ *Henry E. Rohlsen Airport* ☎ *340/778–4663,*

888/264–8894, 340/778–7201 ⊕ budget-stcroix.com. **Hertz.** ✉ Henry E. Rohlsen Airport ☎ 340/778–1402, 888/248–4261, 340/778–9744 ⊕ www.rentacarstcroix.com. **Judi of Croix.** ☎ 340/773–2123, 877/903–2123 ⊕ www.judiofcroix.com. **Olympic.** ✉ Rte. 70, Christiansted ☎ 340/718–3000 ⊕ www.olympicstcroix.com.

TAXI

Taxis are available in downtown Christiansted, at the Henry E. Rohlsen Airport, and at the Frederiksted pier during cruise-ship arrivals, or they can be called. In Frederiksted, all the shops are a short walk away, as is a great beach, so there's no need for a taxi if you are staying in town. Most cruise-ship passengers visit Christiansted on a tour since a taxi will cost $24 for one person plus $11 for each additional passenger (one way). ⚠ **There is no Uber or Lyft on St. Croix.**

CONTACTS St. Croix Taxi Association. ✉ Henry E. Rohlsen Airport ☎ 340/778–1088.

Essentials

BANKS

St. Croix has branches of Banco Popular in the Orange Grove and Sunny Isle shopping centers. FirstBank is in Sunny Isle, Frederiksted, and Orange Grove. Scotiabank, now owned by Oriental, has branches in Sunny Isle, Christiansted, and Sunshine Mall. Bank of St. Croix has locations in Gallows Bay and Peters Rest.

BEACHES

St. Croix's beaches aren't as spectacular as those on St. Thomas. But that's not to say you won't find some good places to spread out for a day on the water. The best beach is on nearby Buck Island, a national monument where a marked snorkeling trail leads you through an extensive coral reef while a soft, sandy beach beckons a few yards away. Other

great beaches are the West End beaches both south and north of Frederiksted.

HOTELS

You can find everything from plush resorts to simple beachfront digs in St. Croix. If you sleep in either the Christiansted or Frederiksted area, you'll be closest to shopping, restaurants, and nightlife. Most of the island's other hotels will put you just steps from the beach. St. Croix has several small but special properties that offer personalized service. If you like all the comforts of home, you may prefer to stay in a condominium or villa. Whether you stay in a hotel, a condominium, or a villa, you'll enjoy up-to-date amenities.

Although a stay right in historic Christiansted may mean putting up with a little urban noise, you probably won't have trouble sleeping. Christiansted rolls up the sidewalks fairly early, and humming air-conditioners drown out any noise. Solitude is guaranteed at hotels and inns outside Christiansted and on the outskirts of sleepy Frederiksted.

Families and groups may find more value in a condo that allows you to do a bit of cooking but still has access to a pool or a limited array of resort-style amenities. There are a lot of condos and apartment buildings on St. Croix, particularly along the North Shore and East End.

Our hotel reviews have been shortened. For full information, go to Fodors.com.

PRIVATE CONDOS AND VILLAS

St. Croix has more than 350 private villas scattered all over the island, from modest two-bedroom houses with just the basics to lavish and luxurious five-bedroom compounds with every imaginable amenity. But most are located in the center or in the East End. Renting a villa gives you all the convenience of home as well as top-notch amenities. Many have pools, hot tubs, and deluxe furnishings. Most companies meet you at the airport, arrange for a rental car, and provide helpful information about the island.

If you want to be close to the island's restaurants and shopping, look for a condominium or villa in the hills above Christiansted or on either side of the town. An East End location gets you out of Christiansted's hustle and bustle, but you're still only 15 minutes from town. North Shore locations are lovely, with gorgeous sea views and lots of peace and quiet.

Vacation St. Croix
✉ 400 La Grande Princess, Christiansted ☎ 340/718–0361 ⊕ www.vacationstcroix. com.

RESTAURANTS
Seven flags have flown over St. Croix, and each has left its legacy in the island's cuisine. You can feast on Italian, French, and American dishes; there are even Chinese and Mexican restaurants in Christiansted. Fresh local seafood is plentiful and always good; wahoo, mahimahi, and conch are most popular. Island chefs often add Caribbean twists to familiar dishes. For a true island experience, stop at a local restaurant for goat stew, curried chicken, or ribs. Regardless of where you eat, your meal will be an informal affair. As is the case everywhere in the Caribbean, prices are higher than you'd pay on the mainland. Some restaurants may close for a week or two in September or October, so if you're traveling during these months it's best to call ahead.

St. Croix has restaurants scattered from one end to the other, so it's usually not hard to find a place to stop when you're exploring the island. Most travelers eat dinner near their hotel so as to avoid long drives on dark, unfamiliar roads. Christiansted has the island's widest selection of restaurants. Don't rule out Frederiksted, especially if you're out exploring the island. It has a handful of delightful restaurants.

WHAT IT COSTS in U.S. Dollars

	$	$$	$$$	$$$$
RESTAURANTS				
	under $13	$13–$20	$21–$30	over $30
HOTELS				
	under $276	$276–$375	$376–$475	over $475

NIGHTLIFE AND PERFORMING ARTS
The island's nightlife is ever changing, and its arts scene is eclectic, ranging from holiday performances of The Nutcracker to locally organized shows. Folk-art traditions, such as quadrille dancers, are making a comeback. To find out what's happening, pick up the local newspapers—V.I. Daily News and St. Croix Avis—available at newsstands. Christiansted has a lively and eminently casual club scene near the waterfront. Frederiksted has a couple of restaurants and clubs offering weekend entertainment.

SAFETY
Don't wander the streets of Christiansted or Frederiksted alone at night. Don't leave valuables in your car, and keep it locked wherever you park. Don't leave cameras, purses, and other valuables lying on the beach while you snorkel for an hour (or even for a minute).

SCUBA DIVING EMERGENCIES
Roy L. Schneider Hospital on St. Thomas has the territory's only hyperbaric chamber.

Juan F. Luis Hospital
Top on-island medical center on St. Croix. ✉ 4007 Estate Diamond Ruby, Christiansted ☎ 340/778–6311 ⊕ jflusvi.org.

Schneider Regional Medical Center
✉ Charlotte Amalie ☎ 340/776–8311 ⊕ www.rlshospital.org.

SHOPPING

Although the shopping on St. Croix isn't as varied or extensive as that on St. Thomas, the island does have several small stores with unusual merchandise. St. Croix shop hours are usually Monday through Saturday 9 to 5, but there are some shops in Christiansted open in the evening. Stores are often closed on Sunday.

If you've rented a condominium or a villa, you'll appreciate St. Croix's excellent stateside-style supermarkets (albeit with prices that are at least 30% higher than on the U.S. mainland). Fresh vegetables, fruits, and meats arrive from the mainland frequently and are always available. Try the open-air stands strung out along Route 70 for island produce.

In Christiansted the best shopping areas are the **Pan Am Pavilion** and **Caravelle Arcade,** off Strand Street, and along **King** and **Company Streets.** These streets give way to arcades filled with boutiques. **Gallows Bay** has a blossoming shopping area in a quiet neighborhood.

TOUR OPTIONS

Sweeny's St. Croix Safari Tours offers van tours of St. Croix. Excursions depart from Christiansted and last about five hours starting at $70 per person. Walking tours of Christiansted's historic sites run $25.

CONTACTS Sweeny's St. Croix Safari Tours. ☎ *340/773–6700 ⊕ www.gotostcroix. com/guided-tours/sweenys-tours.*

VISITOR INFORMATION

If you want some friendly advice, stop by the St. Croix Visitor Center weekdays between 8 and 5 for maps and brochures.

CONTACTS St. Croix Visitor Center. ☎ *340/773–0357 ⊕ www.visitusvi. com.* **USVI Department of Tourism.** ⊠ *321 King St., Frederiksted ☎ 340/772–0357 ⊕ www.visitusvi.com.*

Christiansted

Christiansted is a historic Danish-style town that always served as St. Croix's commercial center. Your best bet is to see the historic sights in the morning, when it's still cool. Break for lunch at an open-air restaurant before spending as much time as you like shopping.

In the 1700s and 1800s Christiansted was a trading center for sugar, rum, and molasses. Today there are law offices, tourist shops, and restaurants, but many of the buildings, which start at the harbor and go up the gently sloped hillsides, still date from the 18th century. You can't get lost. All streets lead back downhill to the water.

Sights

Apothecary Hall

MUSEUM | If you're strolling downtown Christiansted's streets, it's worth a peek into the Christiansted Apothecary Hall. Although the exhibits are behind Plexiglas, they give you a glimpse into a 19th-century pharmacy. This tiny museum is at the original location of a pharmacy that operated from 1820 to 1970. ⊠ *39 Queen Cross St., Christiansted ⊕ www. stcroixlandmarks.org ⊠ Free.*

★ D. Hamilton Jackson Park

CITY PARK | When you're tired of sightseeing, stop at this shady park on the street side of Fort Christiansvaern for a rest. It's named for a famed labor leader, judge, and journalist who started the first newspaper not under the thumb of the Danish crown (his birthday, November 1, is a territorial holiday celebrated with much fanfare in St. Croix). ⚠ **There are no facilities.** ⊠ *Between Fort Christiansvaern and Danish Customs House, Christiansted.*

Christiansted

KEY
- 1 Sights
- 1 Restaurants
- 1 Hotels
- ℹ️ Tourist Information

Sights ▶
1 Apothecary Hall........... F2
2 D. Hamilton Jackson Park............... F1
3 Fort Christiansvaern...... G1
4 Government House....... F2
5 Old Danish Customs House............ F2
6 Scale House............... F1
7 Steeple Building F2

Restaurants ▶
1 BES....................... E2
2 Café Christine F2
3 40 Strand Street........... E2
4 Martha's Deli.............. C3
5 Nate's Boathouse......... D1
6 Rum Runners.............. D1
7 Savant..................... G2
8 Too.Chez................... E2
9 Zion Modern Kitchen..... E2

Hotels ▶
1 Club Comanche Hotel St. Croix............... E2
2 Company House Hotel... F2
3 Hotel Caravelle............ D1
4 Hotel on the Cay F1

Fort Christiansvaern, a National Historic site

★ Fort Christiansvaern

HISTORIC SITE | FAMILY | The large yellow fortress dominates the waterfront. Because it's so easy to spot, it makes a good place to begin a walking tour. In 1749 the Danish built the fort to protect the harbor, but the structure was repeatedly damaged by hurricane-force winds and had to be partially rebuilt in 1771. It's now a National Historic site, the best preserved of the few remaining Danish-built forts in the Virgin Islands. The park's visitor center is here. Rangers are on hand to answer questions. ■ TIP→ **Your paid admission also includes the Steeple Building and the Scale House.** ✉ *Hospital St., Christiansted* ☎ *340/773–1460* ⊕ *www. nps.gov/chri* ✉ *$7.*

Government House

HISTORIC SITE | One of the town's most elegant structures was built as a home for a Danish merchant in 1747. Today it houses offices and serves as the residence of the governor of the Virgin Islands. A sweeping staircase leads to a second-story ballroom, still used for official government functions. Out front, the traditional red guard booth with its pointed top is a popular photo op. ✉ *105 King St., Christiansted* ☎ *340/773–1404.*

Old Danish Customs House

HISTORIC SITE | FAMILY | Built in 1830 on foundations that date from a century earlier, the historic building, which is near Fort Christiansvaern, originally served as both a customs house and a post office. In 1926 it became the Christiansted Library, and it's been a national park facility since 1972. It's closed to the public, but the sweeping front steps make a nice place to take a break. ✉ *King St., Christiansted* ☎ *340/773–1460* ⊕ *www. nps.gov/chri.*

Scale House

HISTORIC SITE | FAMILY | Constructed in 1856, this was once the spot where goods passing through the port were weighed and inspected. The park staffers here have on offer a good selection of books about St. Croix history and its flora and fauna. ✉ *King St., Christiansted* ☎ *340/773–1460* ⊕ *www.nps.gov/chri.*

★ Steeple Building

HISTORIC SITE | The first Danish Lutheran church on the island when it was built in 1753, the Steeple Building is now used as a museum. It's worth the short walk to see the archaeological artifacts and exhibits on plantation life, the architectural development of Christiansted, the island's native inhabitants, and Alexander Hamilton, who grew up in St. Croix. Hours are irregular, so ask at the visitor center. Your paid admission includes Fort Christiansvaern and the Scale House, too. ⊠ *Church St., Christiansted* ☎ *340/773–1460* ⊕ *www.nps.gov/chri* ⓢ *$7.*

Restaurants

BES

$ | CARIBBEAN | Owner Frank Robinson's skilled mixologist's hand draws big crowds to this compact cocktail bar. Tapas are served alongside drinks carefully crafted with local rums and custom infusions; Robinson serves as both chef and bartender, so food and drink pairings are a cinch. **Known for:** handcrafted cocktails; island-inspired small bites; lively atmosphere. ⓢ *Average main: $10* ⊠ *53 B Company St., Christiansted* ☎ *340/773–2985.*

Café Christine

$$ | FRENCH | At this local favorite the presentation is as dazzling as the food and the tropical artwork hanging in the dining room. The small menu changes daily, but look for dishes like croque monsieur or madame, a homemade falafel pita with local tomatoes and pickled onions drizzled with cucumber yogurt sauce, and daily quiche specials. **Known for:** perfect lemon tart; views of historic Christiansted; daily changing menu. ⓢ *Average main: $14* ⊠ *Apothecary Hall Courtyard, 6 Company St., Christiansted* ☎ *340/713–1500* ▤ *No credit cards* ⊗ *Closed Sept. and Oct.*

Big Event

St. Croix celebrates Carnival in late December with the St. Croix Christmas Festival. If you don't book far ahead, it can be hard to find a room because of the influx of visitors from around the region and around the world. ⊕ *www.vicarnivalschedule.com/stcroix*

★ 40 Strand Street

$$$ | ECLECTIC | This trendy place is small and cozy with a casual atmosphere all its own. The menu selections include fresh fish prepared in creative ways and salads made with fresh local greens. **Known for:** macaroni and cheese; craft cocktails; seafood. ⓢ *Average main: $25* ⊠ *40 Strand St., Christiansted* ☎ *340/692–0524* ⊗ *Closed Sun.*

Martha's Deli

$ | CARIBBEAN | This modest storefront eatery fills up with locals getting to-go orders of the restaurant's traditional Crucian breakfast, including salt fish, johnnycakes, eggs, cucumber salad, sautéed spinach, and—in a nod to the island's Danish heritage—herring. Lunch options include chicken, shrimp, and fish rotis, and a popular vegetable lentil soup. **Known for:** traditional Crucian breakfast; numerous roti options; delicious lentil soup. ⓢ *Average main: $12* ⊠ *300 Peters Rest, Christiansted* ☎ *340/773–6054* ⊗ *Closed Sun. and Mon.*

Nate's Boathouse

$$$ | ECLECTIC | Serving breakfast, lunch, and dinner indoors and out, the dockside spot has something for everyone on its extensive menu. Dinner can be as fancy as tilapia and garlic shrimp with mushrooms, white wine, and garlic butter, or as basic as a burger or chicken sandwich. **Known for:** fresh seafood; extensive menu; Sunday brunch. ⓢ *Average main: $25* ✉ *1201 King Cross St., at the boardwalk, Christiansted* ☎ *340/692–6283* ⊕ *www.natesboathouse.com.*

★ Rum Runners

$$$ | ECLECTIC | FAMILY | Sitting right on the Christiansted boardwalk, Rum Runners serves a little bit of everything, including a to-die-for tropical salad topped with fresh local mango (in season) or pineapple. Heartier fare includes chili and lime shrimp and spaghetti tossed with crab and bacon. **Known for:** stellar views; local hangout; boardwalk location. ⓢ *Average main: $30* ✉ *Hotel Caravelle, 44A Queen Cross St., Christiansted* ☎ *340/773–6585* ⊕ *www.rumrunnersstcroix.com* ⊗ *Closed Tues.*

Savant

$$$$ | ECLECTIC | Savant is one of those small but special spots that locals love. The locally sourced cuisine is an unusual fusion of Mexican, Thai, and Caribbean that includes anything from fresh fish to Thai curry with chicken to a fillet of beef stuffed with portobello mushrooms and goat cheese. **Known for:** lively atmosphere; creative dishes; reservations are a must. ⓢ *Average main: $35* ✉ *4C Hospital St., Christiansted* ☎ *340/713–8666* ⊕ *www.savantstx.com* ⊗ *Closed Sun. No lunch.*

Too.Chez

$$$ | FRENCH | This beautiful courtyard restaurant serves French-inspired American cuisine; the barbecued ribs are excellent, and you can do a partially healthy offset by ordering the roasted brussels sprouts dip and scooping it onto flatbread. Don't skip the desserts, particularly the apple crisp topped with homemade vanilla ice cream. **Known for:** desserts that are worth the calories; courtyard dining; creative Caribbean cuisine. ⓢ *Average main: $29* ✉ *53 King St., Christiansted* ☎ *340/713–8888* ⊗ *Closed Mon. and Tues.*

Zion Modern Kitchen

$$$$ | CONTEMPORARY | Find this farm-to-table restaurant, with courtyard seating surrounded by herbs and tropical plants, tucked away in a historic home on a Christiansted side street. Like the food, the drinks are also locally sourced from brewers like Leatherback and distillers like Cruzan Rum and Mutiny vodka. **Known for:** historic setting; creative Caribbean cuisine; handcrafted cocktails. ⓢ *Average main: $36* ✉ *Quin House, 2132 Company St., Christiansted* ☎ *340/773–9466* ⊕ *zionmodernkitchen. com.*

Hotels

Club Comanche Hotel St. Croix

$ | HOTEL | This historic town house built in 1756 is located in the center of town and has a rum and wine bar on the first floor. **Pros:** located near shopping and restaurants; friendly staff. **Cons:** no elevator; no close parking. ⓢ *Rooms from: $199* ✉ *1 Strand St., Christiansted* ☎ *340/773–0210, 855/680–3239* ⊕ *www.clubcomanche.com* ➪ *23 rooms* ⦿ *No meals.*

Company House Hotel

$ | HOTEL | With an elegant lobby, including a grand piano, and serviceable rooms, this hotel provides affordable accommodations in the heart of Christiansted. **Pros:** convenient location; inexpensive. **Cons:** no parking; no beach; busy neighborhood. ⓢ *Rooms from: $229* ✉ *2 Company St., Christiansted* ☎ *340/773–1377* ⊕ *www.hotelcompanyhouse.com* ➪ *31 rooms, 2 suites* ⦿ *No meals.*

Hotel Caravelle

$ | HOTEL | A stay at the Caravelle, which is near the harbor, puts you at the waterfront end of a pleasant shopping arcade and steps from shops and restaurants. **Pros:** good restaurant; convenient location; parking and pool on-site. **Cons:** no beach; busy neighborhood. ⓢ *Rooms from: $219* ✉ *44A Queen Cross St., Christiansted* ☎ *340/773–0687,*

["

★ Hotheads Boutique

CLOTHING | This small store sells hats, hats, and more hats, which are often perched on top of cotton shifts, comfortable shirts, and trendy tropical wear. If you forgot your bathing suit, this store has a good selection. ✉ *1244 Queen Cross St., Christiansted* ☎ *340/773–7888.*

GIFTS

Many Hands

GIFTS/SOUVENIRS | This shop sells pottery in bright colors, paintings of St. Croix and the Caribbean, prints, and maps. They are all made by local artists, and they all make for perfect take-home gifts. ■ TIP➔ The owners ship all over the world. ✉ *6 Pan Am Pavilion, 1103 Strand St., Christiansted* ☎ *340/514–0281.*

Mitchell-Larsen Studio

GIFTS/SOUVENIRS | This glass gallery offers an interesting amalgam of carefully crafted glass plates, suncatchers, and more. The pieces, all made on-site by St. Croix glassmaker Jan Mitchell Larsen, are often whimsically adorned with tropical fish, flora, and fauna. Photography from Steffen Larsen also is on display and for sale. ✉ *2000 Company St., Christiansted* ☎ *340/719–1000* ⊕ *www.mitchelllarsenstudio.com.*

JEWELRY

Chaney Chicks and Island Gifts

JEWELRY/ACCESSORIES | Chaney is jewelry made from shards of the antique Danish pottery that can be found all over St. Croix; local residents find it in the ocean or buried in the ground and sell it to the owners of this Christiansted jewelry shop, who clean it, polish it, wrap it in silver wire, and sell it as earrings, necklaces, and bracelets. The shop also sells locally made seaglass jewelry, beach bags, hats, and other giftware. ✉ *55 Kings Alley, Suite 1C, Christiansted* ☎ *305/896–3135* ⊕ *chaneychicks.com.*

★ Crucian Gold

JEWELRY/ACCESSORIES | St. Croix native Brian Bishop's trademark piece is the Turk's Head ring (a knot of interwoven gold strands). His son, Nathan Bishop, is now creating contemporary sterling and gold pendants, rings, and earrings. Stop by to meet the family, browse the jewelry, and "Feel the Love." ✉ *1112 Strand St., Christiansted* ☎ *340/244–2996, 877/773–5241* ⊕ *www.cruciangold.com.*

★ ib designs

JEWELRY/ACCESSORIES | This small shop showcases the handcrafted jewelry of local craftsman and "Island Boy" Whealan Massicott, including his signature, "infinity" style Crucian hook bracelet. Whether in silver or gold, the designs are simply elegant. ✉ *2108 Company St., Christiansted* ☎ *340/773–4322* ⊕ *www.ibdesignsvi.com.*

Sonya Ltd.

JEWELRY/ACCESSORIES | This store is owned and operated by Sonya Hough, who invented the popular hook bracelet (wear the hook facing out if you're "available," inward if you're attached). Bracelets are priced from about $65 and up, depending on size and materials. In addition to the original silver and gold hooks in a variety of diameters, the shop sells variations that incorporate hurricane symbols, dolphins, hibiscus flowers, and infinity symbols. If you're going to splurge on one nice souvenir in St. Croix, make it a hook bracelet and you'll be recognized as an honorary Crucian whenever you wear it. ✉ *2101 Company St., Christiansted* ☎ *340/773–8924, 800/766–9284* ⊕ *www.sonyaltd.com.*

Under the Sun VI

JEWELRY/ACCESSORIES | The jewelers at Under the Sun VI can create one-of-a-kind pieces to your design. The shop specializes in gold jewelry but also carries diamonds, emeralds, rubies, and sapphires, and jewelry made from "Chaney" (vintage shards of Danish pottery). ✉ *1102 Strand St., Christiansted* ☎ *340/773–0365* ⊕ *underthesunvi.com.*

LIQUOR AND TOBACCO

Baci Duty Free

GIFTS/SOUVENIRS | The walk-in humidor here has a good selection of Arturo Fuente, Partagas, Padron, and Macanudo cigars. Baci also carries high-end liquor, sleek watches from Tissot, Frederick Constance, Alpina, Mido, Luminox, Citizen, and Bering, Steiner binoculars from Germany, and fine jewelry. ✉ *1235 Queen Cross St., Christiansted* ☎ *340/773–5040* ⊕ *www.facebook.com/bacidutyfree.*

West of Christiansted

Heading west from Christiansted there are few sights worth seeing, but it's a busy area with a handful of condos, a standout bed-and-breakfast, as well as a few restaurants in Estates Golden Rock and Princesse.

 Restaurants

Breezez Restaurant

$$$ | **ECLECTIC** | **FAMILY** | This aptly named restaurant, *the* place on the island for Sunday brunch, is poolside at the Club St. Croix condominiums. Locals also gather for lunch, when the menu includes everything from burgers to blackened prime rib with a horseradish sauce. **Known for:** reasonable prices; amaretto cheesecake. $ *Average main: $25* ✉ *Club St. Croix, 220 Estate Golden Rock, off Rte. 752, Estate Golden Rock* ☎ *340/781–7077.*

 Hotels

Club St. Croix

$ | **RENTAL** | **FAMILY** | Sitting beachfront just outside Christiansted, this modern condominium complex faces a lovely sandy beach. **Pros:** beachfront location; good restaurant; full kitchens. **Cons:** need car to get around; sketchy neighborhood. $ *Rooms from: $195* ✉ *3280 Golden Rock, Estate Golden Rock* ☎ *340/718–4800, 800/524–2025, 340/718–9150* ⊕ *www.antillesresorts.com* ⇄ *53 apartments* ♙ *No meals.*

Colony Cove

$ | **RENTAL** | **FAMILY** | In a string of condominium complexes, Colony Cove lets you experience comfortable beachfront living. **Pros:** beachfront location; comfortable units; good views; swimming pool. **Cons:** sketchy neighborhood; need car to get around. $ *Rooms from: $240* ✉ *3221 Golden Rock, Estate Golden Rock* ☎ *340/718–1965, 800/524–2025* ⊕ *www.antillesresorts.com* ⇄ *62 apartments* ♙ *No meals.*

The Palms at Pelican Cove

$ | **RESORT** | A 10-minute drive from Christiansted's interesting shopping and restaurants, this resort, with its mixed bag of guests, has a gorgeous strand of white sand at its doorstep. **Pros:** nice beach; good dining options; friendly staff. **Cons:** need car to get out and about; neighborhood not the best. $ *Rooms from: $225* ✉ *4126 La Grande Princess, La Grande Princesse* ☎ *340/718–8920, 800/548–4460* ⊕ *www.palmspelicancove.com* ⇄ *39 rooms* ♙ *No meals.*

Sugar Beach

$$$ | **RENTAL** | **FAMILY** | With all the conveniences of home, Sugar Beach's apartments are immaculate and breezy. **Pros:** pleasant beach; full kitchens; space to spread out. **Cons:** sketchy neighborhood; need car to get around. $ *Rooms from: $425* ✉ *3245 Golden Rock, Estate Golden Rock* ☎ *340/718–5345, 800/524–2049* ⊕ *www.sugarbeachstcroix.com* ⇄ *46 apartments* ♙ *No meals.*

St. Croix

↑
TO
ST. THOMAS

A B C D E

1
2
3
4
5
6
7

Cane Bay

Salt River Bay

North Star

Hams Bluff

Hams Bay

Davis Bay

80

11 9

1

12

9

6

6

Blue Mt.

75

Northside Rd.

7

Annaly

69

Mt. Victory Camp

4

Rain Forest

Mahogany Rd.

7

76

72

Midland Rd.

Northside Rd.

5

Sunny Isle

West End Beaches

Frederiksted Pier

63

St. George Hill

Kingshill

70

69

2

HOVENSA Oil Refinery

Frederiksted
see detail map

Centerline Rd.

8

3

Henry E. Rohlsen Airport

5

Melvin H. Evans Hwy.

66

Krause Pt.

Long Pt. Bay

Long Pt.

KEY

1 Sights

1 Restaurants

1 Hotels

Beaches

Dive Sites

Cruise Ship Terminal

0   2 miles
0   3 km

Sights ▼

1 Buck Island Reef National Monument **H1**

2 Captain Morgan Distillery **D4**

3 Cruzan Rum Distillery **C5**

4 Estate Mount Washington Plantation **A3**

5 Estate Whim Museum **B5**

6 Mt. Eagle **C3**

7 Point Udall **J3**

8 St. George Village Botanical Garden **C4**

9 Salt River Bay National Historical Park and Ecological Preserve **E2**

Restaurants ▼

1 AMA at Cane Bay **C2**

2 Breezez Restaurant **F3**

3 Cheeseburgers in America's Paradise **H3**

4 The Galleon **G3**

Buck Island

Buck Island

Long
Reef

Christiansted
see detail
map

Tamarind
Reef
Beach

Green
Cay

Pull
Pt.

Coakley
Bay

Cramer's
Park

Cottongarden
Pt.

Christiansted
Harbor

Teague
Bay

Little
Princess
Estate

Gallow's
Bay

East End Rd.

Isaacs Bay

Sugarloaf Hill

Prospect
Hill

Grapetree
Bay

Recovery
Hill

South Side Rd.

Grassy Pt.

Robin
Bay

Great Pond
Bay

Milord
Pt.

South Side Rd.

Canegarden
Bay

Manchenil
Bay

Caribbean Sea

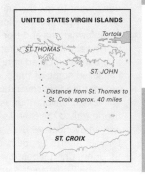

UNITED STATES VIRGIN ISLANDS

Tortola

ST. THOMAS

ST. JOHN

Distance from St. Thomas to
St. Croix approx. 40 miles

ST. CROIX

Shopping

Pueblo
FOOD/CANDY | Pueblo is a chain supermarket selling dry goods, fresh produce, meat, and seafood. ✉ *Golden Rock Shopping Center, Rte. 75, Christiansted* ☎ *340/774–4200* ⊕ *wfmpueblo.com.*

East End

An easy drive (roads are flat and well marked) to St. Croix's eastern end takes you through some choice real estate. Ruins of old sugar estates dot the landscape. You can make the entire loop on the road that circles the island in about an hour, a good way to end the day. If you want to spend a full day exploring, you can find some nice beaches and easy walks with places to stop for lunch.

Sights

★ Buck Island Reef National Monument
REEF | Buck Island has pristine beaches that are just right for sunbathing, but there's also some shade for those who don't want to fry. The snorkeling trail set in the reef allows close-up study of coral formations and tropical fish. Overly warm seawater temperatures have led to a condition called coral bleaching that has killed some of the coral. The reefs are starting to recover, but how long it will take is anyone's guess. There's a hiking trail to the island's highest point and an overlook where you are rewarded for your efforts by spectacular views of St. John. Charter-boat trips leave daily from the Christiansted waterfront or from Green Cay Marina, about 2 miles (3 km) east of Christiansted. Check with your hotel for recommendations. ✉ *Off East End of St. Croix* ☎ *340/773–1460* ⊕ *www.nps.gov/buis.*

Point Udall
VIEWPOINT | This rocky promontory, marked by a large stone sundial sculpture, is the easternmost point in the United States; it's about a half-hour drive east of Christiansted. A paved road takes you to an overlook with glorious views; it's an especially popular gathering spot on New Year's Day for those who want to be the first to greet the first sunrise of the year. Adventurous visitors can hike down to the pristine beach below. On the way back, look for the Castle Aura, an enormous Moorish-style mansion. It was built by the late Nadia Farber, the former Contessa de Navarro, an extravagant local character. ✉ *Rte. 82, Whim.*

Beaches

★ Buck Island
BEACH—SIGHT | Part of Buck Island Reef National Monument, this is a must-see for anyone in St. Croix. The beach is beautiful, but its finest treasures are those you can see when you plop off the boat and adjust your mask, snorkel, and fins to swim over colorful coral and darting fish. Don't know how to snorkel? No problem—the boat crew will have you outfitted and in the water in no time. Take care not to step on those black-pointed spiny sea urchins or touch the mustard-color fire coral, which can cause a nasty burn. Most charter-boat trips start with a snorkel over the lovely reef before a stop at the island's beach. A hike leads uphill to an overlook for a bird's-eye view of the reef below. **Amenities:** none. **Best for:** snorkeling; swimming. ☎ *340/773–1460* ⊕ *www.nps.gov/buis.*

Restaurants

Cheeseburgers in America's Paradise
$$ | **AMERICAN** | **FAMILY** | A perennial favorite with local and visiting families, this open-air restaurant in the middle of a field serves up terrific New York strip

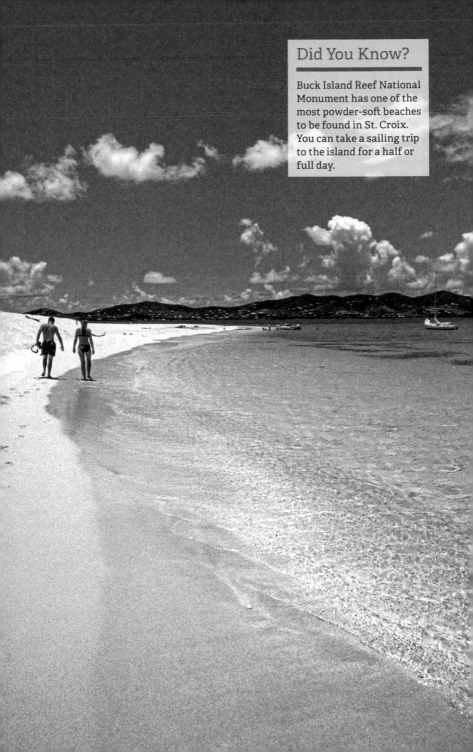

Did You Know?

Buck Island Reef National Monument has one of the most powder-soft beaches to be found in St. Croix. You can take a sailing trip to the island for a half or full day.

steak, burgers with toppings that run from mushrooms to fried onions, and, of course, cheeseburgers. There's room for kids to run around before dinner. **Known for:** kid-friendly dining; lively atmosphere. ⑤ *Average main: $17* ⊠ *67 Southgate, Christiansted* ☎ *340/773–1118* ⊕ *www. cheeseburgersstx.com.*

The Galleon

$$$ | ECLECTIC | This popular dockside restaurant is the place to get Southern soul food in St. Croix (chef-owner Charles Mereday is a graduate of the Charleston, S.C., branch of Johnson and Wales University, after all), but you'll also find hand-cut steaks alongside island favorites like barbecued ribs, grilled chicken, and mahimahi on the menu. Take Route 82 out of Christiansted, and then turn left at the sign for Green Cay Marina. **Known for:** shrimp and grits; island classics; marina views. ⑤ *Average main: $30* ⊠ *Tamarind Reef Resort, Green Cay Marina off Rte. 82, Annas Hope* ☎ *340/718–9948* ⊕ *www.tamarindreefresort.com.*

The New Deep End Bar & Grill

$$$ | ECLECTIC | A favorite with locals and vacationers, this poolside restaurant serves up terrific burgers, steak, and seafood, as well as delicious pasta dishes and popular salads. Come for disco bingo on Thursday with dancing between games, crab races on Friday, Sunday brunch, and live music on weekends. **Known for:** lively atmosphere; beach setting; Sunday brunch. ⑤ *Average main: $23* ⊠ *Tamarind Reef Resort, 5001 Estate Southgate, Annas Hope* ☎ *340/718–7071* ⊕ *www.newdeepend.com.*

 ## Hotels

The Buccaneer

$$$ | RESORT | FAMILY | Aimed at travelers who want everything at their fingertips, this resort has sandy beaches, multiple restaurants, golf, tennis, a spa, and swimming pools. **Pros:** beachfront location; numerous activities; nice

golf course. **Cons:** pricey rates; insular environment; need car to get around. ⑤ *Rooms from: $463* ⊠ *Rte. 82, Shoys* ☎ *340/712–2100, 800/255–3881* ⊕ *www. thebuccaneer.com* ⇋ *138 rooms, 1 villa* ⑩ *Free Breakfast.*

Chenay Bay Beach Resort

$ | RESORT | FAMILY | The seaside setting and complimentary tennis and water-sports equipment make this resort a real find, particularly for families with active kids. **Pros:** beachfront location; pretty grounds; friendly staff. **Cons:** need car to get around; lacks pizzazz. ⑤ *Rooms from: $149* ⊠ *5000 Estate Chenay Bay, Christiansted* ☎ *340/201–1309* ⊕ *www. chenaybay.com* ⇋ *50 rooms* ⑩ *No meals.*

Tamarind Reef Resort

$ | HOTEL | Spread out along a sandy beach, these low-slung buildings offer casual comfort. **Pros:** good snorkeling; tasty restaurant; rooms have kitchenettes. **Cons:** need car to get around; motel-style rooms. ⑤ *Rooms from: $261* ⊠ *5001 Tamarind Reef, off Rte. 82, Cotton Valley* ☎ *340/718–4455, 800/619–0014* ⊕ *www.tamarindreefresort.com* ⇋ *40 rooms* ⑩ *No meals.*

Villa Madeleine

$$ | RENTAL | If you like privacy and your own private pool, you'll like Villa Madeleine, where villas flow downhill from a West Indian plantation greathouse. **Pros:** pleasant decor; full kitchens; private pools. **Cons:** lower units sometimes lack views; need car to get around; no beachfront. ⑤ *Rooms from: $285* ⊠ *Off Rte. 82, Teague's Bay* ☎ *800/533–6863* ⊕ *villamadeleine-stcroix.com* ⇋ *43 villas* ⑩ *No meals.*

 ## Nightlife

Divi Carina Bay Casino

CASINOS | The larger of St. Croix's two casinos (the other is in downtown Christiansted) is located across the street from the Divi Carina Bay resort. For a

Family-friendly resort The Buccaneer sits on the grounds of a 300-acre former sugar plantation in St. Croix.

night out on the island's East End the casino has reel-type slot machines, video poker, and table games including black-jack, poker, roulette, and craps. Guests of the all-inclusive Divi Carina Bay eat and drink free at the Carina Cafe. ⊠ *25 Rte. 60, Estate Turner Hole* ☎ *340/773–7529* ⊕ *www.divicarina.com.*

Shopping

Seaside Market and Deli

FOOD/CANDY | Although it's on the small side, this market has good-quality deli items, local produce, West Indian prepared foods, and a bakery and pastry shop. ⊠ *2001 Mount Welcome Rd., Christiansted* ☎ *340/719–9393* ⊕ *www. seasidemarketstx.com.*

Mid Island

A drive through the countryside between Christiansted and Frederiksted will take you past ruins of old plantations, many bearing the names bestowed by early

owners (Morningstar, Solitude, Upper Love). The traffic moves quickly—by island standards—on the main roads, but you can pause and poke around if you head down some side lanes. It's easy to find your way west, but driving from north to south requires good navigation. Allow an entire day for this trip, so you'll have enough time for a swim at a North Shore beach. Although you can find lots of casual eateries on the main roads, pick up a picnic lunch if you plan to head off the beaten path.

Sights

Captain Morgan Distillery

WINERY/DISTILLERY | The base for Captain Morgan–brand rum is made from molasses at this massive, industrial-scale distillery. The tour includes exhibits on island and rum history, a movie about the process, and a tram ride through the distillery. An extensive gift shop features a wide variety of branded clothing and keepsakes as well as rum for purchase. The tour ends with tastings of the many varieties of Captain Morgan rum (the original spiced, white, aged, dark, and fruit flavored) plus two cocktails. ⌧ *Melvin Evans Hwy. and Rte. 66, Annaberg and Shannon Grove* ☎ *340/713–5654* ⌑ *$10* ⊙ *Weekend tours by appointment only.*

★ Cruzan Rum Distillery

WINERY/DISTILLERY | A tour of this distillery, established in 1760, culminates in a rum tasting, all of which are sold here at good prices—including more than a dozen flavored rums you'll find in popular St. Croix cocktails like the Cruzan Confusion. The distillery is also the best place to pick up a bottle or two of Cruzan's premium single-barrel and Estate Diamond rums. It's worth a stop to look at the charming old buildings and learn about the distillation process, even if you're not a rum connoisseur. ⌧ *3A Estate Diamond, Frederiksted* ☎ *340/692–2280* ⊕ *www.cruzanrum.com* ⌑ *$10* ⊙ *Closed Sun.*

Estate Whim Museum

HISTORIC SITE | **FAMILY** | The restored estate, with a windmill, cookhouse, and other buildings, gives a sense of what life was like on St. Croix's sugar plantations in the 1800s. The oval-shape greathouse has high ceilings and antique furniture and utensils. Notice its fresh, airy atmosphere—the waterless stone moat around the greathouse was used not for defense, but for circulating cooling air. The estate produced sugar and molasses from 1767 to 1934, first with animal power, then wind, and finally with a steam engine to crush the cane. If you have kids, the grounds are the perfect place for them to run around, perhaps while you browse in the museum gift shop or attend a food demonstration using the still functioning ovens in the cookhouse. It's just outside of Frederiksted. ⌧ *Rte. 70, Whim* ☎ *340/772–0598* ⊕ *www.stcroixlandmarks.org* ⌑ *$10.*

★ St. George Village Botanical Garden

GARDEN | At this 17-acre estate, fragrant flora grows amid the ruins of a 19th-century sugarcane plantation (the former overseer's house has been left open to the elements as a habitat for native fruit bats). There are miniature versions of each ecosystem on St. Croix, from a semiarid cactus grove to a verdant rain forest, along with hiking trails, a small museum, and a collection of seashells. The garden's orchid and bromeliad blooms are impressive. Free meditation classes are offered on Tuesday and yoga on Friday. ⌧ *Rte. 70, Estate Saint George* ⌖ *Turn north at sign* ☎ *340/692–2874* ⊕ *www.sgvbg.org* ⌑ *$8.*

 ## Restaurants

★ La Reine Chicken Shack

$$ | **CARIBBEAN** | This barnlike "Crucian-Rican" restaurant is the first stop that locals make before heading to the airport and after arriving back home. Out back, dozens of chickens slowly rotate on a giant rotisserie; in front, locals and a smattering of in-the-know visitors queue up for the juicy birds, traditional johnnycakes, and local food like stewed oxtail and conch in butter sauce. **Known for:** finger-licking-good rotisserie chicken; traditional johnnycakes; local atmosphere. ⑂ *Average main: $15* ⌧ *24-I, La Reine* ☎ *340/778–5717.*

Mt. Pellier Domino Club

$ | **CARIBBEAN** | You don't have to eat like a pig at this West End restaurant and bar in the rain forest, but you can feed a whole can of beer to one. The giant hogs residing here have developed a taste for the suds, and for $3 you can buy a nonalcoholic beer and offer it up to a pig who will crush the can in its powerful jaws, chug down the ingredients, and spit out the crushed aluminum when done. **Known for:** beer-drinking pigs; daily specials; "mamawana," a mix of Cruzan rum, honey, roots, leaves, and spices alternatively touted for its hallucinogenic and aphrodisiacal qualities. ⑂ *Average main: $10* ⌧ *Mahogany Rd., Montpellier* ☎ *340/713–9052.*

Nightlife

Leatherback Brewing

BREWPUBS/BEER GARDENS | St. Croix's first large-scale brewing operation has a plant and tasting room near the oil refinery by the airport; drop by to try some of the more than two dozen beers produced here, including the popular Island Life lager, IPAs flavored with guava and soursop, and a chocolate-coconut stout. The kitchen is also open seven days a week serving sandwiches and apps. ■ **TIP→ You can find the beers at bars throughout the U.S. Virgin Islands and British Virgin Islands, but they can't be shipped to the mainland.** ⊠ *William Roebuck Industrial Park, Industrial Rd., off Melvin H. Evans Hwy., Frederiksted* ☎ *340/277–2337* ⊕ *leatherbackbrewing.com.*

Shopping

FOOD

Plaza Extra East

FOOD/CANDY | Full-service supermarket that stocks both locally grown and imported produce as well as duty-free liquor and a pharmacy. ⊠ *Rte. 70, Sion Farm* ☎ *340/778–6240.*

Plaza Extra West

FOOD/CANDY | This supermarket has a good selection of Middle Eastern foods, in addition to the usual grocery-store items. ⊠ *14 Plessen, Frederiksted* ☎ *340/719–1870* ⊕ *www.plazaextrawest. com.*

Frederiksted

St. Croix's second-largest town, Frederiksted was founded in 1751. While Christiansted is noted for its Danish buildings, Frederiksted is better known for its Victorian architecture. One long cruise-ship pier juts into the sparkling sea. It's the perfect place to start a tour of this quaint city. A stroll around its historic sights will take you no more than an hour. Allow a little more time if you want to duck into the few small shops.

Sights

Caribbean Museum Center for the Arts

MUSEUM | Sitting across from the waterfront in a historic building, this small museum hosts an always-changing roster of exhibits and also houses a bookstore and a gift shop. Some works are cutting-edge multimedia efforts that you might be surprised to find in such an out-of-the way location. Openings are popular events, as are the occasional jazz concerts presented in the upstairs galleries. The back courtyard is a peaceful space, where sculptures and statues are on display; free Wi-Fi is an added inducement to linger. ⊠ *10 Strand St., Frederiksted* ☎ *340/772–2622* ⊕ *www.cmcarts. org* 🎫 *Free* ⊗ *Closed Sun. and Mon.*

Fort Frederik

HISTORIC SITE | FAMILY | On July 3, 1848, some 8,000 slaves marched on this fort to demand their freedom. Danish governor Peter von Scholten, fearing they would burn the town to the ground, stood up in his carriage parked in front of the fort and granted their wish. The fort, completed in 1760, houses an art gallery and a number of interesting exhibits, including a collection of mahogany furniture. The walls, constructed of coral and rubble bound together with molasses, are a testament to the ingenuity and durability of 18th-century engineering. Climb the battlements for great views of the cruise dock and the Caribbean Sea. ⊠ *Waterfront, Frederiksted* ☎ *340/772–2021* ⊕ *nps.gov/places/fort-frederiksted-usvi.htm* 🎫 *$5* ⊗ *Closed weekends.*

Frederiksted Welcome Center

INFO CENTER | Located on the pier, Frederiksted's welcome center has brochures from numerous St. Croix businesses, as well as a few exhibits about the island.

Just past the clear water lapping Frederiksted's pier is Fort Frederik.

It's only open when cruise ships are in port. When the welcome center is not open, visitors can check with the tourism office in the old Custom House at 321 King Street (Suite 7). ⊠ *Frederiksted Pier, Frederiksted* ☎ *340/772–0357.*

Little La Grange Farm and Lawaetz Museum
FARM/RANCH | For a trip back in time, tour this circa-1750 farm, in a valley at La Grange. Tours include the lovely two-story house, aqueducts once used to transport water and cane juice, and the Little La Grange Farm, which produces organic crops for sale through the Ridge to Reef program. The greathouse includes the four-poster mahogany bed 19th-century owner Carl Lawaetz shared with his wife, Marie, the china Marie painted, family portraits, and the fruit trees that fed the family for several generations. Initially a sugar plantation, the farm was subsequently used to raise cattle and grow produce. ⊠ *Rte. 76 (Mahogany Rd.), Estate Little La Grange* ☎ *340/473–1557* ⊕ *www.llgfarm.com* ⊠ *$15* ⊗ *Closed Sun.–Tues., Thurs., and Fri.*

Sandy Point National Wildlife Refuge
NATURE PRESERVE | Located at the western tip of St. Croix, this 383-acre wildlife sanctuary provides critical habitat for leatherback, green, and hawksbill sea turtles, which nest on the refuge's long, sandy beaches. The beaches are open to visitors when not occupied by turtles. The mangrove-fringed West End Salt Pond, which lies partly within the refuge's boundaries, is a bird-watcher's delight. ⊠ *Veteran's Shore Dr., Hesselberg* ☎ *340/773–4554* ⊕ *www.fws.gov/ refuge/Sandy_Point/* ⊗ *Closed weekdays, turtle nesting season (Apr.–Aug.).*

 Beaches

West End beaches
BEACH—SIGHT | There are several unnamed beaches along the coast road north of Frederiksted, but it's best if you don't stray too far from civilization. Most vacationers plop down their towel near one of the casual restaurants spread out along Route 63. The beach at the Rainbow Beach Club, a five-minute

drive outside Frederiksted, has the lively Rhythms beach bar, a casual restaurant decorated with license plates from around the world, and West End Watersports, which rents Jet Skis, Flyboards, and stand-up paddleboards by the half hour and beach chairs and umbrellas by the day. The beach is broad and sandy, the waters clear and calm. If you want to be close to the cruise-ship pier, just stroll on over to the adjacent sandy beach in front of Fort Frederik. On the way south out of Frederiksted, the stretch near Sandcastle on the Beach hotel is also lovely. **Amenities:** food and drink; water sports. **Best for:** snorkeling; swimming; walking. ⊠ *Rte. 63, north and south of Frederiksted, Frederiksted.*

🍴 Restaurants

Beach Side Café

$$$ | ECLECTIC | Sunday brunch is big here, but locals and visitors also flock to this oceanfront bistro at Sand Castle on the Beach resort for lunch and dinner. Both menus include burgers and salads, but at dinner the daily pasta specials shine. **Known for:** oceanfront setting; hummus plate; daily pasta specials. $ *Average main: $29* ⊠ *Sand Castle on the Beach, 127 Smithfield, Frederiksted* ☎ *340/772–1266* ⊕ *sandcastleonthebeach.com/dine.*

840 STX Cafe

$ | CAFÉ | A dollar will buy you an infusion of CBD oil—a nonpsychoactive ingredient in cannabis, said to have various health benefits—in any of the smoothies, lattes, and espresso drinks sold here. Also on the menu are acai bowls, local beers on draft, and a variety of CBD oils, salves, tinctures, and vaping refills. **Known for:** open daily; happy, hempy, cool; a variety of CBD products. $ *Average main: $7* ⊠ *69 C King St., Frederiksted* ☎ *340/713–0840* ▭ *No credit cards.*

Louie and Nachos Beach Bar

$ | MEXICAN | The fare here is the farthest thing from traditional Mexican food—in addition to the usual ingredients you can get a taco stuffed with chicken Parmesan, buffalo chicken, or jambalaya. Bar and restaurant are one story up, so the views of the beach and surf are nice. **Known for:** tacos stuffed with nontraditional fillings; Cassie's Punch made with Cruzan's coconut, black cherry, and pineapple rum mixed with orange juice and grenadine; great ocean views. $ *Average main: $10* ⊠ *37 Strand St., Frederiksted* ☎ *340/772–5151* ⊕ *www.louieandnachos.com.*

Polly's at the Pier

$$ | ECLECTIC | With an emphasis on fresh ingredients, this casual spot right on the waterfront serves delicious fare. For breakfast, the BELT (bacon, egg, lettuce, and tomato) sandwich is the go-to, and at lunch, the gourmet grilled-cheese sandwich comes with your choice of three cheeses as well as delicious additions like basil, fresh Bosc pears, and avocado. **Known for:** local ingredients; waterfront location; neighborhood eatery. $ *Average main: $13* ⊠ *3 Strand St., Frederiksted* ☎ *340/719–9434* ⊕ *pollysatthepierstcroix.com.*

Turtles Deli

$ | DELI | FAMILY | Huge sandwiches at this tiny spot start with homemade bread and can be as basic as turkey and cheddar or as imaginative as the Beast, piled high with hot roast beef, raw onion, and melted Swiss cheese with horseradish and mayonnaise. The menu also features salads and lots of outdoor seating in the shade. **Known for:** corned beef on rye; specialty tacos; waterfront location. $ *Average main: $12* ⊠ *625 Strand St., Frederiksted* ☎ *340/772–3676* ▭ *No credit cards* ⊙ *Closed weekends.*

Sights ▼

1 Caribbean Museum
   Center for the Arts...... **B2**
2 Fort Frederik............ **B1**
3 Frederiksted
   Welcome Center........ **B1**
4 Little La Grange
   Farm and Lawaetz
   Museum **E1**
5 Sandy Point National
   Wildlife Refuge.......... **B5**

Restaurants ▼

1 Beach Side Café........ **B5**
2 840 STX Cafe **C1**
3 Louie and Nachos
   Beach Bar............... **B4**
4 Polly's at the Pier **B2**
5 Turtles Deli.............. **B4**

Quick Bites ▼

1 Armstrong
   Ice Cream................ **D5**
2 Nidulari
   Artisan Bakery........... **E1**

Hotels ▼

1 Cottages by the Sea.... **B5**
2 The Fred **B4**
3 Inn on Strand Street..... **C3**
4 Sand Castle on the
   Beach **B5**

Marching on Frederiksted

On July 3, 1848, more than 8,000 slaves demanding their freedom marched half a mile from La Grange to Frederiksted. Their actions forever changed the course of history. Governor General Peter von Scholten stood up in his carriage in front of Fort Frederick to declare: "You are now free. You are hereby emancipated. Go home peacefully."

Von Scholten was relieved of his position and charged with dereliction of duty by the Danish government. He departed from St. Croix on July 14, leaving behind his lover, a free black woman named Anna Heegaard. He never returned, and died in Denmark in 1852.

The revolt had its roots in the 1834 emancipation of slaves in Great Britain's Caribbean colonies, including what are now called the British Virgin Islands. The Danish government,

sensing what was coming, began to "improve" the working conditions for its slaves. These efforts, however, failed, falling short of the demand for full freedom.

On July 28, 1847, Danish King Christian VIII ruled that slavery would continue a dozen more years, but those born during those 12 years would be free. This further angered the island's slaves. On July 2, 1848, a conch shell sounded, signifying that the slaves should start gathering. The die was cast, and the rest, as they say, is history.

After emancipation, the former slaves were forced to sign yearly contracts with plantation owners. Those contracts could only be renegotiated on October 1, still called Contract Day. This angered the plantation workers and gave rise to other uprisings throughout the late 1800s.

☕ Coffee and Quick Bites

Armstrong Ice Cream

$ | CARIBBEAN | FAMILY | This family-run business has been using the same Danish ice cream recipe with local flavorings since 1900. Stop in for a sweet treat that includes a wide variety of tropically flavored homemade ice cream—almond, ginger, peanut, coconut, pumpkin—plus seasonal varieties like gooseberry, guava, mango, soursop, and passion fruit. **Known for:** homemade ice cream; seasonal flavors; the restaurant is open early so ice cream for breakfast is definitely an option. ⑤ *Average main: $3* ⊠ *78-B Whim, Queen Mary Hwy., Whim* ☎ *340/772–1919* ⊘ *Closed Sun.*

Nidulari Artisan Bakery

$$ | BAKERY | A distinctive gypsy cart on the side of Mahogany Road (Route 76) spills open with fresh baked breads, tarts, sandwiches, and toasties filled with black bean hummus or homegrown banana. The farm-to-table menu, which changes daily to reflect what's available, includes local fare, Indian curries, British-influenced dishes, and Southern comfort food. **Known for:** fresh baked goods made in a traditional brick oven; chocolate made from local ingredients; everything is made from scratch. ⑤ *Average main: $12* ⊠ *Little La Grange Village, 606 Little La Grange, Mahogany Rd., Frederiksted* ☎ *978/850–2924* ⊕ *nidulari. com* ⊘ *Closed Mon., Tues., and Thurs.* ▭ *No credit cards.*

Camping on St. Croix

Out on the West End, where few tourists stay, **Mount Victory Camp** (✉ *Creque Dam Rd., Frederiksted* ☎ *340/201–7983* ⊕ *www.mtvictorycamp.com*) offers a remarkable quietude that distinguishes this out-of-the-way spread on 8 acres in the island's rain forest. If you really want to commune with nature, you'll be hard-pressed to find a better way to do it on St. Croix. Hosts Matt and Carmen are on hand to explain the environment. You sleep in a screened-in tent-cottage ($90) perched on a raised platform and covered by a roof. Each has electricity and a rudimentary outdoor kitchen. There is also an apartment built into the ruins of a historic schoolhouse ($110 per night) and some bare tent sites for $30 per night. The shared, spotlessly clean bathhouse is an easy stroll away. The location feels remote, but a lovely sand beach is a 2-mile (3-km) drive down the hill. In another 10 minutes you're in Frederiksted. Reservations are preferred.

 Hotels

Cottages by the Sea

$ | RENTAL | Step out your door and onto a stunning stretch of white beach at this string of cottages beneath towering palm trees. **Pros:** beachfront location; delightful decor; friendly hosts. **Cons:** neighborhood sketchy at night; need car to get around; some rooms need freshening. ⑤ *Rooms from: $220* ✉ *127A Smithfield Rd., Frederiksted* ☎ *340/772–0495, 800/323–7252* ⊕ *www.caribbeancottages.com* ⇱ *25 cottages* ⦿| *No meals.*

★ The Fred

$ | HOTEL | This boutique hotel on the Frederiksted waterfront saucily beckons you to "Sleep with Fred" in one of a dozen bright and stylishly appointed guest rooms housed in a quartet of new and restored colonial buildings. **Pros:** spacious rooms; waterfront location; LGBTQ+ friendly. **Cons:** not kid friendly; beach is a mix of sandy and rocky sections. ⑤ *Rooms from: $188* ✉ *605 Strand St., Frederiksted* ☎ *340/777–3733, 844/789–8784* ⊕ *www.sleepwithfred.com* ⇱ *12 rooms* ⦿| *No meals.*

Inn on Strand Street

$ | HOTEL | If you want a laid-back atmosphere steps from interesting restaurants and shops, this is a decent choice offering basic but comfortable waterfront rooms for budget travelers. **Pros:** close to restaurants; walk to public beach; reasonable rates. **Cons:** neighborhood sketchy at night; need car to get around. ⑤ *Rooms from: $179* ✉ *442 Strand St., Frederiksted* ☎ *340/772–0500* ⊕ *www.innonstrandstreet.com* ⇱ *35 rooms* ⦿| *No meals.*

★ Sand Castle on the Beach

$ | RESORT | Right on a gorgeous stretch of white beach, Sand Castle has a tropical charm that harks back to a simpler time in the Caribbean; its nearness to Frederiksted's interesting dining scene is also a plus. **Pros:** lovely beach; close to restaurants; very clean. **Cons:** no children's activities—adults-only resort; some rooms are small or lack views; public areas can be noisy. ⑤ *Rooms from: $209* ✉ *127 Smithfield, Frederiksted* ☎ *340/772–1205, 800/524–2018* ⊕ *www.sandcastleonthebeach.com* ⇱ *25 units* ⦿| *No meals.*

ⓨ Nightlife

★ Sunset Jazz

MUSIC | This outdoor event is a hot ticket in Frederiksted, drawing crowds of visitors and locals at 6 pm on the third Friday of every month to watch the sun go down and listen to good music on the waterfront in Buddhoe (Emancipation) Park. Occasional cultural performances are also staged in the gazebo at the center of the park. ✉ *Waterfront, Frederiksted* ☎ *340/690–1741.*

🛍 Shopping

The best shopping in Frederiksted is along **Strand Street** and in the side streets and alleyways that connect it with **King Street.** Most stores close on Sunday, except when a cruise ship is in port.

Susan Mango

CLOTHING | Austin native and fashion wholesaler Susan Connett brings her sense of style to St. Croix with a dazzling variety of resort wear, beachwear, and fabrics sourced from women producers in Bali, Africa, Guatemala, and elsewhere. Come on Wednesday for free interior design advice from the owner. ✉ *54 King St., Frederiksted* ☎ *512/689–7049* ⊕ *www.susanmango.com.*

North Shore

👁 Sights

Estate Mount Washington Plantation

ARCHAEOLOGICAL SITE | Several years ago, while surveying the property, its owners discovered the ruins of a sugar plantation beneath the rain forest brush. The grounds have since been cleared and opened to the public. The estate is private property, but the owners allow visitors to take a self-guided walking tour of the mill, the rum distillery, and other ruins. An oversize wind chime ringing softly in the breeze and a stone-lined labyrinth create a sense of serenity. ✉ *Rte. 63, Estate Mount Washington and Washington Hill* ⊕ *www.estatemtwashington.com.*

Mt. Eagle

MOUNTAIN—SIGHT | At 1,165 feet, this is St. Croix's highest peak. Determined hikers can follow an unpaved road to the summit, or take a jeep tour with Tan Tan Tours. Route 69 climbs the shoulder of the mountain; look for a mark on the pavement with the words "The Beast" and a set of giant paw prints. The hill you're about to climb is the famous Beast of the St. Croix Half Ironman Triathlon, an annual event during which participants must cycle up this intimidating slope. ✉ *Rte. 69, Estate Fountain.*

Salt River Bay National Historical Park and Ecological Preserve

NATIONAL/STATE PARK | If you want to learn more about St. Croix's indigenous Carib people while appreciating beautiful preserves that protect endangered species, head to this joint national and local park. Christopher Columbus's men skirmished with the Carib people here in 1493, on his second visit to what he deemed the New World. The peninsula on the bay's east side is named for the event: Cabo de las Flechas (Cape of the Arrows). A ball court, used by the Caribs in religious ceremonies, was discovered at the spot where the taxis park. Take a short hike up the dirt road to the ruins of an old earthen fort for great views of Salt River Bay. The area also encompasses a coastal estuary with the region's largest remaining mangrove forest, a submarine canyon, and several endangered species, including the hawksbill turtle and the roseate tern. The water at the beach can be on the rough side, but it's a nice place for sunning when the turtles aren't nesting. Local tour companies offer tours, including to a pair of bioluminescent bays, by kayak and pontoon boat. ✉ *Rte. 75 to Rte. 80, Estate Salt River* ☎ *340/773–1460* ⊕ *www.nps.gov/sari.*

Sea turtles nest in several places on St. Croix, including Sandy Point National Wildlife Refuge.

 Beaches

Cane Bay

BEACH—SIGHT | On the island's breezy North Shore, Cane Bay does not always have gentle waters but the scuba diving and snorkeling are wondrous. You can see elkhorn and brain corals, and less than 200 yards out is the drop-off called the Cane Bay Wall. Make Cane Bay an all-day destination by combining a dive with food and drinks at the casual bars and restaurants that line the waterfront, including the excellent AMA at Cane Bay and Eat at Cane Bay. **Amenities:** food and drink. **Best for:** snorkeling; swimming. ⊠ *Rte. 80, Cane Bay* ✛ *About 4 miles (6 km) west of Salt River.*

 Restaurants

AMA at Cane Bay

$$ | CARIBBEAN | Chef Digby Stridiron's waterfront restaurant—on the back deck of the Waves at Cane Bay hotel—serves sustainably sourced Caribbean-American food that pairs wonderfully with a craft cocktail list that highlights classics like a Singapore Sling and the Old Cuban made with 18-year-old Matusalem rum. The dining room overlooks Cane Bay, a perfect backdrop to try Stridiron's unique dishes like ceviche made with local angelfish, conch and clam pasta, or the pork porterhouse from the Alcor artisan farm in Puerto Rico that's served with farro and West Indian pumpkin. **Known for:** location overlooking Cane Bay; sustainable seafood from local purveyors; guava berry cheesecake. ⑤ *Average main: $20* ⊠ *Waves at Cane Bay, 112C Cane Bay, Cane Bay* ☏ *340/227–3432* ⊕ *www.amacanebay.com* ⊘ *Closed Sun. and Mon.*

Leatherback Landing at Cane Bay

$$ | SEAFOOD | Grilled mahimahi sandwiches, falafel, tacos, and burgers are among the local favorites at this open-air bar across the street from Cane Bay beach. Some dishes are prepared using local Leatherback beer, which is available behind the bar. **Known for:** fresh-off-the-boat seafood; live music; ocean views.

Turtles on St. Croix

Like creatures from the prehistoric past, green, leatherback, and hawksbill turtles crawl ashore during the annual April-to-November turtle nesting season to lay their eggs. They return from their life at sea every two to seven years to the beach where they were born. Since turtles can live for up to 100 years, they may return many times to nest in St. Croix.

The leatherbacks like Sandy Point National Wildlife Refuge and other spots on St. Croix's western end, but the hawksbills prefer Buck Island and the East End. Green turtles are also found primarily on the East End. Access to the pristine beach at Sandy Point is restricted during turtle nesting season.

All of these sea turtles are endangered species that face numerous predators, some natural, some the result of the human presence. Particularly in the Frederiksted area, dogs and cats prey on the nests and eat the hatchlings. Occasionally a dog will attack a turtle about to lay its eggs, and cats train their kittens to hunt at turtle nests, creating successive generations of turtle-egg hunters. In addition, turtles have often been hit by fast-moving boats, leaving large gashes in their shells if not killing them outright. The St. Croix Leatherback Project conducts an annual census of the Sandy Point sea turtles, and also runs a program that allows visitors to "adopt" turtles who are tagged and named each season.

$ Average main: $18 ⊠ 110c Cane Bay, Cane Bay ☎ 340/718–0362 ⊕ www.leatherbacklanding.com.

Off the Wall

$$ | **AMERICAN** | Divers fresh from a plunge at the North Shore's popular Cane Bay Wall gather at this breezy spot on the beach, where every sunset is celebrated with free shots at the beach bar. The menu includes deli sandwiches, burgers, and hot dogs, but the stars are the calzones and pizzas, which run the gamut from vegetarian to meat-lovers. **Known for:** hammocks on the beach; great pizza. $ Average main: $19 ⊠ Rte. 80, Cane Bay ☎ 340/718–4771 ⊕ www.otwstx.com ⊘ Closed Fri.

 Hotels

Arawak Bay: The Inn at Salt River

$ | **B&B/INN** | With stellar views of St. Croix's North Shore and an affable host, this small B&B allows you to settle into island life at a price that doesn't break the bank. **Pros:** 20 minutes from Christiansted; good prices. **Cons:** no beach nearby; can be some road noise. $ Rooms from: $160 ⊠ Rte. 80, Estate Salt River ☎ 888/772–1684 ⊕ www.arawakhotelstcroix.com ⚲ 14 rooms ¶⊚¶ Free Breakfast.

★ Renaissance St. Croix Carambola Beach Resort and Spa

$$ | **RESORT** | This resort has a stellar beachfront setting and peaceful ambience as well as lovely rooms with attractive palm-theme accessories that match the resort's atmosphere. **Pros:** lovely beach; relaxing atmosphere; close to golf. **Cons:** remote location; need car to get around; renovations mean only some amenities are available. $ Rooms from: $299 ⊠ Rte. 80, Estate Davis Bay, Estate Fountain ☎ 340/778–3800, 888/503–8760, 800/627–7468 ⊕ www.marriott.com ⚲ 151 rooms ¶⊚¶ No meals.

Divers love the sponge-encrusted Rosa Maria, off the west end of St. Croix.

Villa Margarita

$ | **B&B/INN** | This quiet retreat provides a particularly good base if you want to admire the dramatic views of the wind-swept coast. **Pros:** friendly host; great views; snorkeling nearby. **Cons:** isolated location; need car to get around; limited amenities. ⑤ *Rooms from: $220* ⊠ *22 Salt River Road, off Rte. 80, Estate Salt River* ☎ *340/692–1408* ⊕ *www.villamargarita.com* ⌇ *3 units* ⎟◯⎟ *No meals.*

The Waves at Cane Bay

$ | **HOTEL** | The famed Cane Bay Wall is just offshore from this hotel, giving it an enviable location. **Pros:** great diving; restaurants nearby; beaches nearby. **Cons:** need car to get around; on main road; bland decor. ⑤ *Rooms from: $149* ⊠ *Rte. 80, 112C Cane Bay, Cane Bay* ☎ *340/718–1815* ⊕ *www.thewavescanebay.com* ⌇ *10 rooms* ⎟◯⎟ *No meals.*

Activities

BOAT TOURS

Almost everyone takes a day trip to Buck Island aboard a charter boat. Most leave from the Christiansted waterfront or from Green Cay Marina and stop for a snorkel at the island's eastern end before dropping anchor off a gorgeous sandy beach for a swim, a hike, and lunch. Sailboats can often stop right at the beach; a larger boat might have to anchor a bit farther offshore. A full-day sail runs about $100, with lunch included on most trips. A half-day sail costs about $70.

Big Beard's Adventure Tours

SAILING | From catamarans that depart from the Christiansted waterfront, you can head to Buck Island for half- and full-day snorkeling tours. The 42-foot *Adventure* has a glass viewing platform for those who want to see the fish but don't want to get in the water. The full-day tour on the *Renegade* concludes with dropping anchor at a private beach for an all-you-can-eat-and-drink barbecue.

Sunset sails and tours of Salt River Bay also are offered. ✉ *1247 Queen Cross St., Christiansted* ☎ *340/773–4482* ⊕ *www.bigbeards.com.*

Buck Island Charters

SAILING | Scheduled half-day trips to Buck Island on the trimaran *Teroro II* leave Green Cay Marina in the morning and afternoon. Bring your own lunch and drinks; cost is $75 for adults. Private charters for up to six passengers are also available on the 38-foot trimaran *Dragonfly.* ✉ *Green Cay Marina, Annas Hope* ☎ *340/718–3161.*

Caribbean Sea Adventures

SAILING | With boats leaving from the Christiansted waterfront, Caribbean Sea Adventures has both half- and full-day trips to Buck Island. Sunset sails and fishing excursions are also available. ✉ *Christiansted Boardwalk, Christiansted* ☎ *340/773–2628* ⊕ *www.caribbean-seaadventures.com.*

Lyric Sails

ADVENTURE TOURS | This sailing adventure on a 63-foot, custom-built catamaran called the *Jolly Mon* features live musical entertainment from local performers Wednesday to Sunday. Visitors can choose a private day sail, a sunset sail, or a full-moon evening sail. Trips can also be centered on special foods or wines. ✉ *1D Strand St., Christiansted* ☎ *340/201–5227* ⊕ *www.lyricsails.com.*

DIVING AND SNORKELING

At **Buck Island,** a short boat ride from Christiansted or Green Cay Marina, the reef is so nice that it's been named a national monument. You can dive right off the beach at **Cane Bay,** which has a spectacular drop-off called the Cane Bay Wall. Dive operators also do boat trips along the Wall, usually leaving from Salt River or Christiansted. **Frederiksted Pier** is home to a colony of sea horses, creatures seldom seen in the waters of the Virgin Islands. At **Green Cay,** just outside Green

Cay Marina in the East End, you can see colorful fish swimming around the reefs and rocks. Two exceptional North Shore sites are **North Star** and **Salt River,** which you can reach only by boat. At Salt River you can float downward through a canyon filled with colorful fish and coral.

The island's dive shops take you out for one- or two-tank dives. Plan to pay about $70 for a one-tank dive and $95 for a two-tank dive, including equipment and an underwater tour. All companies offer certification and introductory courses called resort dives.

Which dive outfit you pick usually depends on where you're staying. Your hotel may have one on-site. If so, you're just a short stroll away from the dock. If not, other companies are close by. Where the dive boat goes on a particular day depends on the weather, but in any case, all St. Croix's dive sites are special. All shops are affiliated with PADI, the Professional Association of Diving Instructors.

★ Cane Bay Dive Shop

SCUBA DIVING | This is the place to go if you want to do a shore dive or boat dive along the North Shore, including the famous Cane Bay Wall. ✉ *2 Strand St., Frederiksted* ✛ *Across from cruise pier* ☎ *340/772–0715* ⊕ *www.canebayscuba. com.*

Dive Experience

SCUBA DIVING | Convenient for those staying in Christiansted, Dive Experience runs trips to the North Shore walls and reefs, in addition to offering the usual certification and introductory classes. It's a PADI Five Star facility. ✉ *1000 King St., Suite 6, Christiansted* ☎ *340/773–3307, 800/235–9047* ⊕ *www.divexp.com.*

St. Croix Ultimate Bluewater Adventures

SCUBA DIVING | This company can take you to your choice of more than 75 dive sites; it also offers a variety of packages that include hotel stays, stylish and comfortable island wear, and dive gear available at the dive shop. ✉ *81 Queen Cross St., Suite 14, Christiansted* ☎ *340/773–5994* ⊕ *www.stcroixscuba.com.*

FISHING

Since the early 1980s some 20 world records—many for blue marlin—have been set in these waters. Sailfish, skipjack, bonito, tuna (allison, blackfin, and yellowfin), and wahoo are abundant. A charter runs about $500 to $800 for a half day (for up to six people), with most boats going out for a four-, six-, or eight-hour trips.

Caribbean Sea Adventures

FISHING | This charter company can take your group out fishing for marlin, wahoo, tuna, and mahi on a 32-foot Boston Whaler, the *Smooth Recovery*, or the 42-foot Cape Dory, *Betty Ann.* ✉ *59 Kings Wharf, Christiansted* ☎ *340/773–2628* ⊕ *www. caribbeanseaadventures.com.*

Gone Ketchin'

FISHING | Captain Grizz, a true old salt, heads half, three-quarter, and full-day fishing charter trips in pursuit of marlin, wahoo, mahimahi, king mackerel, barracuda, and tuna. ✉ *Salt River Marina, Rte. 80, Estate Salt River* ☎ *340/713–1175, 340/998–2055* ⊕ *www.goneketchin.com.*

GOLF

St. Croix's three courses welcome you with spectacular vistas. Check with your hotel or the tourism department to determine when major celebrity tournaments will be held. There's often an opportunity to play with the pros.

★ Buccaneer Golf Course

GOLF | The Buccaneer Resort 18-hole course, near Christiansted, mixes fun with risk. Some of the par fours are within reach of a long drive, making birdies possible. However, miscues on holes that run near the ocean or have ponds can be costly for those keeping score. Most golfers' memories are of the beautiful views, not the sand traps. The signature 3rd hole with the green sitting above a rocky coastline has some calling this course the Caribbean Pebble Beach. ✉ *Rte. 82, Christiansted* ☎ *340/712–2144* ⊕ *www.thebuccaneer.com* 🖙 *$115 (discounts for guests)* ⅃. *18 holes, 5169 yards, par 70.*

Carambola Golf Club

GOLF | Golfers should enjoy the exotic beauty of this difficult course in the rain forest designed by Robert Trent Jones Sr., because they might not enjoy their score. An extra sleeve of balls might also be required. The long water holes never return splash balls and the jungle rough seldom does. Most fairways are forgiving with ample landing area, but the length of many holes makes it challenging. ✉ *Rte. 69, Estate River* ☎ *340/778–5638* ⊕ *www.golfcarambola.com* 🖙 *$115 with cart* ⅃. *18 holes, 5727 yards, par 72.*

Reef Golf Course

GOLF | If you want to enjoy panoramic Caribbean views without paying high costs, the public, 9-hole Reef Golf course on the island's East End is the place to go. The course design is basic, but the views from the hillside are spectacular. Trees on this course very seldom enter into play, and sand traps are absent. The 7th hole with its highly elevated tee is the most interesting. No good with a club in your hand? Try nine holes of disc (Frisbee) golf, instead. ✉ *Rte. 82, Teague's Bay* ☎ *340/773–8844* 🖙 *$23 greens fee, $17 for cart* ⅃. *9 holes, 2395 yards, par 35.*

GUIDED TOURS

Joseph's VIP Taxi Tours

DRIVING TOURS | Guided island van tours are available with expert commentary on the sights, history, and culture of St. Croix. Cost is $125 for three hours or $350 for a full day with up to six passengers; larger groups are $50 per person. ☎ *340/277–6133* ✉ *shaggy95144@gmail.com.*

Sweeny's St. Croix Safari Tours

DRIVING TOURS | These open-air (but covered) safari truck tours of St. Croix depart from Christiansted and last about five

Scenic horseback riding on the beach on St. Croix

hours. Costs run from $65 per person, plus admission fees to attractions like the St. George Village Botanical Garden and the Whim Plantation Museum ✉ *Christiansted* ☎ *340/773–6700* ⊕ *www.gotostcroix.com.*

HIKING

Although you can set off by yourself on a hike through a rain forest or along a shore, a guide will point out what's important and tell you why.

Crucian Heritage And Nature Tourism (CHANT)

HIKING/WALKING | CHANT runs several educational tours focused on St. Croix's natural and cultural heritage. Ras Lumumba Corriette takes hikers up hill and down dale in some of St. Croix's most remote places, including Annaly Bay, Maroon Ridge, and Estate Hermitage to see some of St. Croix's uniquely acclimatized Senopol Cattle. The cost is $50 per person for a 3½-hour hike. There's a three-person minimum. Other CHANT tours visit historic Frederiksted, follow in the boyhood footsteps of Alexander Hamilton, and explore the Ridge to Reef ecofarm. ☎ *340/277–4834* ⊕ *www.chantvi.org.*

HORSEBACK RIDING

Paul and Jill's Equestrian Stables

HORSEBACK RIDING | From Sprat Hall, just north of Frederiksted, co-owner Jill Hurd will take you through the rain forest, across the pastures, along the beaches, and through valleys—explaining the flora, fauna, and ruins on the way. A 1½-hour morning or afternoon group ride costs $100. ✉ *Sprat Hall, Rte. 58, Frederiksted* ☎ *340/772–2880, 340/332–0417* ⊕ *www.paulandjills.com.*

KAYAKING

Caribbean Adventure Tours

KAYAKING | These kayak tours take you on trips through Salt River Bay National Historical Park and Ecological Preserve, one of the island's most pristine areas, including night paddles through the park's bioluminescent bay. All tours cost $50. ✉ *Salt River Marina, Rte. 80, Estate Salt River* ☎ *340/778–1522, 800/532–3483* ⊕ *www.stcroixkayak.com.*

Virgin Kayak Tours

KAYAKING | Virgin runs guided daytime, sunset, and evening kayak trips on Salt River Bay, including tours to see the bay light up with bioluminescent marine life on moonless nights. A women-only stand-up paddleboard (SUP) tour has a wellness focus that features a yoga session and a clay bath in Mermaid Cove. The company also rents kayaks and SUPs so you can tour around by yourself. Tours start at $50, and kayak rentals are $50 for the entire day. ⌧ *Rte. 80, Salt River Marina, Estate Salt River* ☎ *340/514–0062* ⊕ *www.virginkayaktours.com.*

TENNIS

The public courts in Frederiksted (near the fort) and Christiansted (in Canagata Park) are generally in good condition. You can also pay a fee and play at one of the hotel courts. Costs vary by resort, but count on paying about $10 an hour per person.

The Buccaneer

TENNIS | There are eight courts (two are lighted), plus a full tennis shop. ⌧ *The Buccaneer, Rte. 82, Shoys* ☎ *340/773–3036* ⊕ *www.thebuccaneer.com.*

Club St. Croix

TENNIS | There are two turf tennis courts, one with lights. ⌧ *Club St. Croix, Rte. 752, Estate Golden Rock* ☎ *340/718–4800* ⊕ *www.antillesresorts.com.*

Chapter 6

TORTOLA

Updated by
Robert Curley

◉ Sights   🍴 Restaurants   🛏 Hotels   🛍 Shopping   🍸 Nightlife

★★★★☆   ★★★★☆   ★★★★☆   ★★★☆☆   ★★★★☆

WELCOME TO TORTOLA

TOP REASONS TO GO

★ **Charter a boat:** Tortola is the charter-yacht capital of the Caribbean and a popular destination for boaters.

★ **Hit the road:** You'll get the real flavor of the island by heading out in whatever direction you choose. The views are dramatic, and the traffic is light enough to allow for easy driving.

★ **Shop in Road Town:** The island's largest community is also home to an eclectic collection of stores.

★ **Hit the trail:** Tortola is home to Sage Mountain National Park, a small but quite nice nature reserve.

★ **Dive in:** Dive trips to spectacular locations leave from Tortola. If you're not certified to dive, an introductory course can teach you the basics and whet your appetite for more adventures under the sea.

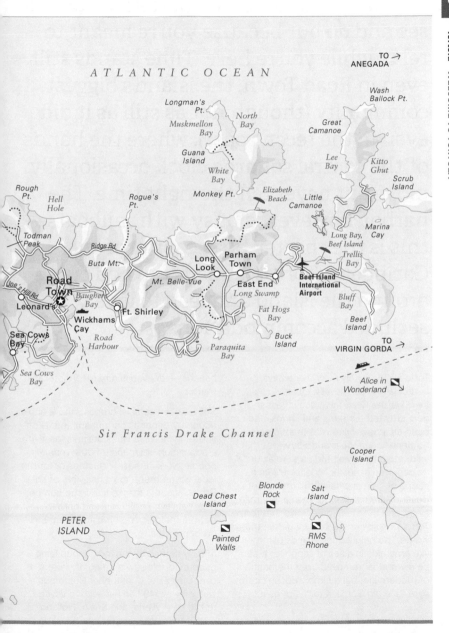

A day might not be enough to tour this island—all 21 square miles (56 square km) of it—not because there's so much to see and do but because you're meant to relax while you're here. Time stands still even in Road Town, the island's biggest community (though not as still as it did even in the recent past), where the hands of the central square's clock occasionally move but never tell the right time. The harbor, however, is busy with sailboats—this is the charter-boat capital of the Caribbean. Tortola's roads dip and curve around the island and lead to lovely, secluded accommodations.

Tortola is definitely busy these days, particularly when several cruise ships tie up at the Road Town dock. Passengers crowd the streets and shops, and open-air jitneys filled with them create bottlenecks on the island's byways. That said, most folks visit Tortola to relax on its deserted sands or linger over lunch at one of its many delightful restaurants. Beaches are never more than a few miles away, and the steep green hills that form Tortola's spine are fanned by gentle trade winds. The neighboring islands glimmer like emeralds in a sea of sapphire. It can be a world far removed from the hustle of modern life, but it simply doesn't compare to Virgin Gorda in terms of beautiful beaches—or even luxury resorts, for that matter.

Still a British colonial outpost, the island's economy depends on tourism and its offshore financial-services businesses. With a population of around 24,000, most people work in those industries or for the local government. You'll hear lots of crisp British accents thanks to a large number of expats who call the island home, but the melodic West Indian accent still predominates.

Initially settled by the indigenous Taíno people, Tortola saw a string of visitors over the years. Christopher Columbus sailed by in 1493 on his second voyage to the New World, and Spain, Holland,

and France made periodic visits about a century later. Sir Francis Drake arrived in 1595, leaving his name on the channel between Tortola and sister islands like Norman Island, Cooper Island, and Virgin Gorda. Pirates and buccaneers followed, the British finally laying claim to the island in the late 1600s. In 1741, John Pickering became the first lieutenant governor of Tortola, and the seat of the British government moved from Virgin Gorda to Tortola. As the agrarian economy continued to grow, slaves were imported from Africa. The slave trade was abolished in 1807, but slaves in Tortola and the rest of the BVI did not gain their freedom until August 1, 1834, when the Emancipation Act was read at Sunday Morning Well in Road Town. That date is celebrated every year as part of the island's annual Carnival.

Getting Here and Around

AIR
There's no nonstop air service from the continental United States to Tortola; connections are usually made through San Juan, Puerto Rico, or St. Thomas, U.S.V.I.

CAR
You might get by with taxis, especially if you are staying in Road Town, but if you are in a villa or an isolated resort, a car is a necessity here. Remember that driving is on the *left* even though cars are generally American-made. Tortola's main roads are well paved for the most part, but there are exceptionally steep hills and sharp curves; driving demands your complete attention. A main road circles the island, and several roads cross it, mostly through mountainous terrain.

Road Town's traffic and parking can be horrific, so avoid driving along Waterfront Drive during morning and afternoon rush hours. ■TIP→ **It's longer—but often quicker—to drive through the hills above Road Town. (And the views are great as well.)** Parking can also be very difficult in Road

Town, particularly during high season. There's parking along the waterfront and on the inland side on the eastern end of downtown, but if you're planning a day of shopping, go early to make sure you snag a space. Or, take a taxi.

CAR RENTALS
Only Hertz and National have offices at the airport, but most companies will pick you up. It's usually best to reserve a car in advance.

CONTACTS Avis. ✉ *Tortola Pier Park, Wickham's Cay, Road Town* ☎ *284/495–4973 West End, at Road Town cruise pier, 284/495–0110 airport branch* ⊕ *www.avis. com.* **Denzil Clyne Jeep Rentals.** ✉ *West End Rd.* ☎ *284/495–4900* ⊕ *denzilclyne-rentals.com.* **Itgo Car Rental.** ✉ *Mill Mall, Wickham's Cay I, Road Town* ☎ *284/494–5150, 284/494–2639* ⊕ *www.itgobvi. com.* **National.** ✉ *Terrance B Lettsome International Airport* ☎ *284/495–2626, 284/494–3197 Road Town (Maria's By the Sea)* ⊕ *www.nationalcar.com.*

FERRY
Frequent daily ferries connect Tortola with St. Thomas, which many vacationers decide to use as their main air gateway. Ferries go to and from both Charlotte Amalie and Red Hook. There's huge competition between the Tortola-based ferry companies on the St. Thomas–Tortola runs, with boats leaving close together. As you enter the ferry terminal to buy your ticket, crews may try to convince you to take their ferry. Ferries also link Tortola to St. John, where all Red Hook–bound ferries stop in Cruz Bay to clear customs and immigration. Ferries also link Tortola with Jost Van Dyke, Norman Island, Peter Island, and Virgin Gorda. You can also connect to Anegada from Road Town and Trellis Bay on Beef Island. Tortola has two ferry terminals—one at West End and one in Road Town—and a jetty at Beef Island where ferries depart for Virgin Gorda, so make sure you hop a ferry that disembarks closest to where you want to go. Ferry schedules vary, and not all

companies make daily trips. Departures can be suddenly canceled, particularly in the summer. The BVI Tourist Board website (⊕ *www.bvitourism.com*) has links to all the ferry companies.

TAXI

Taxi rates are set on Tortola, but you should still check with your driver before you start your trip. Fares are per destination, not per person here, so it's cheaper to travel in groups, because the fare will be the same whether you have one, two, or three passengers. On Tortola the BVI Taxi Association has stands in Road Town near Wickham's Cay I. The Waterfront Taxi Association picks up passengers from the Road Town ferry dock. The Airport Taxi Association operates at the Terrance B. Lettsome Airport on Beef Island. You can also usually find a West End Taxi Association taxi at the West End ferry dock.

CONTACTS Beef Island Taxi Association.
☎ *284/495–1982*.

Essentials

BANKS

On Tortola, banks are near the waterfront at Wickham's Cay I. All have ATMs. Look for Banco Popular, First Caribbean International Bank, First Bank, and Scotiabank, among others.

BEACHES

Beaches in the BVI are less developed than those on St. Thomas or St. Croix, but they are also less inviting. The best BVI beaches are on deserted islands reachable only by boat, so take a snorkeling or sailing trip at least once. Tortola's north side has several palm-fringed, white-sand beaches that curl around turquoise bays and coves, but none really achieves greatness. Nearly all are accessible by car (preferably a four-wheel-drive vehicle), albeit down bumpy roads that corkscrew precipitously. Some of these beaches, like Cane Garden Bay, are lined with bars and restaurants as well as water-sports

equipment stalls; others have absolutely nothing.

HOTELS

Tortola resorts are intimate—only a handful have more than 50 rooms. Guests are treated as more than just room numbers, and many return year after year. This can make booking a room at popular resorts difficult, even off-season, despite the fact that more than half the island's visitors stay aboard their own or chartered boats. Hotels in Road Town don't have beaches, but they do have pools and are within walking distance of restaurants, bars, and shops. Accommodations outside Road Town are relatively isolated, but most face the ocean. Some places close during the peak of hurricane season—August through October—to give their owners a much-needed break.

Luxury on Tortola is more about a certain state of mind—serenity, seclusion, gentility, and a bit of Britain in the Caribbean—than about state-of-the-art amenities and fabulous facilities. Some properties, especially the vacation villas, are catching up with current trends, but others seem stuck in the 1980s. But don't let a bit of rust on the screen door or a chip in the paint on the balcony railing mar your appreciation of the ambience. You will likely spend most of your time outside, so the location, size, or price of a hotel should be more of a deciding factor than the decor.

A stay at any one of the hotels and guesthouses on Tortola's north side will put you closer to the beach, but not to worry: it doesn't take that long to get from one side of the island to the other. Visitors who want to be closer to Road Town's restaurants and shops can find a handful of places in and around the island's main town.

Hotel reviews have been shortened. For full information, visit Fodors.com.

PRIVATE VILLAS

Renting a villa is growing in popularity. Vacationers like the privacy, the space to spread out, and the opportunity to cook meals. As is true everywhere, the most important thing is location. If you want to be close to the beach, opt for a villa on the North Shore. If you want to dine out in Road Town every night, a villa closer to town may be a better bet. Prices per week during the winter season run from around $2,000 for a one- or two-bedroom villa up to $10,000 for a five-room beachfront villa. Rates in summer are substantially less. Most, but not all, villas accept credit cards.

McLaughlin-Anderson Luxury Villas

The St. Thomas–based McLaughlin-Anderson Luxury Villas manages nearly two dozen properties on Tortola and Virgin Gorda. Villas range from one to six bedrooms and come with full kitchens and stellar views. Most have pools. The company can hire a chef and stock your kitchen with groceries. ☎ 340/776–0635, 800/537–6246 ⊕ www.mclaughlinanderson.com.

Smiths Gore

Smiths Gore has properties all over the island available as long-term (a month or more) rental. They range from two to four bedrooms: all have stellar views, lovely furnishings, and lush landscaping. ✉ Brittanic Hall, Main St., Road Town ☎ 284/494–2446 ⊕ villavacationsbvi.com.

RESTAURANTS

Local seafood is plentiful on Tortola, and although other fresh ingredients are scarce, the island's chefs are a creative lot who apply their skills to whatever the boat delivers. Contemporary American dishes with Caribbean influences are very popular, but you can find French and Italian fare as well. The more expensive restaurants have dress codes: long pants and collared shirts for men and elegant but casual resort wear for women. Prices are often a bit higher than you'd expect to pay back home, and the service can

sometimes be a tad slow, but enjoy the chance to linger over the view.

Restaurants are scattered from one end of the island to the other, so you're never far from a good meal. Cane Garden Bay, with a handful of restaurants along the beach, is a popular dining destination. Eateries in Road Town are a short stroll from each other, making it easy to find a place that pleases everyone. Most hotels have restaurants that welcome nonguests.

6

Tortola

WHAT IT COSTS in U.S. Dollars

	$	$$	$$$	$$$$
RESTAURANTS				
	under $13	$13–$20	$21–$30	over $30
HOTELS				
	under $276	$276–$375	$376–$475	over $475

SAFETY

Although crime is rare, use the same common sense you would on any vacation. Don't leave your camera on the beach while you take a dip, for example.

SIGHTS

Tortola doesn't have an abundance of historic sights, but it does have lots of spectacular natural scenery and beautiful beaches. Although you could explore the island's 21 square miles (56 square km) in a few hours, opting for such a whirlwind tour would be a mistake. There's no need to live in the fast lane when you're surrounded by some of the Caribbean's most breathtaking panoramas. In any event, you come to Tortola to relax, read in the hammock, and spend hours at dinner, not to dash madly around the island ticking yet another sight off your list. Most island sights are best seen when you stumble upon them on your round-the-island drive.

NIGHTLIFE

Like any other good sailing destination, Tortola has watering holes that are popular with salty and not-so-salty dogs. Many offer entertainment; check the weekly *Limin' Times* for schedules and up-to-date information. The local beverage is the Painkiller, an innocent-tasting mixture of fruit juices and rums. It goes down smoothly but packs quite a punch, so give yourself time to recover before you order another. Road Town and Cane Garden Bay are your best bets for nightlife that goes later than 10 pm.

TOUR OPTIONS

Romney Associates/Travel Plan Tours can arrange island tours, boat tours, snorkeling and scuba-diving trips, dolphin swims, and yacht charters from its Tortola base. Tours can also be booked directly with operators including taxis, scuba diving operators, and power- and sail- charter boats. Their contacts can be found at the BVI Tourism Board website and on the BVI Now mobile app.

CONTACTS Romney Associates/Travel Plan Tours. ☎ *284/494–4000* ⊕ *romascogroup. com.*

VISITOR INFORMATION

CONTACTS BVI Tourist Board. ☎ *212/563–3117, 800/835–8530 in the U.S.* ⊕ *www. bvitourism.com.*

Road Town

The bustling capital of the BVI looks out over Road Harbour. It takes only an hour or so to stroll down Main Street and along the waterfront, checking out the traditional West Indian buildings painted in pastel colors and with corrugated-tin roofs, bright shutters, and delicate fretwork trim. For sightseeing brochures and the latest information on everything from taxi rates to ferry schedules, stop in the BVI Tourist Board office. Or just choose a seat on one of the benches in Sir Olva Georges Plaza, on Waterfront Drive, and watch the people come and go from the ferry dock and customs office across the street.

Sights

Fort Burt

HISTORIC SITE | The most intact historic ruin on Tortola was built by the Dutch in the early 17th century to safeguard Road Harbour. It sits on a hill at the western edge of Road Town and is now the site of a small hotel and restaurant. The foundations and magazine remain, and the structure offers a commanding view of the harbor. ⊠ *Waterfront Dr., Road Town* ☎ *284/494–2587* ⊕ *www.fortburt. com* 🖲 *Free.*

Her Majesty's Prison Museum

JAIL | Road Town's formidable prison was constructed in the mid-19th century and went on to hold prisoners in relatively primitive conditions for more than a century before closing in 2007. The prisoners confined to the humid barred cells were lucky compared to those who were hung in a creepy chamber, where the gallows claimed its last victim in the 1970s. Informative, docent-led tours offer insights into island history and the administration of justice from the colonial period into the early 21st century. ⊠ *Main St., Road Town* ☎ *284/494–3132* 🖲 *$5* ⊗ *Closed weekends.*

J.R. O'Neal Botanic Gardens

GARDEN | This 3-acre showcase of plant life has sections devoted to prickly cacti and succulents, hothouses for ferns and orchids, gardens of medicinal herbs, and plants and trees indigenous to the seashore. From the tourist office in Road Town, cross Waterfront Drive and walk one block over to Main Street and turn right. Keep walking until you see the high school. The gardens are on your left. ⊠ *Botanic Station, Road Town* ☎ *284/345–3650* ⊕ *www.bvinpt.org/ jr-o-neal-botanical* 🖲 *$3.*

Tortola Pier Park

PEDESTRIAN MALL | Tortola's Pier Park is the point of disembarkation for cruise ship passengers visiting the island. This Road Town development has a cigar bar, pizza joint, a hot dog eatery, Caribbean fusion restaurant, and an ice cream parlor. Diverse shopping options include jewelry stores, art galleries, and clothing boutiques. You can rent a car here or join in one of the frequent festivals and special events held at the complex. ☎ 284/494–8775 ⊕ www.tortolapier.com.

 Restaurants

★ Brandywine Estate

$$$$ | MEDITERRANEAN | At this Brandywine Bay restaurant, candlelit outdoor tables have sweeping views of nearby islands. The menu has a Mediterranean bistro flair but changes often; you might find grilled local king fish or a classic paella. **Known for:** gardenlike atmosphere; stunning Caribbean views; Mediterranean bistro cuisine. 🛇 *Average main: $32* ⊠ *Sir Francis Drake Hwy., east of Road Town, Brandywine Bay* ☎ *284/495–2301, 284/494–2200 Brandywine Rooftop* ⊕ *brandywine.vg* ☉ *Closed Mon.*

★ Capriccio di Mare

$$ | ITALIAN | Stop by this casual, authentic Italian outdoor café for an espresso, a fresh pastry, a bowl of perfectly cooked penne, or a crispy tomato-and-mozzarella pizza. Drink specialties include a mango Bellini, an adaptation of the famous cocktail served at Harry's Bar in Venice. **Known for:** authentic Italian; lively street café setting; specialty cocktails. 🛇 *Average main: $16* ⊠ *Waterfront Dr., Road Town* ☎ *284/494–5369* ☉ *Closed Sun.*

Captain Mulligan's

$$ | BURGER | FAMILY | Located at the entrance to Nanny Cay, this sports bar attracts expats, locals, and sailors with its promise to have "the second-best burger on the island," underlining the eatery's irreverent tone (we never found

out who has the best!). Hot wings, pizza, ribs, and burgers are on the menu, and most people come to watch the game on the big-screen TVs. **Known for:** bar scene; family- and pet-friendly atmosphere; minigolf. 🛇 *Average main: $16* ⊠ *Nanny Cay* ☎ *284/494–0602.*

Island Roots Cafe on Main

$ | CARIBBEAN | Located in the historic Customs House, Island Roots is part café and part art gallery. You can order sandwiches, salads, espresso, or smoothies from the counter and browse unique artwork and historic prints while waiting for your meal. **Known for:** coffee; light fare; evening cocktails. 🛇 *Average main: $12* ⊠ *Main St., Road Town* ☎ *284/343–8985* ☉ *Closed Sun.*

Peg Legs

$$$ | SEAFOOD | Take in views of Sir Francis Drake Channel and sidle up to the outdoor beach bar to hear yachties swap sea stories at this mariner-friendly eatery. Menu offerings range from burgers and pizzas to daily fresh seafood. **Known for:** people-watching; great views; Spring Regatta after-parties. 🛇 *Average main: $29* ⊠ *Nanny Cay* ☎ *284/494–0028* ⊕ *nannycay.com.*

The Pub

$$$ | ECLECTIC | Hamburgers, salads, and sandwiches are typical lunch offerings at this Road Town eatery, along with classic British fare such as shepherd's pie and liver and onions. In the evening you can also choose grilled fish, sautéed conch, sizzling steaks, or barbecued ribs. **Known for:** billiards and bar games; pub fare; live entertainment Thursday and Friday. 🛇 *Average main: $26* ⊠ *Columbus Centre, Waterfront Dr., Road Town* ☎ *284/345–1122* ☉ *No lunch Sun.*

Pusser's Road Town Pub

$$ | ECLECTIC | FAMILY | Almost everyone who visits Tortola stops here at least once to have a bite and to sample the famous Pusser's rum Painkiller (fruit juice and rum). The nonthreatening menu

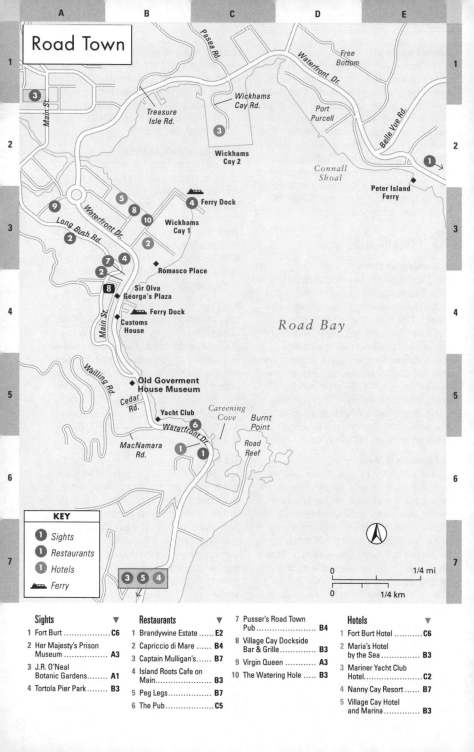

Road Town

A **B** **C** **D** **E**

Paseа Rd.

Waterfront Dr.

Free Bottom

Treasure Isle Rd.

Wickhams Cay Rd.

Port Purcell

Belle Vue Rd.

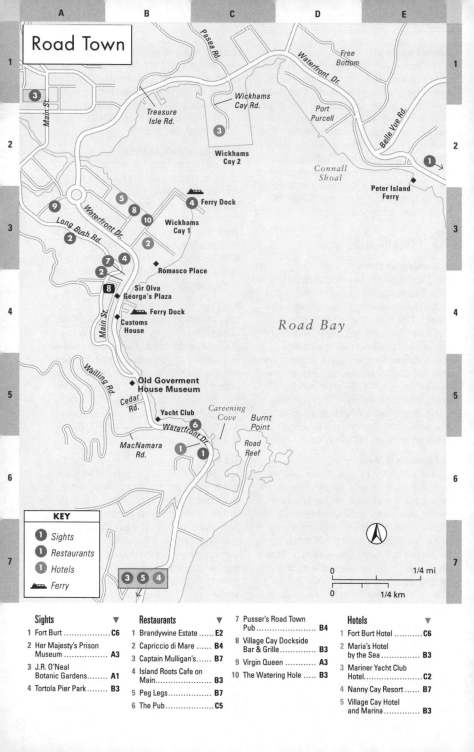 3

Main St.

Wickhams Cay 2

Connall Shoal

Peter Island Ferry

Long Bush Rd.

Waterfront Dr.

Ferry Dock

Wickhams Cay 1

Road Bay

Romasco Place

Sir Olva Georga's Plaza

Ferry Dock

Customs House

Main St.

Wailling Rd.

Old Goverment House Museum

Cedar Rd.

Yacht Club

Careening Cove

Burnt Point

Road Reef

MacNamara Rd.

Waterfront Dr.

KEY

1 Sights
1 Restaurants
1 Hotels
Ferry

0 _____ 1/4 mi
0 _____ 1/4 km

Sights ▼

1 Fort Burt **C6**
2 Her Majesty's Prison
  Museum **A3**
3 J.R. O'Neal
  Botanic Gardens........ **A1**
4 Tortola Pier Park **B3**

Restaurants ▼

1 Brandywine Estate **E2**
2 Capriccio di Mare **B4**
3 Captain Mulligan's....... **B7**
4 Island Roots Cafe on
  Main..................... **B3**
5 Peg Legs................. **B7**
6 The Pub **C5**

7 Pusser's Road Town
  Pub **B4**
8 Village Cay Dockside
  Bar & Grille............. **B3**
9 Virgin Queen **A3**
10 The Watering Hole **B3**

Hotels ▼

1 Fort Burt Hotel **C6**
2 Maria's Hotel
  by the Sea **B3**
3 Mariner Yacht Club
  Hotel.................... **C2**
4 Nanny Cay Resort **B7**
5 Village Cay Hotel
  and Marina **B3**

includes cheesy pizza, shepherd's pie, fish-and-chips, and hamburgers. (The "potato-chip tree" may threaten your beach body, however.) Dine inside in air-conditioned comfort or outside on the verandah, which looks out on the harbor. **Known for:** maritime decor; Pusser's rum; pub fare. $ *Average main: $15* ⊠ *Waterfront Dr., Road Town* ☎ *284/494–2467* ⊕ *www.pussers.com.*

Village Cay Dockside Bar & Grille

$$$ | **ECLECTIC** | Docked sailboats stretch nearly as far as the eye can see at this busy Road Town restaurant. Its alfresco dining and convivial atmosphere make it popular with both locals and visitors. **Known for:** lunch buffet; happy hour; outdoor dining. $ *Average main: $25* ⊠ *Wickham's Cay I, Road Town* ☎ *284/494–2771* ⊕ *villagecaybvi.com.*

Virgin Queen

$$$ | **ECLECTIC** | The sailing and rugby crowds head here to play darts, drink beer, and eat Queen's Combo pizza—a crusty, cheesy pie topped with sausage, onions, green peppers, and mushrooms. Also on the menu is excellent West Indian and English fare: barbecued ribs with beans and rice, curry chicken, bangers and mash, shepherd's pie, and grilled sirloin steak. **Known for:** pizza; West Indian and English fare; local bar scene. $ *Average main: $21* ⊠ *Flemming St., Road Town* ☎ *284/494–2310* ☽ *Closed Sun. No lunch Sat.*

The Watering Hole

$$ | **MODERN BRITISH** | Quietly tucked into a corner in Road Town's waterfront, the Watering Hole is a quiet oasis amidst the jungle of concrete government buildings and banks in downtown Road Town. Imported wine and beer, coffee, Wi-Fi, and light lunch fare make this a popular lunch spot for Road Town professionals and charter-yacht crews, while the after-work crowd is also drawn in with nightly weekday specials. **Known for:** South African wine; breakfast; popular lunch spot. $ *Average main: $18* ⊠ *Road*

Town ✢ *Wickham's Cay* ☎ *284/346–5950* ⊕ *www.wateringholebvi.com* ☽ *Closed Sun.*

Hotels

Fort Burt Hotel

$ | **HOTEL** | The Fort Burt Hotel surrounds the ruins of an old Dutch fort, giving you a sense of history along with a night's sleep. **Pros:** nice views; historic site; walk to shops and restaurants. **Cons:** little parking; long walk to Road Town; need car to get around. $ *Rooms from: $115* ⊠ *Waterfront Dr., Road Town* ☎ *284/494–2587* ⊕ *www.fortburt.com* ➳ *18 rooms* ❖ *No meals.*

Maria's Hotel by the Sea

$ | **HOTEL** | Sitting near the water in busy Road Town, Maria's Hotel by the Sea is perfect for budget travelers who want to be near shops and restaurants but who don't need many frills. **Pros:** good location; spacious rooms; walk to shops and restaurants. **Cons:** busy street; little parking; need car to get around. $ *Rooms from: $170* ⊠ *Waterfront Dr., Road Town* ☎ *284/494–2595* ⊕ *www.mariasbythesea.com* ➳ *67 rooms* ❖ *No meals.*

Mariner Yacht Club Hotel

$ | **HOTEL** | If you enjoy the camaraderie of a busy marina, this inn on the edge of Road Town may appeal to you. **Pros:** good dining options; friendly guests; excellent spot to charter boats. **Cons:** busy location; long walk to Road Town; need car to get around. $ *Rooms from: $250* ⊠ *Waterfront Dr., Road Town* ☎ *284/393–2331, 800/416–0820* ⊕ *www.moorings.com* ➳ *16 rooms* ❖ *No meals.*

Nanny Cay Resort

$ | **HOTEL** | This quiet oasis is far enough from Road Town to give it a secluded feel but close enough to make shops and restaurants convenient. **Pros:** nearby shops and restaurants; pleasant rooms; marina atmosphere. **Cons:** busy location; need car to get around; 20 minutes to the nearest beach. $ *Rooms from: $160*

✉ *Waterfront Dr., Nanny Cay* ☎ *284/394–2512* ⊕ *www.nannycay.com* ➦ *15 rooms* ❍ *No meals.*

Village Cay Hotel and Marina

$ | **HOTEL** | If you want to be able to walk to restaurants and shops, you simply can't beat Village Cay's prime location in the heart of Road Town. **Pros:** prime location; restaurant on-site; nautical ambience. **Cons:** little parking; busy street; need a car to get to the beach. ⑤ *Rooms from: $165* ✉ *Wickham's Cay I, Road Town* ☎ *284/494–2771* ⊕ *www.villagecaybvi.com* ➦ *22 rooms* ❍ *No meals.*

Nightlife

The Pub

BARS/PUBS | At this popular watering hole, there's live music and a happy hour from 5 to 7 every day. ✉ *Waterfront St., Road Town* ☎ *284/345–1122.*

Pusser's Road Town Pub

BARS/PUBS | Try Pusser's famous mixed drink, called the Painkiller, and snack on the excellent pizza. The tin Painkiller cup is a must-have BVI souvenir. ✉ *Waterfront St., Road Town* ☎ *284/494–2467* ⊕ *www.pussers.com.*

Shopping

Many shops and boutiques are clustered along and just off Road Town's **Main Street.** You can shop in Road Town's **Wickham's Cay I** adjacent to the marina. The **Crafts Alive Market** on the Road Town waterfront is a collection of colorful West Indian–style buildings with shops that carry items made in the BVI. You might find pretty baskets or interesting pottery or perhaps a bottle of home-brewed hot sauce.

ART

Allamanda Gallery

ART GALLERIES | Photography by the gallery's owner, Amanda Baker, as well as books, gifts, and cards are on display

and available to purchase. A second location is at the Baths in Virgin Gorda. ✉ *Pier Park, Road Town* ☎ *284/494–6680, 284/495–5935* ⊕ *www.theallamandagallery.com.*

CLOTHES AND TEXTILES

Arawak Surf

CLOTHING | This boutique carries batik sundresses, sportswear, swimwear, and resort wear for men and women. There's also a selection of furniture and children's clothing and books. A second location is in Leverick Bay. ✉ *Nanny Cay Marina, Nanny Cay* ☎ *284/494–5240* ⊕ *www.arawakvi.com.*

FOODSTUFFS

Ample Hamper

FOOD/CANDY | This grocer has an outstanding collection of cheeses, wines, fresh fruits, and canned goods from the United Kingdom and the United States, as well as wine, beer, and liquor. The staff will stock your yacht or rental villa. ✉ *Inner Harbour Marina, Road Town* ☎ *284/494–2494, 284/494–2784* ⊕ *www.amplehamper.com.*

RiteWay

FOOD/CANDY | This supermarket has fresh produce, deli, prepared foods, meats, bakery, and all the grocery items you'll need for your villa or yacht. You can shop for yourself or set up a provisioning order. You'll find RiteWay locations all over Tortola, and there's also one on Virgin Gorda. ✉ *Waterfront Dr. at Pasea Estate, Road Town* ☎ *284/494–2263, 384/347–1188 Provisioning Dept.* ⊕ *www.rtwbvi.com.*

GIFTS

Crafts Alive Village

CRAFTS | The collection of colorful West Indian cottages offering handicrafts, cloths, and souvenirs at the Crafts Alive Village makes for excellent one-stop souvenir shopping. ✉ *Waterfront Dr., Road Town* ☎ *284/342–8595.*

Most of Tortola's shops are in Road Town.

West End

Sights

Fort Recovery

HISTORIC SITE | An unrestored but largely intact 17th-century Dutch fort sits amid a profusion of tropical greenery on the grounds of Fort Recovery Beachfront Villas and Suites. The most interesting thing to see here are the remains of a martello tower, a type of fortification used to make up for the site's lack of elevation; it's rarely found in the Caribbean. There are no guided tours, but you're welcome to stop by and poke around. ⊠ *Waterfront Dr., Pockwood Pond, Road Town* ☎ *284/541–0955* ⊕ *www.fortrecovery. com* ⌨ *Free.*

Soper's Hole

NEIGHBORHOOD | On this little island connected by a causeway to Tortola's western end, you can find a marina and a captivating complex of pastel West Indian–style buildings with shady balconies, shuttered windows, and gingerbread trim that house art galleries, boutiques, and restaurants. The popular Pusser's Landing and Omar's Cafe are here. ⊠ *Soper's Hole.*

Beaches

Long Bay Beach

BEACH—SIGHT | This beach is a stunning, mile-long stretch of white sand; have your camera ready to snap the breathtaking approach. The entire beach is open to the public and is often used by people staying in villas in the Long Bay/Belmont area. The water isn't as calm here as at Cane Garden or Brewers Bay, but it's still swimmable. Turn left at Zion Hill Road; then travel about half a mile. **Amenities:** none. **Best for:** swimming. ⊠ *Long Bay Rd., Long Bay.*

Smuggler's Cove Beach

BEACH—SIGHT | A beautiful, palm-fringed beach, Smuggler's Cove is down a pothole-filled dirt road. After bouncing your way down, you'll feel as if you've found a

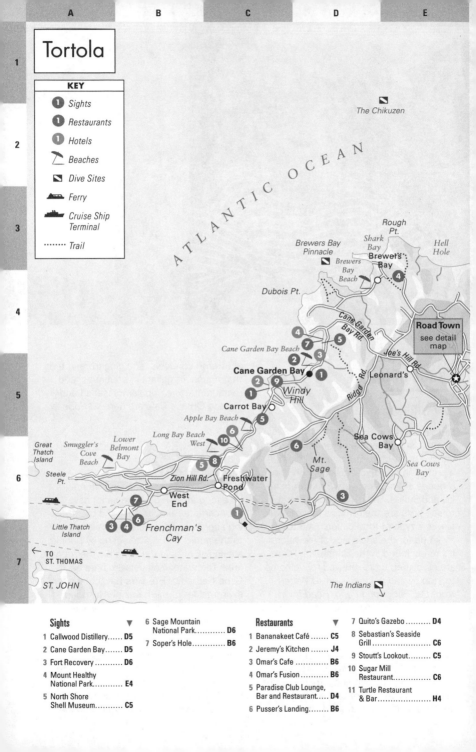

Tortola

KEY

- **1** Sights
- **1** Restaurants
- **1** Hotels
- Beaches
- Dive Sites
- Ferry
- Cruise Ship Terminal
- ········ Trail

A T L A N T I C   O C E A N

The Chikuzen

Rough Pt.

Brewers Bay Pinnacle

Shark Bay

Hell Hole

Brewers Bay Beach

Brewer's Bay

Dubois Pt.

Cane Garden Bay Rd.

Road Town
see detail map

Joe's Hill Rd.

4

Cane Garden Bay Beach

7

5

2 **3**

Cane Garden Bay ● **1**

Leonard's

2

1 **9**

Windy Hill

Ridge Rd.

Carrot Bay

Apple Bay Beach

5

6

Sea Cows Bay

Long Bay Beach West

10

Sea Cows Bay

Great Thatch Island

Smuggler's Cove Beach

Lower Belmont Bay

5 **8**

6

Mt. Sage

Steele Pt.

Zion Hill Rd.

Freshwater Pond

7

West End

3

Little Thatch Island

3 **4**

6

Frenchman's Cay

1

← TO ST. THOMAS

ST. JOHN

The Indians

Sights ▼

1 Callwood Distillery...... **D5**
2 Cane Garden Bay..... **D5**
3 Fort Recovery **D6**
4 Mount Healthy National Park............ **E4**
5 North Shore Shell Museum........... **C5**
6 Sage Mountain National Park............ **D6**
7 Soper's Hole............. **B6**

Restaurants ▼

1 Bananakeet Café **C5**
2 Jeremy's Kitchen **J4**
3 Omar's Cafe **B6**
4 Omar's Fusion **B6**
5 Paradise Club Lounge, Bar and Restaurant..... **D4**
6 Pusser's Landing........ **B6**
7 Quito's Gazebo **D4**
8 Sebastian's Seaside Grill **C6**
9 Stoutt's Lookout......... **C5**
10 Sugar Mill Restaurant............... **C6**
11 Turtle Restaurant & Bar..................... **H4**

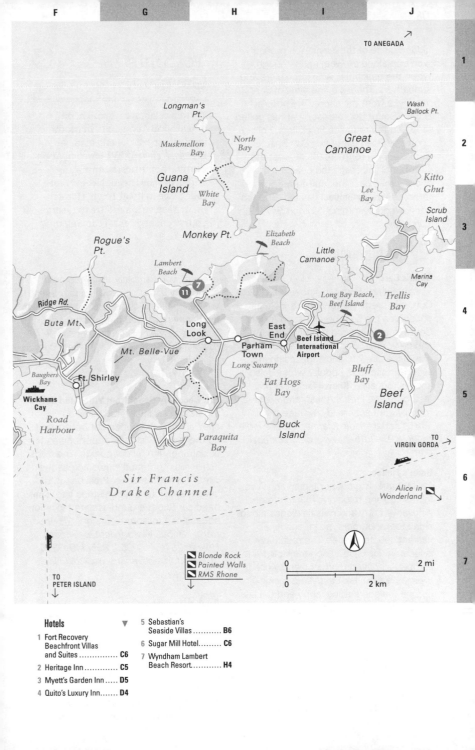

F   **G**   **H**   **I**   **J**

1

TO ANEGADA →

Longman's
Pt.

Wash
Ballock Pt.

2

Muskmellon
Bay

North
Bay

*Great
Camanoe*

Kitto
Ghut

Guana
Island

White
Bay

Lee
Bay

Scrub
Island

3

Monkey Pt.

Elizabeth
Beach

*Little
Camanoe*

Marina
Cay

Rogue's
Pt.

Lambert
Beach

7

11

Long Bay Beach,
Beef Island

*Trellis
Bay*

4

Ridge Rd.

Buta Mt.

Long
Look

East
End

Beef Island
International
Airport

2

Mt. Belle-Vue

Parham
Town

Long Swamp

Bluff
Bay

*Beef
Island*

5

Baughers
Bay

Ft. Shirley

Fat Hogs
Bay

Wickhams
Cay

*Road
Harbour*

Buck
Island

Paraquita
Bay

TO
VIRGIN GORDA →

6

*Sir Francis
Drake Channel*

Alice in
Wonderland ◣

TO
PETER ISLAND
↓

◤ Blonde Rock
◤ Painted Walls
◤ RMS Rhone
↓

0   2 mi

0   2 km

7

Hotels ▼

1 Fort Recovery
  Beachfront Villas
  and Suites **C6**

2 Heritage Inn **C5**

3 Myett's Garden Inn **D5**

4 Quito's Luxury Inn **D4**

5 Sebastian's
  Seaside Villas **B6**

6 Sugar Mill Hotel **C6**

7 Wyndham Lambert
  Beach Resort **H4**

hidden piece of the island. You probably won't be alone on weekends, though, when the beach fills with snorkelers and sunbathers. There's a fine view of Jost Van Dyke from the shore. The popular Nigel's Boom Boom Beach Bar has grilled food and the requisite Painkillers. Follow Long Bay Road past Long Bay Beach Club, keeping to the roads nearest the water until you reach the beach. It's about a mile past the (currently shuttered) resort. **Amenities:** parking. **Best for:** snorkeling; swimming. ⊠ *Long Bay Rd., Long Bay.*

🍴 Restaurants

Omar's Cafe
$ | **CARIBBEAN** | Formerly known as D'Best Cup, this pretty pastel Soper's Hole eatery serves the best breakfast on Tortola. Chef Omar Hurst and his wife, Ashanti, and crew dish out omelets, French toast, waffles, espresso, and cappuccino in a lively atmosphere, popular with locals and visitors alike. **Known for:** great breakfast; omelets, French toast, and waffles; friendly atmosphere. ⑤ *Average main: $13* ⊠ *Soper's Hole Marina, Soper's Hole* ☎ *284/495–8015* ⊕ *www.omarscafebvi. com.*

Omar's Fusion
$$$ | **INDIAN** | The best of Indian and West Indies cooking traditions mix to create innovative curry and masala dishes alongside steaks, burgers, pizza, and local fish and lobster dishes. The restaurant is located dockside at Soper's Hole with an open-air dining room cooled by ocean breezes. **Known for:** East/West fusion cuisine; unique setting; curry and masala dishes. ⑤ *Average main: $24* ⊠ *Soper's Hole Marina* ☎ *284/495–8015, 284/346–7771* ⊕ *omarfusion.com* ⊙ *Closed Sept.– late Oct.*

Pusser's Landing
$$$ | **AMERICAN** | Yachties navigate their way to this waterfront restaurant. Downstairs, from late morning to well into the

Tortola's Carnival

Tortola celebrates Carnival on and around August 1 to mark the anniversary of the end of slavery in 1834. A slew of BVI Emancipation Festival activities, culminating with a parade through the streets, take place in Road Town. Hotels fill up fast, so make sure to reserve your room and rental car well in advance.

evening, you can belly up to the outdoor mahogany bar or sit downstairs for sandwiches, fish-and-chips, and pizzas. **Known for:** happy hour; pub fare; outdoor deck. ⑤ *Average main: $26* ⊠ *Soper's Hole* ☎ *284/495–4554* ⊕ *www.pussers.com.*

🛏 Hotels

Fort Recovery Beachfront Villas and Suites
$$ | **RESORT** | **FAMILY** | This small but special property stands out because of its friendly service and opportunities for socializing with fellow guests, and all of its rooms have good views across the water toward St. John. **Pros:** beautiful beach; spacious units; historic site. **Cons:** need car to get around; isolated location; not as posh as some locations. ⑤ *Rooms from: $345* ⊠ *Waterfront Dr., Soper's Hole* ☎ *284/541–0955, 855/349–3355* ⊕ *www.fortrecovery.com* ⇥ *24 villas* ⑩ *No meals.*

🛍 Shopping

There's an ever-growing number of art and clothing stores at **Soper's Hole** in West End.

CLOTHES AND TEXTILES
Arawak
CLOTHING | This shop carries batik sundresses, sportswear, and resort wear for

Cane Garden Bay has a popular beach lined with bars and restaurants.

men and women. There's also a selection of children's clothing. ✉ *Soper's Hole Marina* ☎ *284/495–4262.*

Pusser's Company Store

CLOTHING | Pusser's West End store sells clothing for both men and women, handsome decorator bottles of Pusser's rum, and gift items bearing the Pusser's logo. ✉ *Soper's Hole Marina, Soper's Hole* ☎ *284/495–4554.*

North Shore

Sights

Callwood Distillery

WINERY/DISTILLERY | Nobody is really sure how long rum has been made at the Callwood Distillery, but it has been at least 200 years, and one thing is certain: it houses the longest continuously operated copper pot still in the Caribbean. Located on a side street in Cane Garden Bay, the ancient distillery offers tours and tastings of its uniquely flavored rums,

made directly from the juice of pressed sugar cane, not molasses or refined sugar. For a true taste of the BVI, it doesn't get more authentic than Callwood's barrel-aged spirits. ✉ *Cane Garden Bay, Cane Garden Bay* ☎ *284/495–9383.*

★ Cane Garden Bay

NEIGHBORHOOD | Once a sleepy village, Cane Garden Bay has become one of Tortola's most popular destinations. Stay at a small hotel or guesthouse here, or stop by for lunch, dinner, or drinks at a seaside restaurant, and nightlife at Quito's and the Paradise Club. You can find a few small stores selling clothing and basics such as suntan lotion, and one of Tortola's most popular beaches is at your feet. Myett's offers hotel rooms almost directly on the beach, while the new, high-rise Quito's Inn has stylish modern rooms across the street. The Callwood Distillery has been making rum from sugar cane grown around the bay for at least 200 years. The roads in and out of this area are dauntingly steep, so use caution when driving. ✉ *Cane Garden Bay.*

North Shore Shell Museum

MUSEUM | Egbert Donovan, the "shell man" of Carrot Bay, entertains passing buses full of tourists with tunes on his guitar and welcomes those who tarry longer to visit his museum crammed with thousands of sea shells, gathered over the course of 25 years from the nearby waters and shoreline. Donovan's shell-gathering boat was a victim of Hurricane Irma, so now he spends more time showing off his shells and serving bush tea and turtle soup to visitors. ⊠ *Carrot Bay, Cane Garden Bay* ☎ *284/343–7581.*

 Beaches

Apple Bay Beach

BEACH—SIGHT | Along with nearby Little Apple Bay and Capoon's Bay, this is your spot if you want to surf—although the white, sandy beach itself is narrow. Sebastian's, a casual hotel, caters to those in search of the perfect wave. Otherwise, there's nothing else in the way of amenities. Good waves are never a sure thing, but you're more apt to find them in January and February. If you're swimming and the waves are up, take care not to get dashed on the rocks. **Amenities:** none. **Best for:** surfing; swimming. ⊠ *North Shore Rd. at Zion Hill Rd., Apple Bay.*

Brewers Bay Beach

BEACH—SIGHT | This beach is easy to find, but the steep, twisting roads leading down to it can be a bit daunting. An old sugar mill and the ruins of a rum distillery are off the beach along the road. Nicole's Beach Bar provides Painkiller cocktails to thirsty sunbathers. You can actually reach the beach from either Brewers Bay Road East or Brewers Bay Road West. **Amenities:** food and drink. **Best for:** snorkeling; swimming. ⊠ *Brewers Bay Rd. E, off Cane Garden Bay Rd., Brewers Bay.*

★ Cane Garden Bay Beach

BEACH—SIGHT | This silky stretch of sand boasts exceptionally calm crystalline waters—except when storms at sea turn the water murky. Snorkeling is good along the edges. Casual guesthouses, restaurants, bars, and shops are steps from the beach in the village of the same name. The beach is a laid-back, even somewhat funky place to put down your towel. It's the closest beach to Road Town (one steep uphill and downhill drive) and one of the BVI's best-known anchorages. Unfortunately, it can be very crowded with day-trippers when cruise ships dock in Road Town. Water-sports shops rent equipment. **Amenities:** food and drink; toilets; water sports. **Best for:** snorkeling; swimming; partiers. ⊠ *Cane Garden Bay Rd., off Ridge Rd., Cane Garden Bay.*

🍽 Restaurants

★ Bananakeet Café

$$$ | ECLECTIC | The sunset sea-and-mountain views are stunning at this poolside restaurant at Heritage Inn hotel, so arrive early for the predinner happy hour. "Caribbean fusion" best describes the fare, with an emphasis on seafood, including local Anegada conch swimming in an herb-butter broth. Those without a taste for seafood won't go hungry—the menu also includes lamb, beef, and chicken dishes. **Known for:** sunset happy hour; panoramic views; Anegada conch. $ *Average main: $30* ⊠ *Heritage Inn, North Coast Rd., Great Carrot Bay* ☎ *284/494–5842* ⊕ *www.heritageinn.vg* ☷ *No lunch. Closed Sept. 15–Oct. 15.*

Paradise Club Lounge, Bar and Restaurant

$$ | PIZZA | Find this Cane Garden Bay eatery and bar on the beach by the "I Love BVI" sign—it's known for its traditional Caribbean breakfast, brick-oven pizza, and daily drink specials. DJs get a good beach jam going at night, including monthly full-moon parties and themed events. **Known for:** Caribbean breakfast; pizza; beach parties. $ *Average main: $15* ⊠ *Cane Garden Bay* ☎ *284/345–2541.*

Continued on page 188

TRY A YACHT CHARTER

IT'S SURPRISINGLY AFFORDABLE

Savoring a freshly brewed mug of coffee, I sat on the front deck of our chartered 43-foot catamaran and watched the morning show. Laserlike rays of sunlight streamed through a cottony cloud bank, bringing life to the emerald islands and turquoise seas. What would it have been like to sail with Columbus and chart these waters for the first time? How would it feel to cast about the deserted beaches for the perfect place to bury plundered treasure? The aroma of freshly made banana pancakes roused me from my reverie.

Once considered an outward-bound adventure or exclusive domain of the rich and famous, chartering a boat can be a surprisingly affordable and attractive vacation alternative. Perhaps you're already a sailor and want to explore beyond your own lake, river, or bay. Or maybe your idea of sailing has always been on a cruise ship, and now you're ready for a more intimate voyage. Or perhaps you've never sailed before, but you are now curious to cast off and explore a whole new world.

By Carol M. Bareuther

CREWED CHARTER

On a crewed charter, you sit back and relax while the crew provides for your every want and need. Captains are licensed by the U.S. Coast Guard or the equivalent in the British maritime system. Cooks—preferring to be called chefs—have skills that go far beyond peanut butter and jelly sandwiches. There are four meals a day, and many chefs boast certificates from culinary schools ranging from the Culinary Institute of America in New York to the Cordon Bleu in Paris.

The advantage of a crewed yacht charter, with captain and cook, is that it takes every bit of stress out of the vacation. With a captain who knows the local waters, you get to see some of the coves and anchorages that are not necessarily in the guidebooks. Your meals are prepared, cabins cleaned, beds made up every day—and turned down at night, too. Plus, you can sail and take the helm as often as you like. But at the end of the day, the captain is the one who will take responsibility for anchoring safely for the night while the chef goes below and whips up a gourmet meal.

APPROXIMATE COSTS	PROS	CONS
From $4,800 for 2 people for 5 days	■ Passengers just have to lay back and relax (unless they want to help sail)	■ More expensive than a bareboat, especially if you get a catamaran
From $5,500 for 2 people for 7 days	■ Most are catamarans, offering more space than monohulls	■ Less privacy for your group than on a bareboat
From $12,000 for 6 people for 5 days	■ You have an experienced, local hand on board if something goes wrong	■ Captain makes ultimate decisions about the course
From $15,000 for 6 people for 7 days	■ Water toys and other extras are often included	■ Chance for personality conflicts: you have to get along with the captain and chef. This is where a charter yacht broker is helpful in determining what yachts and crews might be a good fit.
Prices are all-inclusive for a 50- to 55-foot catamaran yacht in high season except for 15%–20% gratuity.	■ Competively priced within an all-inclusive resort	

(top) Family sailing in the British Virgin Islands

BAREBOAT

If you'd like to bareboat, don't be intimidated. It's a myth that you must be a graduate of a sailing school in order to pilot your own charter boat. A bareboat company will ask you to fill out a resume. The company checks for prior boat-handling experience, the type of craft you've sailed (whether powerboat or sailboat), and in what type of waters. Real-life experience, meaning all those day and weekend trips close to home, count as valuable know-how. If you've done a bit of boating, you may be more qualified than you think to take out a bareboat.

Costs can be very similar for a bareboat and crewed charter, depending on the time of year and size of the boat. You'll pay the highest rates between Christmas and New Year's, when you may not be allowed to do a charter of less than a week. But there are more than 800 bareboats between the USVI and BVI, so regardless of your budget, you should be able to find something in your price range. Plus, you might save a bit by chartering an older boat from a smaller company instead of the most state-of-the-art yacht from a larger company.

APPROXIMATE COSTS	PROS	CONS
From $3,800 for a small monohull (2–3 cabins)	■ The ultimate freedom to set the yacht's course	■ Must be able to pass a sailing test
From $6,300 for a large monohull (4–5 cabins)	■ A chance to test your sailing skills	■ Those unfamiliar with the region may not find the best anchorages
From $6,500 for a small catamaran (2 cabins)	■ Usually a broader range of boats and prices to choose from	■ You have to cook for and clean up after yourself
From $8,900 for a large catamaran (4 cabins)	■ More flexibility for meals (you can always go ashore if you don't feel like cooking)	■ You have to do your own provisioning and planning for meals
Prices exclude food, beverages, fuel, and other supplies. Most bareboat rates do not include water toys, taxes, insurance, and permits.	■ You can always hire a captain for a few days	■ If something goes wrong, there isn't an experienced hand onboard

Three women rigging the sails.

WHAT TO CONSIDER

Whether bareboat or a crewed yacht, there are a few points to ponder when selecting your boat.

HOW BIG IS YOUR GROUP?

As a general rule, count on one cabin for every two people. Most people also prefer to have one head (bathroom) per cabin. A multihull, also called a catamaran, offers more space and more equal-size cabins than a monohull sailboat.

WHAT TYPE OF BOAT?

If you want to do some good old traditional sailing, where you're heeling over with the seas at your rails, monohulls are a good option. On the other hand, multihulls are more stable, easier to board, and have a big salon for families. They're also ideal if some people get seasick or aren't as gung-ho for the more traditional sailing experience. If you'd like to cover more ground, choose a motor yacht.

DO YOU HAVE A SPECIAL INTEREST?

Some crewed charter boats specialize in certain types of charters. Among these are learn-to-sail excursions, honeymoon cruises, scuba-diving adventures, and family-friendly trips. Your broker can steer you to the boats that fit your specific needs.

WHAT KIND OF EQUIPMENT DO YOU WANT ONBOARD?

Most charter boats have satellite navigation systems and autopilots, as well as regulation safety gear, dinghies with motors, and even stereos and entertainment systems. But do you want a generator or battery-drive refrigeration system? How about a/c? Do you want a satellite phone? Do you want water toys like kayaks, boogie boards, and Windsurfers?

Now that you've decided on bareboat versus crewed charter and selected your craft, all you need to do is confirm the availability of the date with the company or broker and pay a nonrefundable deposit equal to 50% of the charter price.

TO SAIL OR NOT TO SAIL?

If you're not sure whether a charter yacht vacation is right for you, consider this: would you enjoy a floating hotel room where the scenery outside your window changed according to your desires? A "yes" may entice wary companions to try chartering. A single one-week trip will have them hooked.

Two catamaran sailboats seen from behind.

CATAMARANS
Multihulls are more stable, easier to board and have a big salon for families. Seasickness is less of an issue.

MOTOR YACHT
Best if you want to cover more ground, but costs a lot more than a sailboat.

MONOHULLS
Good for more traditional and active sailing, but the movement may not appeal to non-sailors.

CHOOSING A CHARTER

Information on charters is much easier to find now than even a decade ago. Websites for bareboat companies show photos of different types of boats—both interiors and exteriors—as well as layout schematics, lists of equipment and amenities, and sample itineraries. Many sites will allow you to book a charter directly, while others give you the option of calling a toll-free number to speak with an agent first.

There are two types of websites for crewed charters. If you just want some information, the **Virgin Islands Professional Charter Association** (⊕ www.vipca.org) and the **Charter Yacht Society of the British Virgin Islands** (⊕ www.bvicrewedyachts.com) both help you understand what to look for in a crewed charter, from the size of the boat to the amenities. You can't reserve on these sites, but they link to the sites of brokers, who are the sales force for the charter yacht industry. Most brokers, whether they're based in the Caribbean, the United States, or Europe, attend annual charter yacht shows in St. Thomas, Tortola, and Antigua. At these shows, brokers visit the boats and meet the crews. This is what gives brokers their depth of knowledge for "matchmaking," or linking you with a boat that will meet your personality and preferences.

The charter companies also maintain websites. About 30% of the crewed charter yachts based out of the U.S. and British Virgin Islands can be booked directly. This saves the commission an owner has to pay to the broker. But while "going direct" might seem advantageous, there is usually little difference in pricing, and if you use a broker, he or she can help troubleshoot if something goes wrong or find a replacement boat if the boat owner has to cancel.

Timing also matters. Companies may offer last-minute specials that are available only online. These special rates—usually for specific dates, destinations, and boats—are updated weekly or even daily.

PREPARING FOR YOUR CHARTER

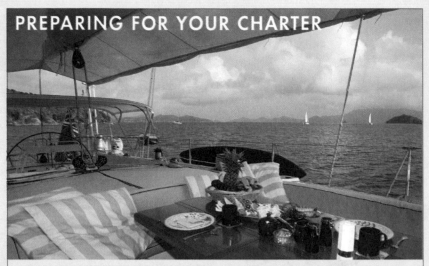

British Virgin Islands—anchorage in a tropical sea with breakfast on board.

PROVISIONING

Bareboaters must do their own provisioning. It's a good idea to arrange provisioning at least a week in advance.

Provisioning packages from the charter company are usually a bit more expensive, at $30 to $35 per person per day, but they save you the hassle of planning the details. You can also shop on arrival. Both St. Thomas and Tortola have markets, though larger grocery stores may require a taxi ride. If you shop carefully, this route can still save you money. Just be sure to allow yourself a few hours after arrival to get everything done.

PLANNING

For a crewed charter, your broker will send a preference sheet for both food and your wishes for the trip. Perhaps you'd like lazy days of sleeping late, sunning, and swimming. Or you might prefer active days of sailing with stops for snorkeling and exploring ashore. If there's a special spot you'd like to visit, list it so your captain can plan the itinerary accordingly.

PACKING TIPS

Pack light for any type of charter. Bring soft-sided luggage (preferably a duffle bag) since space is limited and storage spots are usually odd shapes. Shorts, T-shirts, and swimsuits are sufficient. Bring something a bit nicer if you plan to dine ashore. Shoes are seldom required except ashore, but you might want beach shoes to protect your feet in the water. Most boats provide snorkel equipment, but always ask. Bring sunscreen, but a type that will not stain cockpit cushions and decks.

WHAT YOU'LL SEE IN THE USBVI

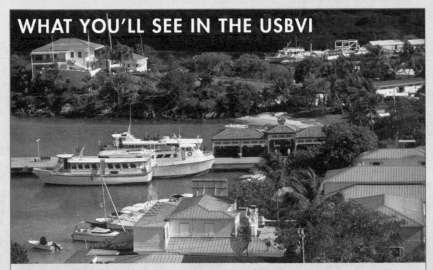

Cruz Bay in St. John

MAIN CHARTER BASES

The U.S. and British Virgin Islands boast more than 100 stepping-stone islands and cays within a 50-nautical-mile radius. This means easy line-of-sight navigation and island-hopping in protected waters, and it's rare that you'll spend more than a few hours moving between islands.

Tortola, in the British Virgin Islands, is the crewed charter and bareboat mecca of the Caribbean. This fact is plainly apparent from the forest of masts rising out from any marina.

The U.S. Virgin Islands fleet is based in **St. Thomas**. Direct flights from the mainland, luxurious accommodations, and duty-free shopping are drawing cards for departures from the U.S. Virgin Islands, whereas the British Virgins are closer to the prime cruising grounds.

POPULAR ANCHORAGES

On a typical weeklong charter you could set sail from Red Hook, St. Thomas, then cross Pillsbury Sound to St. John, which offers popular north-shore anchorages in Honeymoon, Trunk, or Francis bays.

But the best sailing and snorkeling always includes the British Virgin Islands (which require a valid passport or passport card). After clearing customs in West End, Tortola, many yachts hop along a series of smaller islands that run along the south side of the Sir Francis Drake Channel. But some yachts will also visit Guana Island, Great Camanoe, or Marina Cay off Tortola's more isolated east end.

The islands south of Tortola include **Norman Island**, the rumored site of Robert Lewis Stevenson's *Treasure Island*. The next island over is **Peter Island**, famous for it's posh resort and a popular anchorage for yachters. Farther east, off Salt Island, is the wreck of the **RMS Rhone**—the most magnificent dive site in the eastern Caribbean. Giant boulders form caves and grottos called The Baths at the southern end of **Virgin Gorda**.

A downwind run along Tortola's north shore ends at **Jost Van Dyke**, where that famous guitar-strumming calypsonian Foxy Callwood sings personalized ditties that make for a memorable finale.

The hiking trails in Sage Mountain National Park lead to panoramic views.

Quito's Gazebo

$$$ | CARIBBEAN | This beachside bar and restaurant is owned and operated by island native Quito Rymer, a multitalented recording star who plays and sings solo (usually on Wednesdays) and performs with his reggae band, the Edge, on Friday (though there is some sort of live music nearly every night of the week). The menu is Caribbean, with an emphasis on fresh fish; try the conch fritters or the jerk chicken. **Known for:** live music; Caribbean fare; casual picnic table dining. ⑤ *Average main: $26 ⊠ Cane Garden Bay* ☎ *284/495–4837 ⊕ quitosbvi.com.*

Sebastian's Seaside Grill

$$$ | ECLECTIC | The waves practically lap at your feet at this beachfront restaurant on Tortola's North Shore, a perfect spot to stop for lunch on your around-the-island tour. The dinner menu emphasizes seafood—especially lobster, conch, and local fish—but you can also find dishes such as jerk chicken and filet mignon. **Known for:** surfer vibe; beachside dining; local seafood. ⑤ *Average main: $29*

⊠ *Sebastian's on the Beach, North Coast Rd., Apple Bay* ☎ *284/544–4212 ⊕ www. sebastiansbvi.com.*

Stoutt's Lookout

$ | BURGER | Kingfish burgers and long-distance views are on the menu in the reggae-colored Stoutt's Lookout, the domain of gregarious owner Prince Stoutt. Burgers and barbecue ribs round out the lunch menu, all best washed down with a punch made with local Callwood rum and pineapple, guava, and orange juice. **Known for:** views of Cane Garden Bay; burgers; Callwood rum punch. ⑤ *Average main: $12 ⊠ Cane Garden Bay, Cane Garden Bay* ⊹ *At the intersection of Windy Hill and Ridge Rd.* ☎ *284/442–0432.*

★ Sugar Mill Restaurant

$$$$ | ECLECTIC | Candles gleam and the background music is peaceful in this romantic restaurant inside a 17th-century sugar mill. Well-prepared selections on the à la carte menu, which changes nightly, include some pasta and vegetarian entrées. **Known for:** unique historic setting; fine dining; Caribbean specialties.

$ Average main: $49 ✉ Sugar Mill Hotel, North Coast Rd., Apple Bay ☎ 284/495–4355 🌐 www.sugarmillhotel.com ⏲ No lunch. Closed Wed. in summer.

Hotels

Heritage Inn

$ | **B&B/INN** | The gorgeous sea and mountain views are the stars at this small hotel perched on the edge of a cliff. **Pros:** stunning views; fun vibe; room has kitchenette, but there's also a great restaurant on-site. **Cons:** need car to get around; close to road; not on beach. *$ Rooms from: $225 ✉ North Coast Rd., Great Carrot Bay ☎ 284/494–5842 🌐 heritageinnbvi.com 🛏 6 rooms 🍽 No meals.*

Myett's Garden Inn

$ | **HOTEL** | Tucked away in a beachfront garden, this tiny hotel puts you right in the middle of Cane Garden Bay's busy hustle and bustle. **Pros:** beautiful beach; good restaurant; shops nearby. **Cons:** busy location; need a car to venture out; small. *$ Rooms from: $250 ✉ Cane Garden Bay ☎ 284/495–9649 🌐 www.myetts.com 🛏 11 units 🍽 No meals.*

Quito's Luxury Inn

$$ | **HOTEL** | The tireless Quito Rymer, one of the island's most popular musicians, opened this high-rise hotel in 2019 across the street from the beach and his eponymous restaurant-bar (where he still performs). **Pros:** near bars and restaurants; pool and spa on-site; good restaurant. **Cons:** busy location; not on beach; need car to get around. *$ Rooms from: $342 ✉ Cane Garden Bay ☎ 284/495–4837 🌐 quitosbvi.com 🛏 21 rooms 🍽 No meals.*

Sebastian's Seaside Villas

$ | **HOTEL** | Sitting on the island's north coast, Sebastian's definitely has a beachy feel, and that's its primary charm. **Pros:** nice beach; good restaurants; beachfront rooms. **Cons:** on busy road; some rooms nicer than others; need car to get around. *$ Rooms from: $226 ✉ North Coast Rd., Apple Bay ☎ 284/495–4212 🌐 www.sebastiansbvi.com 🛏 35 rooms 🍽 No meals.*

★ **Sugar Mill Hotel**

$$$ | **RESORT** | Though it's not a sprawling resort, the Sugar Mill Hotel has a Caribbean cachet that's hard to beat, and it's a favorite place to stay on Tortola. **Pros:** lovely rooms; excellent restaurants on-site; nice views. **Cons:** on busy road; small beach; need car to get around. *$ Rooms from: $395 ✉ North Coast Rd., Apple Bay ☎ 284/495–4355 🌐 www.sugarmillhotel.com 🛏 22 units 🍽 Free Breakfast.*

Nightlife

★ **Pusser's at Myett's**

BARS/PUBS | Local bands play at this popular spot on the beach, which has live music nightly in season. There's usually a lively dance crowd, and this is the place in Cane Garden Bay to get your obligatory Pusser's Painkiller in a souvenir mug. *✉ Cane Garden Bay ☎ 284/495–9649 🌐 www.myetts.com.*

Quito's Bar and Restaurant

MUSIC CLUBS | BVI recording star Quito Rhymer sings island ballads and love songs at his rustic beachside bar–restaurant. Solo shows are usually Wednesday at 5:30 pm, and every other Friday at 9 pm Quito performs with his band, the Edge. *✉ North Coast Rd., Cane Garden Bay ☎ 284/495–4837 🌐 quitosbvi.com.*

Sebastian's

BARS/PUBS | There's often live music at Sebastian's on Sunday and Wednesday evenings in season, and you can dance under the stars (but call ahead for the schedule). *✉ North Coast Rd., Apple Bay ☎ 284/495–4212 🌐 www.sebastiansbvi.com.*

Rocking the Bay

Cane Garden Bay is the place to go for live music, with Quito Rymer frequently delighting the crowds at his Quito's Bar and Restaurant. Myett's is also a happening place and has live music nightly in season, while Paradise Club and The Elm Beach Bar host lively local music some nights.

There are no chain hotels or sprawling resorts here—all the places to stay are small and locally owned, even the new high-rise Quito's Luxury Inn. In addition to the handful of properties on the beach, there are plenty of others up on the hillsides that have eye-popping views. The area has plenty of places to eat, with lobster the specialty on many a menu.

Mid Island

Sights

Mount Healthy National Park

NATIONAL/STATE PARK | The remains of an 18th-century sugar plantation can be seen here. The windmill structure, the last one standing in the BVI, has been restored, and you can also see the ruins of a factory with boiling houses, storage areas, stables, a hospital, and many dwellings. It's a nice place to picnic and reflect on the island's history. ⊠ *Ridge Rd., Todman Peak* ⊕ *www.bvitourism. com/mount-healthy-national-park* ⊠ *Free.*

Sage Mountain National Park

NATIONAL/STATE PARK | At 1,716 feet, Sage Mountain is the highest peak in the BVI. From the parking area, a trail leads you in a loop not only to the peak itself (and extraordinary views) but also to a small rain forest that is sometimes shrouded in mist. There are a dozen hiking trails total in the park. Most of the forest was cut down over the centuries for timber, to create pastureland, or for growing sugarcane, cotton, and other crops. In 1964, this 127-acre park was established to preserve what remained. Up here you can see mahogany trees, white cedars, mountain guavas, elephant-ear vines, mamey trees, and giant bullet

woods, plus birds like mountain doves and thrushes. Take a taxi from Road Town or drive up Joe's Hill Road and make a left onto Ridge Road toward Chalwell and Doty villages. The road dead-ends at the park. ⊠ *Ridge Rd., Sage Mountain* ☎ *284/852–3650* ⊕ *www.bvitourism.com* ⊠ *$3.*

East End

Beaches

Lambert Beach

BEACH—SIGHT | Home to a small resort, Lambert Beach is a palm-lined, wide, sandy beach with parking along its steep downhill access road. There are no amenities aside from peace and quiet. Turn at the sign for the Wyndham Lambert Beach Resort. If you miss it, you wind up at Her Majesty's Prison. **Amenities:** food and drink; parking; toilets. **Best for:** solitude; swimming. ⊠ *Lambert Rd., off Ridge Rd., East End.*

Long Bay Beach, Beef Island

BEACH—SIGHT | If this beach wasn't located right next to the airport, it probably would show up on lists of the Caribbean's most beautiful strands. Long Bay on Beef Island has superlative scenery: the beach stretches seemingly forever, and you can catch a glimpse of Little

Did You Know?

Beef Island, on the east end of Tortola, is where you'll find the island's airport. It also has one of the best beaches.

Camanoe and Great Camanoe islands. Just keep your eyes out to sea and not on the runway behind you. If you walk around the bend to the right, you can see little Marina Cay and Scrub Island. Swim out to wherever you see a dark patch for some nice snorkeling. Turn left shortly after crossing the bridge to Beef Island. **Amenities:** food and drink; toilets. **Best for:** snorkeling; swimming. ⊠ *Beef Island Rd.*

 Restaurants

Jeremy's Kitchen

$$ | **AMERICAN** | Situated on Trellis Bay's beachfront, brightly painted Jeremy's Kitchen is the ideal spot to enjoy a slow breakfast or lunch while people-watching. Omelets, croque madame and monsieur sandwiches, and eggs Benedict are breakfast favorites, while wholesome sandwiches and quesadillas round out the lunch and dinner menus. **Known for:** creative sandwiches; laid-back island vibes; beachfront dining. $ *Average main: $13* ⊠ *Trellis Bay* ☎ *284/345–5177* ⊕ *www.jeremyskitchen.com.*

Turtle Restaurant & Bar

$$$ | **ECLECTIC** | If you're touring the island, Turtle is a good place to stop for breakfast, lunch, or dinner with Caribbean-Mediterranean flair, including pizza and pasta dishes, West Indian roti, and ginger Thai lobster. Sitting near the ocean at the Wyndham Lambert Beach Resort, this casually elegant restaurant provides a relaxing respite from the rigors of navigating mountain roads. **Known for:** beachfront location; fusion dining; relaxed elegance. $ *Average main: $30* ⊠ *Wyndham Lambert Beach Resort, Lambert Bay, East End* ☎ *284/495–2877* ⊕ *www.wyndhamhotels.com.*

 Hotels

Wyndham Lambert Beach Resort

$ | **RESORT** | Although this isolated location on the northeast coast puts you far from Road Town, Lambert Bay is one of the island's loveliest stretches of sand and the main reason to recommend this resort. **Pros:** lovely beach; beautiful setting; good restaurant. **Cons:** lacks local flavor; isolated location; need car to get around. $ *Rooms from: $169* ☎ *284/495–2877* ⊕ *www.wyndhamhotels.com* ↪ *67 rooms* ⫶◎⫶ *No meals.*

 Activities

BOATING
BigSexy Boat Charters

BOATING | Name aside, BigSexy specializes in small boat charters for sightseeing and fishing. The private half-day and day tours aboard a 36-foot powerboat start at $400. ☎ *284/544–9141* ⊕ *www.bigsexyboatrentals.com.*

Island Time Power Boat Rentals

BOATING | Island Time rents a small fleet of open sportfishing boats (23 to 30 feet) for $445 to $630 per day, and rigid hull inflatables (RIBS) for $255–$310 per day. ⊠ *Nanny Cay* ☎ *284/346–0356, 284/495–9993* ⊕ *islandtimebvi.com.*

CRICKET

Fans of this sport are fiercely loyal and exuberant. Matches are held at Greenland Field at East End. Check local newspapers or ask at your hotel front desk for information on times and teams.

DIVING AND SNORKELING

Clear waters and numerous reefs afford some wonderful opportunities for underwater exploration. In some spots visibility reaches 100 feet, but colorful reefs teeming with fish are often just a few feet below the sea surface. The BVI's system of marine parks means the underwater life visible through your mask will stay protected.

There are several popular dive spots around the islands, including some new sites arising from the destruction of 2017's Hurricane Irma. The *Willy T* party boat, which sunk in Pirate's Bight off Norman Island, has reopened, while several small planes that wrecked at the BVI airport have been repurposed as the **Sharkplano** site near Great Dog Island. **Alice in Wonderland** is a deep dive south of Ginger Island, with a wall that slopes gently from 15 feet to 100 feet. It's an area overrun with huge mushroom-shape coral, hence its name. Crabs, lobsters, and shimmering fan corals make their homes in the tunnels, ledges, and overhangs of **Blonde Rock,** a pinnacle that goes from 15 feet below the surface to 60 feet deep. It's between Dead Chest and Salt Island. When the currents aren't too strong, **Brewers Bay Pinnacle** (20 to 90 feet down) teems with sea life. At the **Indians,** near Pelican Island, colorful corals decorate canyons and grottoes created by four large, jagged pinnacles that rise 50 feet from the ocean floor. The **Painted Walls** is a shallow dive site where corals and sponges create a kaleidoscope of colors on the walls of four long gullies. It's northeast of Dead Chest.

The *Chikuzen,* sunk northwest of Brewers Bay in 1981, is a 246-foot vessel in 75 feet of water; it's home to thousands of fish, colorful corals, and big rays. In 1867 the **RMS *Rhone,*** a 310-foot royal mail steamer, split in two when it sank in a devastating hurricane. It's so well preserved that it was used as an underwater prop in the movie *The Deep.* You can see the crow's nest and bowsprit, the cargo hold in the bow, and the engine and enormous propeller shaft in the stern. Its four parts are at various depths from 30 to 80 feet. Get yourself some snorkeling gear and hop aboard a dive boat to this wreck near Salt Island (across the channel from Road Town). Every dive outfit in the BVI runs scuba and snorkel tours to this part of the BVI National Parks Trust; if you only

have time for one trip, make it this one. Rates start at around $70 for a one-tank dive and $100 for a two-tank dive.

Your hotel probably has a dive company right on the premises. If not, the staff can recommend one nearby. Using your hotel's dive company makes a trip to the offshore dive and snorkel sites a breeze. Just stroll down to the dock and hop aboard. All dive companies are certified by PADI, the Professional Association of Diving Instructors, which ensures that your instructors are qualified to safely take vacationers diving. The boats are also inspected to make sure they're seaworthy. If you've never dived, try a short introductory dive, often called a resort course, which teaches you enough to get you underwater. In the unlikely event you get a case of the bends, a condition that can happen when you rise to the surface too fast, your dive team will whisk you to the decompression chamber at Schneider Regional Medical Center in nearby St. Thomas.

RECOMMENDED DIVE OPERATORS
Blue Water Divers
SCUBA DIVING | If you're chartering a sailboat, Blue Waters Divers will meet yours at Peter, Salt, Norman, or Cooper Island for a rendezvous dive. Or, meet them at their base, Nanny Cay. The company teaches resort, open-water, rescue, and advanced diving courses, and also makes daily dive trips. Rates include all equipment as well as instruction. Reserve two days in advance. ⊠ *Nanny Cay Marina, Nanny Cay* ☎ *284/494–2847, 284/340–4311* ⊕ *www.bluewaterdiversbvi.com.*

FISHING
Most of the boats that take you deep-sea fishing for bluefish, wahoo, swordfish, and shark leave from nearby St. Thomas, but local anglers like to fish the shallower water for bonefish. A three-quarter-day trip runs about $650, a full day around $850. Wading trips are $325. Information on fishing regulations and charter

operations can be found on the BVI Tourism website. ⊕ *www.bvitourism. com/activities/fishing*

Caribbean Fly Fishing

FISHING | Wade into the waters of Tortola in pursuit of bonefish. ✉ *Nanny Cay Marina, Nanny Cay* ☏ *284/441–7739, 284/499–1590* ⊕ *www.caribflyfishing. com.*

HIKING

Sage Mountain National Park attracts hikers who enjoy the quiet trails that crisscross the island's loftiest peak. There are some lovely views and the chance to see rare plant species that grow only at higher elevations.

SAILING

The BVI are among the world's most popular sailing destinations. They're clustered together and surrounded by calm waters, so it's fairly easy to sail from one anchorage to the next. Most of the Caribbean's biggest sailboat charter companies have operations in Tortola. If you know how to sail, you can charter a bareboat (perhaps for your entire vacation); if you're unschooled, you can hire a boat with a captain. Prices vary depending on the type and size of the boat you wish to charter. In season, a weekly charter runs from $1,500 to $35,000. Book early to make sure you get the boat that fits you best. Most of Tortola's marinas have hotels, which give you a convenient place to spend the nights before and after your charter.

If a day sail to some secluded anchorage is more your spot of tea, the BVI have numerous boats of various sizes and styles that leave from many points around Tortola. Prices start at around $135 per person for a full-day sail, including lunch and snorkeling equipment.

Aristocat Charters

SAILING | This company's 45-foot catamaran, *Sugar Rush*, sets sail daily to Jost Van Dyke, Norman Island, Cooper Island, and other small islands. Day-sailing

charters run from Soper's Hole (Frenchman's Cay), West End, and the Village Cay Marina in Road Town. ☏ *284/499–1249* ⊕ *www.aristocatcharters.com.*

The Catamaran Company

SAILING | The catamarans here come with or without a captain. ✉ *Hodges Creek Marina, East End* ☏ *284/344–3722, 800/262–0308* ⊕ *www.catamarans.com.*

Horizon Yacht Charters BVI

SAILING | Horizon rents monohull and catamaran sailing vessels with bareboat, captain-only, or full-crew options. ✉ *Nanny Cay* ☏ *877/877–1888, 284/494–8787, 877/494–8787* ⊕ *www.horizonyachtcharters.com.*

The Moorings

BOATING | One of the world's best bareboat operations, the Moorings has a large fleet of both monohulls and catamarans. Hire a captain or sail the boat yourself. ✉ *Wickham's Cay II, Road Town* ☏ *888/350–3575* ⊕ *www.moorings.com.*

Regency Yacht Vacations

BOATING | If you prefer a powerboat, call Regency Yacht Vacations. It handles captain and full-crew sail and powerboat charters, as well as sail and powered catamarans and everything up to megayachts. ✉ *Wickham's Cay I, Road Town* ☏ *284/524–7676, 800/524–7676* ⊕ *yachtfleet.com.*

Sunsail

SAILING | A full fleet of boats to charter with or without a captain is available here. ✉ *Wickham's Cay II, Road Town* ☏ *866/514–9778* ⊕ *www.sunsail.com.*

Voyage Charters

SAILING | Voyage has a variety of sailboats for charter, with or without a captain and crew. Their fleet includes an electric-powered 48-foot sailing catamaran. ✉ *Soper's Hole Marina* ☏ *443/569–7007, 888/869–2436* ⊕ *www.voyagecharters.com.*

SURFING AND WINDSURFING

Surfing is big on Tortola's North Shore, particularly when the winter swells come in to Josiah's and Apple bays. Rent surfboards starting at $65 for a full day.

Steady trade winds make windsurfing a breeze. Three of the best spots for sailboarding are Nanny Cay, Slaney Point, and Trellis Bay on Beef Island. Rates for sailboards start at about $25 an hour or $100 for a two-hour lesson.

BVISUPCO

WINDSURFING | This water-sports company rents windsurfing equipment as well as stand-up paddleboards, kayaks, and other water toys. ⊠ *Trellis Bay, Road Town* ☎ *284/346–1981* ⊕ *www.bvisupco.com.*

Island Surf and Sail

WATER SPORTS | Based in Soper's Hole, Island Surf and Sail rents kayaks, paddleboards, SUP boards, windsurfers, surfboards, fishing equipment, snorkeling equipment, various water toys, and—amusingly—guitars. The company also offers private sailing day trips and bareboat charters. ⊠ *Soper's Hole* ☎ *284/345—0123, 284/340–0123* ⊕ *www. bviwatertoys.com.*

TENNIS

Tortola's tennis options range from simple, untended, concrete courts to professionally maintained facilities that host organized tournaments. Some hotels have one or two courts for guests.

Tortola Sports Club

TENNIS | The Tortola Sports Club in Road Town has four lighted hard-court tennis courts as well as indoor squash courts and other recreational facilities, including a pool and gym. Members get priority for court time but visitors can play here on a day pass; courts are more available during the day than in the evenings. ⊠ *Long Bay Rd., Road Town* ☎ *284/494–3457* ⊕ *tortolasportsclub.com.*

Chapter 7

VIRGIN GORDA

7

Updated by
Robert Curley

👁 Sights   🍴 Restaurants   🛏 Hotels   🛍 Shopping   🍸 Nightlife

★★★★☆   ★★★★☆   ★★★★☆   ★★★☆☆   ★★★☆☆

WELCOME TO VIRGIN GORDA

TOP REASONS TO GO

★ **Beautiful beaches:** Virgin Gorda's stunning, white, sandy beaches are the number one reason to visit. Spring Bay Beach and The Baths are highly recommended.

★ **The Baths:** The ever-popular Baths, an area strewn with giant boulders—many as big as houses—draw many visitors during peak hours. Go early or late to enjoy some solitude.

★ **Vacation villas:** Virgin Gorda villas come in all sizes and price ranges. Or, stay at a stunning resort like Rosewood Little Dix Bay.

★ **North Sound:** Even if you aren't a guest at one of North Sound's handful of resorts, you still should visit. Stay for lunch, or just enjoy an afternoon drink.

★ **Solitude:** You don't go to Virgin Gorda for the nightlife (although there is some here and there) or endless activities (but you might want to rent a kayak). This is a spot for relaxation.

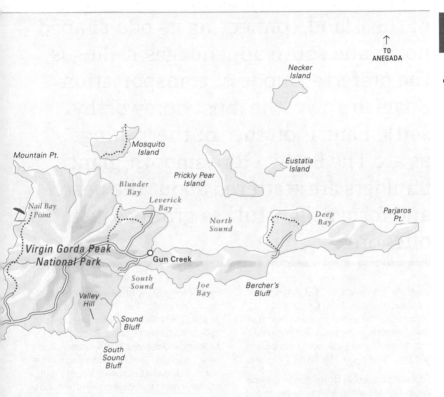

↑
TO
ANEGADA

Necker
Island

Mosquito
Island

Mountain Pt.

Eustatia
Island

Prickly Pear
Island

Blunder
Bay

Leverick
Bay

Nail Bay
Point

North
Sound

Deep
Bay

Parjaros
Pt.

Virgin Gorda Peak
National Park

Gun Creek

South
Sound

Joe
Bay

Bercher's
Bluff

Valley
Hill

Sound
Bluff

South
Sound
Bluff

C a r i b b e a n   S e a

Mountainous and arid Virgin Gorda runs the gamut from laid-back to more laid-back. Its main road sticks to the center of the island, connecting its odd-shaped north and south appendages; sailing is the preferred mode of transportation. Spanish Town, the most noteworthy settlement, is on the southern wing, as are The Baths. Here smooth, giant boulders are scattered about the beach and form delightful sea grottoes just offshore.

Lovely Virgin Gorda, or "Fat Virgin," received its name from Christopher Columbus. The explorer envisioned the island as a reclining pregnant woman, with Virgin Gorda Peak being her belly and the boulders of The Baths her toes.

Compared to other British Virgin Islands, Virgin Gorda runs at a slow pace, and goats still wander across the roads in places like North Sound. But that's changing. Virgin Gorda Yacht Harbour, the center of commerce and activity in Spanish Town, is expanding, and the Oil Nut Bay development has raised the bar on high-end stays on Virgin Gorda along with the return of the luxury Rosewood Little Dix Bay resort. That said, budget travelers can still find modest villas and guesthouses all over the island to while away a few days or more.

Virgin Gorda isn't all that easy to get to, but once you're here you can find enough diversions to make getting out of your chaise longue worthwhile. You can drive from one end of the island to the other in about 20 minutes, but make sure to take time to visit Copper Mine Point to learn about the island's history or to hike up Virgin Gorda Peak to survey the surroundings. At numerous spots with stellar views, the local government has thoughtfully built viewing platforms with adjacent parking. It's worth a stop to snap some photos.

The scenery on the northeastern side of the island is the most dramatic, with a steep road ending at Leverick Bay and Gun Creek in North Sound. Head to the other end of the island for views of the huge boulders that spill over from The Baths into the southwest section of Virgin Gorda. You can find several restaurants dotted around this end of the island.

In truth, though, it's the beaches that make Virgin Gorda special. Stretches of powdery sand fringe aquamarine waters. Popular places like The Baths see hordes of people, but just a quick walk down the road brings you to quieter beaches like Spring Bay. On the other side of Spanish Town you may be the only person at such sandy spots as Savannah Bay.

If shopping's on your agenda, you can find stores in Spanish Town selling items perfect for rounding out your tropical wardrobe or tucking into your suitcase to enjoy when you get home. Additional shops can be found at the Top of the Baths.

Virgin Gorda has very little crime and hardly any frosty attitudes among its more than 4,500 permanent residents. In short, the island provides a welcome respite in a region that's changing rapidly.

Getting Here and Around

AIR

There's no nonstop service from the continental United States to Virgin Gorda. Cape Air flies between Virgin Gorda and San Juan, Puerto Rico. Cape Air and Seaborne offer scheduled flights from St. Thomas to Beef Island, Tortola.

CAR

Virgin Gorda has a small road system, and a single, very steep road links the north and south ends of the island. You will probably need a car to get around for at least a few days of your stay unless you plan on staying put at your resort. If your resort is reachable only by boat, you should rent only for those days when you want to explore the island. Remember that driving is on the *left,* British-style, even though almost all cars are American-made.

The main route sticks resolutely to the center of the island, linking The Baths on the southern tip with Gun Creek and Leverick Bay at North Sound. An alternate route, Nail Bay Road, goes through Nail Bay and connects to the scenic North

Sound Road. Signage is erratic, so come prepared with a map.

CAR RENTAL

Alamo has a rental office in Spanish Town, and you can also rent a car from several local companies like Speedy's and Virgin Gorda Car Rental.

CONTACTS Andy's Car & Jeep Rental. ☎ 284/495–5253. **L&S Jeep Rental.** ☎ 284/495–5297 ⊕ www.landsjeeprental. com. **Mahogany Rentals & Taxi Service.** ☎ 284/495–5469, 284/545–0058 ⊕ www. mahoganycarrentalsbvi.com. **Speedy's Car Rentals.** ☎ 284/495–5240, 284/495–5235, 284/341–7145 mobile ⊕ www.speedy-scarrentals.com.

FERRY

Ferries connect St. Thomas with Virgin Gorda; they leave daily from both Charlotte Amalie and less regularly from Red Hook. Ferries also link St. John and Tortola with Virgin Gorda. Ferries to Virgin Gorda land in Spanish Town. Ferry schedules vary by day, and not all companies make daily trips. The BVI Tourist Board website (⊕ www. bvitourism.com) has links for all the ferry companies, and their individual websites are the best up-to-date sources of information for specific routes and schedules.

■TIP→ **The ferry service from the public dock in Spanish Town can be a tad chaotic. Get there early and ask at the dock whether you're getting on the right boat.**

TAXI

Taxi rates are regulated by the government throughout the BVI, but it's always best to verify the cost of your trip with your driver. It's cheaper to travel in groups; fares are per trip, not per person. The taxi number is also the license plate number. Andy's Rentals & Tours offers service from one end of Virgin Gorda to the other. Mahogany Rentals & Taxi Service provides taxi service all over Virgin Gorda. The Valley Taxi Association, a group of independent taxi operators, also offers service from the ferry dock and around Virgin Gorda.

Essentials

BANKS

Banco Popular is in Virgin Gorda Yacht Harbour.

BEACHES

Although some of the best beaches are reachable only by boat, don't worry if you're a landlubber, because you can find plenty of places to sun and swim. Anybody going to Virgin Gorda must experience swimming or snorkeling among its unique boulder formations, which can be visited at several sites along Lee Road. The most popular is The Baths, but there are several other similar places nearby that are easily reached.

HOTELS

Virgin Gorda's charming hostelries appeal to a select, appreciative clientele; repeat business is extremely high. Those who prefer Sheratons, Marriotts, and the like may feel they get more for their money on other islands, but the peace and pampering offered on Virgin Gorda are priceless to the discriminating traveler. Villas are plentiful on the island and are widely distributed, but most of the resorts are concentrated in three places: The Valley (a catch-all geographic name that encompasses the southwestern part of the island), the Northwest Shore, and the North Sound, which is reachable only by ferry.

Hotel reviews have been shortened. For full information, visit Fodors.com.

PRIVATE VILLAS

Visitors craving seclusion would do well at a villa. Most have full kitchens and maid service. Prices per week in winter run from around $2,000 for a one- or two-bedroom villa, up to $10,000 for a five-room beachfront villa. Rates in summer are substantially less. On Virgin Gorda a villa in the North Sound area means you can pretty much stay put at night unless you want to make the drive on narrow roads. If you opt for a spot near The Baths, it's an easier drive to town.

BOOKING AGENCIES

McLaughlin-Anderson Luxury Villas

The St. Thomas–based McLaughlin–Anderson Luxury Villas represents more than two dozen properties on Virgin Gorda and Tortola. Villas range in size from one bedrooms to five bedrooms, and come with full kitchens, pools, stellar views, and other amenities. The company can hire a chef and stock your kitchen with groceries. Most villas have a seven-night minimum stay during the winter season and a five-night minimum in the off-season. ☎ 340/776–0635, 800/537–6246 ⊕ www.mclaughlinanderson.com.

Villas Virgin Gorda

This management company's dozen-plus properties stretch from The Baths to the Nail Bay area. Several budget properties are included among the pricier offerings. Most houses have private pools, and a few are right on the beach. ☎ 284/540–8002 ⊕ www.villasvirgingorda.com.

Virgin Gorda Villa Rentals

This company's 20-plus properties are all near Leverick Bay Resort and Mahoe Bay, so they are perfect for those who want to be close to activities. Many of the accommodations—from one to six or more bedrooms—have private swimming pools and air-conditioning, at least in the bedrooms. All have full kitchens, are well maintained, and have spectacular views. ⊠ Mahoe Bay ☎ 284/542–4014, 284/542–4011 ⊕ www.vgvirgingordavillarentals.com.

RESTAURANTS

Dining out on Virgin Gorda is a mixed bag, with everything from hamburgers to lobster available; restaurants range from simple to elegant. Most folks opt to have dinner at or near their hotel to avoid driving on Virgin Gorda's twisting roads at night. Hotels that are accessible only by boat will arrange transport in advance upon request from nonguests who wish to dine at their restaurants. Most other independent

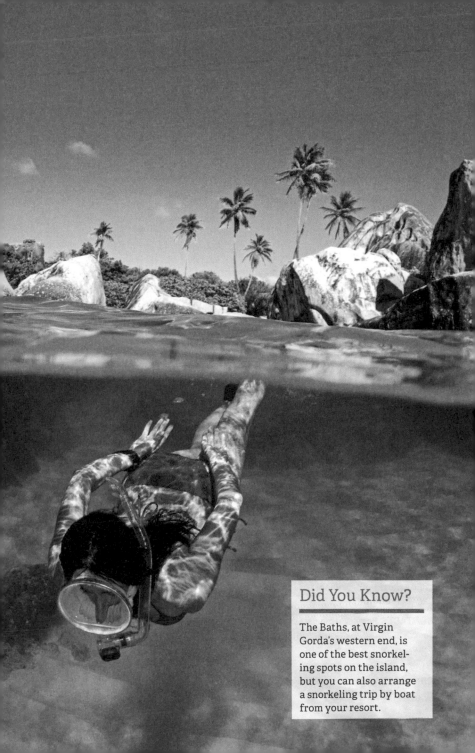

Did You Know?

The Baths, at Virgin Gorda's western end, is one of the best snorkeling spots on the island, but you can also arrange a snorkeling trip by boat from your resort.

restaurants are in The Valley or the vicinity. It's wise to make dinner reservations almost everywhere except at really casual spots.

WHAT IT COSTS in U.S. Dollars			
$	$$	$$$	$$$$
RESTAURANTS			
under $13	$13–$20	$21–$30	over $30
HOTELS			
under $276	$276–$375	$376–$475	over $475

SAFETY
Although crime is rare, use common sense: don't leave your camera on the beach while you take a dip, or your wallet on a hotel dresser when you go for a walk.

SHOPPING
Most boutiques are within hotel complexes or in Spanish Town, but some resorts also have specialty shops.

SIGHTS
Virgin Gorda's most popular attractions are those provided by Mother Nature. Beautiful beaches, crystal clear water, and stellar views are around nearly every bend in the road. That said, remember to get a taste of the island's past at Copper Mine Point.

TOUR OPTIONS
Romney Associates/Travel Plan Tours, Virgin Gorda Tours Association, Speedy's, and Valley Taxi Association can arrange island tours, boat tours, snorkeling and scuba-diving trips, dolphin swims, and yacht charters.

CONTACTS Romney Associates/Travel Plan Tours. ☎ 284/494–4000 ⊕ romascogroup. com.

VISITOR INFORMATION
CONTACTS Virgin Gorda BVI Tourist Board. ☎ 284/852–6020 ⊕ www.bvitourism.com.

The Valley

Sights

★ The Baths National Park
BEACH—SIGHT | FAMILY | At Virgin Gorda's most celebrated sight, giant boulders are scattered about the beach and in the water. Some are almost as large as houses and form remarkable grottoes. Climb between these rocks to swim in the many placid pools. Early morning and late afternoon are the best times to visit if you want to avoid crowds. If it's privacy you crave, follow the shore northward to quieter bays—Spring Bay, the Crawl, Little Trunk, and Valley Trunk—or head south to Devil's Bay. ⊠ *Off Tower Rd., Spanish Town* ☎ *284/494-2069* ⊕ *www. bvitourism.com* ⊠ *$3.*

Copper Mine National Park
HISTORIC SITE | A tall stone shaft silhouetted against the sky, a small stone structure that overlooks the sea, and a deep cistern are part of what was once a copper mine, now in ruins. Established 400 years ago, it was worked first by the Spanish, then by the English, until the early 20th century. ⊠ *Copper Mine Rd., Spanish Town* ⊠ *Free.*

Spanish Town
TOWN | Virgin Gorda's peaceful main settlement, on the island's southern wing, is so tiny that it barely qualifies as a town at all. Also known as "The Valley," Spanish Town has a marina, some shops, a few restaurants and bars, and a couple of car-rental agencies. Just north of town is the ferry slip. At the Virgin Gorda Yacht Harbour you can stroll along the dock, but some facilities are under repair. ⊠ *Spanish Town.*

Beaches

The Baths Beach
BEACH—SIGHT | The most popular tourist destination in the BVI, this stunning maze of huge granite boulders extending into the sea is usually crowded

The Baths are filled with grottoes and hidden pools.

midday with day-trippers, especially when cruise ships are in port (come early in the morning or toward evening for more solitude). The snorkeling is good, and you're likely to see a wide variety of fish. Public bathrooms and a handful of bars and shops are close to the water and at the start of the path that leads to the beach. Divers also come to The Baths from charter boats anchored just offshore; use the swim line to get to shore since boats no longer launch dinghies to transport guests back and forth. Lockers are available to keep belongings safe. **Amenities:** food and drink; parking; toilets. **Best for:** snorkeling; swimming. ✉ *Tower Rd., about 1 mile (1½ km) west of Spanish Town ferry dock, Spanish Town* ☎ *284/494–2069* ⊕ *www.bvitourism.com* 🎫 *$3.*

Spring Bay Beach

BEACH—SIGHT | This national park beach gets much less traffic than the nearby Baths, and has similarly large, imposing boulders that create interesting grottoes for swimming. Plus, there's the added benefit of no admission fee. The snorkeling is excellent, and the grounds include swings and picnic tables. Guavaberry Spring Bay Vacation Homes has villas and cottages right near the beach. **Amenities:** none. **Best for:** snorkeling; swimming. ✉ *Spanish Town* ☎ *284/346–2779* ⊕ *www.bvitourism.com* 🎫 *Free.*

🍴 Restaurants

Bath and Turtle

$$ | ECLECTIC | Co-located with the more upscale Chez Bamboo, this informal tavern with friendly staff is a good spot to sit back and relax for breakfast or lunch. Well-stuffed sandwiches, burgers, homemade pizzas, pasta dishes, and daily specials such as conch soup round out the casual menu. **Known for:** live music; bar scene; pizza. $ *Average main: $19* ✉ *Spanish Town* ☎ *284/545–1861* ⊕ *www.bathandturtle.com.*

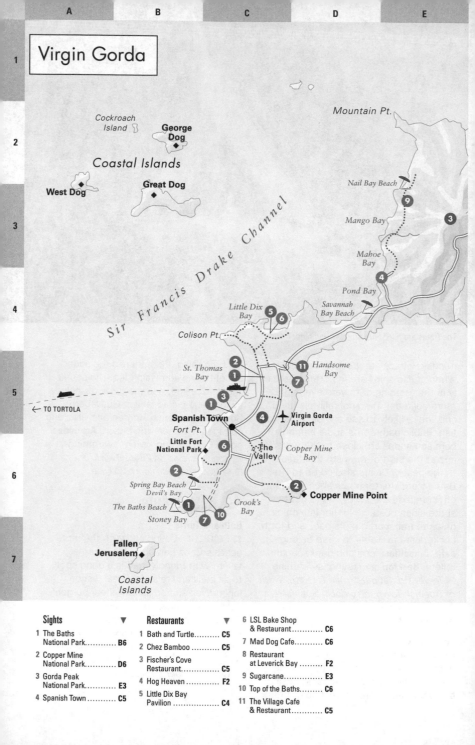

Virgin Gorda

Cockroach Island

George Dog

Coastal Islands

West Dog

Great Dog

Mountain Pt.

Nail Bay Beach

9

3

Mango Bay

Mahoe Bay

Sir Francis Drake Channel

4

Pond Bay

Savannah Bay Beach

Little Dix Bay

5 **6**

Colison Pt.

2

St. Thomas Bay

1

11 *Handsome Bay*

7

← TO TORTOLA

1 **3**

4 **Virgin Gorda Airport**

Spanish Town

Fort Pt.

Little Fort National Park

6

The Valley

Copper Mine Bay

2

Spring Bay Beach
Devil's Bay

1

The Baths Beach

7 **10**

Crook's Bay

2 **Copper Mine Point**

Stoney Bay

Fallen Jerusalem

Coastal Islands

F   G   H   I   J

↑ TO NECKER ISLAND

↑ TO ANEGADA

1

Mosquito Island

Blunder Bay

Prickly Pear Island

Eustatia Island

2

8 **3** Leverick Bay

4

North Sound

Deep Bay

Parjaros Pt.

5

3

Gun Creek

South Sound

Joe Bay

Bercher's Bluff

Valley Hill

Sound Bluff

4

South Sound Bluff

Caribbean Sea

5

KEY

6

1 Sights

1 Restaurants

1 Hotels

🚢 Cruise Ship Terminal

⤲ Beaches

🚢 Ferry

7

0   1 mi

0   1 km

Hotels ▼

1 Fischer's Cove Beach Hotel **C5**

2 Guavaberry Spring Bay Vacation Homes **B6**

3 Leverick Bay Resort and Marina **G2**

4 Mango Bay Resort...... **E4**

5 Oil Nut Bay **J3**

6 Rosewood Little Dix Bay **C4**

7 Virgin Gorda Village **C5**

Spring Bay has boulders similar to those at The Baths.

Chez Bamboo

$$$$ | ECLECTIC | This pleasant little hideaway has candles in the dining room and on the patio creating a mellow atmosphere where you can enjoy a bowl of lobster bisque, something from the tapas menu, or one of the Asian-inspired specialties, such as lobster curry. For dessert, try the chocolate cake or crème brûlée. **Known for:** island chic; gardenlike setting; tapas. ⑤ *Average main: $34* ✉ *Lee Rd., Spanish Town* ☎ *284/545–1861* ⊕ *www.chezbamboo.com.*

Fischer's Cove Restaurant

$$$ | CARIBBEAN | Dine seaside at this alfresco restaurant that's open to the breezes. If pumpkin soup is on the menu, give it a try for a true taste of the Caribbean. **Known for:** friendly staff; great views; local cuisine like the Saturday-night pig roast. ⑤ *Average main: $30* ✉ *Lee Rd., Spanish Town* ☎ *284/495–5253* ⊕ *www.fischerscove.com.*

★ Little Dix Bay Pavilion

$$$$ | CARIBBEAN | For an elegant evening, you can't do better than this—the candlelight in the open-air pavilion is enchanting, the always-changing menu sophisticated, the service attentive. Superbly prepared seafood, meat, and vegetarian entrées, most drawing upon Caribbean cooking traditions, are a hit with locals and visitors alike. **Known for:** elegant atmosphere; fine Caribbean-influenced cuisine; excellent service. ⑤ *Average main: $45* ✉ *Little Dix Bay Resort, off Little Rd., Spanish Town* ☎ *284/495–5555* ⊕ *www.littledixbay.com.*

LSL Bake Shop & Restaurant

$$ | ECLECTIC | Along the road to The Baths, this small restaurant with pedestrian decor is a local favorite for fresh bread, cakes and pastries, and informal dining. You can always find fresh fish on the menu, accompanied by traditional local sides like peas and rice. **Known for:** local flavors; fresh fish; cakes. ⑤ *Average main: $16* ✉ *Tower Rd., Spanish*

Town ☎ 284/495–5151, 284/340–5151, 284/495–6151 ⊕ www.lslbakeshop. com.

Mad Dog Cafe
$ | **AMERICAN** | **FAMILY** | Piña coladas are *the* thing at this breezy bar just outside the entrance to The Baths. The menu includes great triple-decker sandwiches, BLTs, and hot dogs. **Known for:** piña coladas; sandwiches; quick bites. Ⓢ *Average main: $9* ✉ *The Baths, Tower Rd., Spanish Town* ☎ *284/495–5830* ⊗ *No dinner.*

Top of the Baths
$$$ | **ECLECTIC** | **FAMILY** | At the entrance to The Baths, this popular restaurant has tables on an outdoor terrace or in an open-air pavilion; all have stunning views of the Sir Francis Drake Channel. The restaurant starts serving at 8 am for breakfast; for lunch, hamburgers, coconut chicken sandwiches, and fish-and-chips are among the offerings. **Known for:** great location; stunning views; key lime pie. Ⓢ *Average main: $23* ✉ *Spanish Town* ☎ *284/495–5497* ⊕ *topofthebaths.com.*

The Village Cafe & Restaurant
$$$ | **ECLECTIC** | Meals are served poolside under the shade of umbrellas at this casual eatery at the Virgin Gorda Village condo complex. The lunch menu includes salads, pizzas, wraps, rotis, and burgers, but the lobster tacos are a must-have. **Known for:** lobster tacos; casual lunch; fish-and-chips with Cajun spices. Ⓢ *Average main: $24* ✉ *Virgin Gorda Village, North Sound Rd., Spanish Town* ☎ *284/343–8092, 284/545–0283, 284/495–5350* ⊕ *www.virgingordavillage. com* ⊗ *Closed Mon.*

Hotels

Fischer's Cove Beach Hotel
$ | **RESORT** | The rooms are modest, the furniture is discount-store-style, and the walls are thin, but you can't beat the location right on the beach and within walking distance of Spanish Town's shops and restaurants. **Pros:** beachfront location; budget price; good restaurant. **Cons:** very basic units; thin walls; no air-conditioning in some rooms. Ⓢ *Rooms from: $175* ✉ *Lee Rd., Spanish Town* ☎ *284/495–5253* ⊕ *www.fischerscove. com* ⤴ *14 units* ⏐⏐ *No meals.*

Guavaberry Spring Bay Vacation Homes
$$ | **RENTAL** | Rambling back from the beach, these hexagonal one- and two-bedroom villas give you all the comforts of home—and that striking boulder-fringed beach is just minutes away. **Pros:** short walk to The Baths (and excellent snorkeling); easy drive to town; great beaches nearby. **Cons:** few amenities; older property; basic decor. Ⓢ *Rooms from: $303* ✉ *Tower Rd., Spanish Town* ☎ *284/544–7186* ⊕ *www. guavaberryspringbay.com* ▤ *No credit cards* ⤴ *19 units* ⏐⏐ *No meals.*

★ Rosewood Little Dix Bay
$$$$ | **RESORT** | **FAMILY** | This laid-back luxury resort offers a gorgeous crescent of sand, plenty of activities, and good restaurants. **Pros:** convenient location; lovely grounds; near many restaurants. **Cons:** expensive; very spread out; insular though not isolated. Ⓢ *Rooms from: $850* ✉ *Off Little Rd., Spanish Town* ☎ *284/495–5555, 888/767–3966* ⊕ *www.littledixbay.com* ⤴ *80 rooms* ⏐⏐ *No meals.*

Virgin Gorda Village
$ | **RENTAL** | All the condos in this upscale complex a few minutes' drive from Spanish Town have at least partial ocean views. **Pros:** close to Spanish Town; lovely pool; recently built units. **Cons:** no beach; on a busy street; noisy roosters nearby. Ⓢ *Rooms from: $265* ✉ *North Sound Rd., Spanish Town* ☎ *284/495–5544* ⊕ *www.virgingordavillage.com* ⤴ *30 condos* ⏐⏐ *No meals.*

Rosewood Little Dix Bay resort has two pools that overlook the beach.

Nightlife

Pick up a free copy of the *Limin' Times*—available at most resorts and restaurants—for the most current local entertainment schedule.

Bath and Turtle/Chez Bamboo

BARS/PUBS | During high season, the Bath and Turtle (and the adjacent Chez Bamboo) is one of the liveliest spots on Virgin Gorda, hosting island bands several nights a week. ⊠ *Lee Rd., Spanish Town* ☎ *284/495–5752* ⊕ *www.bathturtle.com.*

Little Dix Bay

BARS/PUBS | The Rum Room at Little Dix Bay presents live entertainment several nights a week in season. ⊠ *Little Dix Bay Resort, Little Rd., Spanish Town* ☎ *284/495–5555* ⊕ *www.littledixbay. com.*

Shopping

FOOD

RiteWay Cash & Carry

WINE/SPIRITS | The store isn't much to look at, inside or out, but it has the best wine prices on Virgin Gorda, along with the usual basic supermarket items. ⊠ *Lee Rd., Spanish Town* ☎ *284/347–1200* ⊕ *www.rtwbvi.com.*

Rosy's Supermarket

FOOD/CANDY | This store carries the basics plus an interesting selection of ready-to-cook meals, such as whole seasoned chickens. ⊠ *Rhymer Rd., Spanish Town* ☎ *284/495–5245* ⊕ *www.rosysvg.com.*

GIFTS

The Beach House at Little Dix Bay Resort

CLOTHING | This shop has the latest in resort wear for men and women, as well as jewelry, books, housewares, and expensive T-shirts. ⊠ *Little Dix Bay Resort, Little Rd., Spanish Town* ☎ *284/495–5555* ⊕ *www.littledixbay.com.*

Northwest Shore

 Sights

Gorda Peak National Park

NATIONAL/STATE PARK | There are two trails at this 254-acre park, which contains the island's highest point, at 1,359 feet. Signs on North Sound Road mark both entrances. It's a short but steep 30- to 50-minute hike (depending on which trail you take) through a rare Caribbean dry forest to a small clearing, where you can enjoy some high-level views. ⊠ *North Sound Rd., Gorda Peak* ⊕ *www.bvinpt. org* ⊠ *Free.*

Beaches

Fallen Jerusalem Island and the Dog Islands

BEACH—SIGHT | You can easily reach these quaintly named islands by boat, which you can rent in either Tortola or Virgin Gorda. They're all part of the National Parks Trust of the Virgin Islands, and their seductive beaches and unparalleled snorkeling display the BVI at their beachcombing, hedonistic best. **Amenities:** none. **Best for:** solitude; snorkeling. ⊕ *www.bvitourism.com* ⊠ *Free.*

Nail Bay Beach

BEACH—SIGHT | At the island's north tip, the three beaches on Nail Bay are ideal for snorkeling. Mountain Trunk Bay is perfect for beginners, and Nail Bay and Long Bay beaches have coral caverns just offshore. **Amenities:** none. **Best for:** snorkeling; swimming. ⊠ *Nail Bay Resort, off Plum Tree Bay Rd., Nail Bay* ⊠ *Free.*

Savannah Bay Beach

BEACH—SIGHT | This is a wonderfully private beach close to Spanish Town. It may not always be completely deserted, but you can find a spot to yourself on this long stretch of soft white sand. Bring your own mask, fins, and snorkel, as there are no facilities. Villas are available through rental property agencies. The view from above is a photographer's

Carnival on Virgin Gorda

Carnival coincides with Easter on Virgin Gorda. The celebration is smaller than those you'll find on more heavily touristed islands, but people visiting family and friends do come from around the Caribbean. If you're heading to Virgin Gorda during the three-day annual event, make sure you've booked your room well in advance.

delight. **Amenities:** none. **Best for:** solitude; snorkeling; swimming. ⊠ *Off N. Sound Rd., ¾ mile (1¼ km) east of Spanish Town ferry dock, Savannah Bay* ⊠ *Free.*

 Restaurants

Sugarcane

$$$ | **CARIBBEAN** | Spectacular island views round out the romantic atmosphere here, creating the perfect setting for an intimate dinner of fresh local fish prepared in a variety of ways. The conch fritters are the stars on the menu—they're light, fluffy, nicely seasoned, and stuffed with conch. **Known for:** outdoor dining; romantic ambience; jerk chicken. ⑤ *Average main: $30* ⊠ *Nail Bay Sports Club, Off Plum Tree Bay Rd., Nail Bay* ☎ *284/545–8640* ⊕ *www.sugarcane.vg.*

Hotels

Mango Bay Resort

$ | **RENTAL** | Facing west to capture sunsets, this collection of contemporary condos and villas will make you feel right at home. **Pros:** nice beach; lively location an easy drive from restaurants; homes come with floats, kayaks, and snorkeling equipment. **Cons:** drab decor; some units have lackluster views; need car to get around. ⑤ *Rooms from: $195* ⊠ *Plum*

Sailing is a popular pastime on Virgin Gorda.

Tree Bay Rd., Pond Bay ☎ *284/340–9500*
⊕ *www.mangobayresort.com* ⇥ *22 units*
🍽 *No meals.*

North Sound

Restaurants

★ Hog Heaven

$ | BARBECUE | FAMILY | The million-dollar
view is the thing at this simple wooden
restaurant perched on a hillside overlooking the North Sound. If the scenery alone
isn't enough to make you feel as if you're
ready to be singing with the angels, this
barbecue joint's succulent pork, local
fish, and conch in butter sauce will help.
Known for: spectacular views; barbecue;
rum drinks. $ *Average main: $12* ⊠ *North
Sound* ☎ *284/547–5964.*

Restaurant at Leverick Bay

$$$$ | ECLECTIC | The laid-back menu at
this marina restaurant draws cruise ship
passengers on tour as well as hotel
guests, locals, and mariners. The upscale

restaurant serves dinner with dishes that
feature wild salmon and Anegada lobster.
Known for: Friday-night beach barbecue party; happy hour with live music;
Anegada lobster. $ *Average main: $38*
⊠ *Leverick Bay Resort & Marina, Leverick
Bay Rd., Leverick Bay* ☎ *284/541–8879,
284/346–7241, 284/340–3005* ⊕ *www.
leverickbayvg.com* ⊙ *Closed Fri.*

Hotels

This area of Tortola was particularly hard
hit by the hurricane season of 2017
followed by closures from COVID-19 in
2020. The good news? Well-loved **Bitter
End Yacht Club** and **Saba Rock Resort** have
plans to reopen after renovations. In
the meantime, there are other worthy
options to consider here, including the
new Oil Nut Bay.

Leverick Bay Resort and Marina

$ | RESORT | With its colorful buildings
and bustling marina, Leverick Bay is
a good choice for visitors who want
easy access to water-sports activities.

Getting Your Goat

Roaming livestock is a fact of life in the tropics, particularly in less-developed places like Virgin Gorda. Indeed, residents who leave their car windows open occasionally return to find a freshly laid egg on the front seat. If you have time to sit a spell at places like Virgin Gorda Yacht Harbour, you might see a mother hen followed by a string of little ones.

While crowing roosters can rouse annoyingly early, grazing goats pose traffic hazards. Some have owners, but many of them wander off to forage for food. Be particularly careful when you're driving around bends or over the top of hills. You might find a herd of goats, or maybe a sheep or two, camped out in the middle of the road. Sound your horn and be patient. They'll move in their own time.

And should you happen to see a vendor selling local dishes, the relatives of those goats and chickens are probably bubbling in the pot.

7

Virgin Gorda NORTH SOUND

Pros: fun location; good restaurant; small grocery store. **Cons:** small beach; no laundry in units; 15-minute drive to town; basic rooms. ⑤ *Rooms from: $237* ✉ *Off Leverick Bay Rd., Leverick Bay* ☎ *284/542–4011, 284/542–4014* ⊕ *www.leverickbayvg.com* ⤴ *13 rooms* ❍ *No meals.*

Oil Nut Bay

$$$$ | RENTAL | Part luxury resort and part villa community, Oil Nut Bay has rooms ranging from one-bedroom suites to six-bedroom villas, most with private swimming pools and spectacular views of Virgin Gorda's east end and the Caribbean Sea. Activities available on property include diving, water sports, tennis, and hiking. **Pros:** luxurious accommodations; ample amenities including spa and restaurants; fantastic views. **Cons:** expensive; far from other attractions; only accessible by boat or helicopter. ⑤ *Rooms from: $550* ☎ *284/393–1000, 800/761–0377* ⊕ *www.oilnutbay.com* ⤴ *18 villas* ❍ *No meals.*

Nightlife

Restaurant at Leverick Bay

BARS/PUBS | This resort's main restaurant hosts bands several nights a week, including steel pan music on Monday, and things really get going at the Friday night beach barbecue. Call for lineup. ✉ *Leverick Bay Resort & Marina, Leverick Bay Rd., Leverick Bay* ☎ *284/541–8879, 284/346–7241, 284/340–3005* ⊕ *www. leverickbayvg.com.*

Shopping

CLOTHING
Pusser's Gift Shop

CLOTHING | A trademark line of sportswear, rum products, and gift items is available here. ✉ *Leverick Bay Marina, Leverick Bay Rd., Leverick Bay* ☎ *284/495–5423, 284/495–6952* ⊕ *www. pussers.com.*

FOOD

Buck's Food Market

FOOD/CANDY | Buck's is the closest to a full-service supermarket the island offers, and has everything from an in-store bakery and deli to fresh fish and produce departments. ✉ *North Sound Rd., Spanish Town* ☎ *284/495–5423* ⊕ *www. bucksmarkets.com.*

Chef's Pantry

FOOD/CANDY | This store has the fixings for an impromptu party in your villa or on your boat—fresh seafood, specialty meats, imported cheeses, daily baked breads and pastries, and an impressive wine and spirits selection. ✉ *Leverick Bay Marina, Leverick Bay Rd., Leverick Bay* ☎ *284/344–1621* ⊕ *www.leverickbayvg. com.*

Activities

DIVING AND SNORKELING

Where you go snorkeling and what company you pick depends on where you're staying. Many hotels have on-site dive outfitters, but if yours doesn't, one won't be far away. If your hotel does have a dive operation, just stroll down to the dock and hop aboard—no need to drive anywhere. The dive companies are all certified by PADI. Costs vary, but count on paying about $75 for a one-tank dive and $110 for a two-tank dive. All dive operators offer introductory courses as well as certification and advanced courses. Should you get an attack of the bends, which can happen when you ascend too rapidly, the nearest decompression chamber is at Schneider Regional Medical Center in St. Thomas.

There are some terrific snorkel and dive sites off Virgin Gorda, including areas around The Baths, the North Sound, and the Dogs. The BVI Art Reef features a sculpture of a giant kraken engulfing the sunken hull of a historic U.S. Navy ship. The Chimney at Great Dog Island has a coral archway and canyon covered with a wide variety of sponges. At Joe's Cave, an underwater cavern on West Dog Island, huge groupers, eagle rays, and other colorful fish accompany divers as they swim. At some sites you can see 100 feet down, but snorkelers and divers who don't want to go that deep will find plenty to look at just below the surface.

Dive BVI

SCUBA DIVING | In addition to day trips, Dive BVI also offers expert instruction and certification. The Yacht Harbour location is housed in a shipping container. ✉ *Virgin Gorda Yacht Harbour, Lee Rd., Spanish Town* ☎ *284/541–9818* ⊕ *www. divebvi.com.*

Sunchaser Scuba

SCUBA DIVING | Resort, advanced, and rescue courses are all available here along with dive charters to northern BVI sites, the Dog Islands, and other destinations—all 15 to 45 minutes away. ✉ *North Sound* ☎ *284/344–2766* ⊕ *www.sunchaserscuba.com.*

SAILING AND BOATING

The BVI waters are calm and terrific places to learn to sail. You can also rent sea kayaks, waterskiing equipment, dinghies, and powerboats, or take a parasailing trip.

Double "D" Charters

BOATING | If you just want to sit back, relax, and let the captain take the helm, choose a sailing or power yacht from Double "D" Charters. Rates run from $300 for a day trip. Private full-day cruises or sails for up to eight people run from $1,100. ✉ *Virgin Gorda Yacht Harbour, Lee Rd., Spanish Town* ☎ *284/499–2479* ⊕ *www.doubledbvi.com.*

WATER SPORTS

Blue Rush Water Sports

WATER SPORTS | This company rents a variety of fun water toys, including flyboards, Jet Skis, clear-bottomed kayaks, Hobie Cats, and stand-up paddleboards. ✉ *Leverick Bay Marina, North Sound* ☎ *284/499–7515* ⊕ *www.bluerushwatersports.com.*

Chapter 8

OTHER BRITISH VIRGIN ISLANDS

8

Updated by
Robert Curley

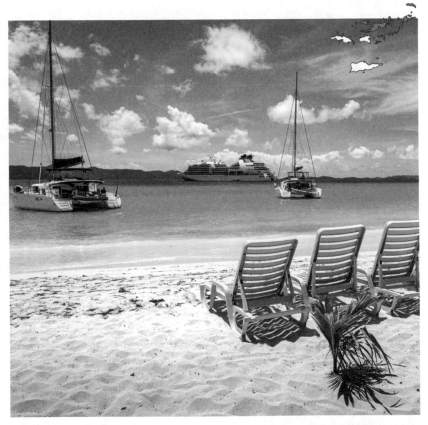

👁 Sights	🍴 Restaurants	🛏 Hotels	🛍 Shopping	🍸 Nightlife
★★★★★	★★★★☆	★★★★★	★★★☆☆	★★★★☆

WELCOME TO THE OTHER BRITISH VIRGIN ISLANDS

TOP REASONS TO GO

★ **Snorkeling and diving in Anegada:** The wrecks and reefs draw divers from all over the world to this beautiful, beach-fringed island.

★ **Barhopping in Jost Van Dyke:** The BVI's nightlife (and day drinking) capital is the place to go, especially for Foxy's Halloween and New Year's parties. The Soggy Dollar and Foxy's Tamarind are favorites.

★ **Communing with nature on Guana Island:** This private island resort has a world-famous conservation program and extensive hiking trails through rain forests and to secluded beaches.

★ **Turning back the clock at Cooper Island:** Although it's been updated in recent years with a rum bar and brewery, a stay here is like visiting the old Caribbean, and that's exactly how guests want it.

★ **Sailing the BVI:** Pick up a charter yacht in Tortola and enjoy a variety of experiences throughout the 50-some islands that make up the BVI.

West End Pt. Bones Bight Red Pond Loblolly Bay
Table Bay
Flamingo Pond The Settlement Budrock Pond
Lower Bay White Bay
Anegada (15 miles north of Necker Is.) Horse Shoe Reef

OCEAN

Necker Island
Prickly Pear Island
Mosquito Island George Dog Eustatia Island
Long Pt. Towing Pt. Great Camanoe Cockroach Island North Sound
Guana Island North Bay North Bay West Dog Great Dog Long Bay Virgin Gorda Peak Berchers Bay
Little Camanoe Kitto Ghut **Scrub Island** Pond Bay South Sound
Trunk Bay Monkey Pt. Josiah's Bay Marina Cay Handsome Bay VIRGIN GORDA
East End **Beef Island International Airport** Spanish Town **Virgin Gorda Airport**
ROAD TOWN Fort Shirley Fat Hogs Bay Beef Island Copper Mine Pt. Anegada Passage
Road Harbour Sir Francis Drake Channel Buck Island Fallen Jerusalem
TORTOLA Broken Jerusalem
Manchioneel Bay Quart-a-Nancy Pt. Round Rock
Great Harbour Dead Man's Bay Dead Chest South Bay Ginger Island
Rock Hole Salt Island **Cooper Island** Markoe Pt.
Pelican Island White Bay Salt Island Bluff
Privateer Bay Big Reef Bay **Peter Island**
Money Bay Peter Island Bluff
Norman Island

Caribbean Sea

Tortola and Virgin Gorda are the largest—and most visited—of the British Virgin Islands, but the chain is made up of 50-some islands and cays, many of them small and uninhabited. Of these outlying islands, Jost Van Dyke and Anegada get the lion's share of visitors, but several other smaller islands have notable resorts.

Anegada is most popular with snorkelers, sailors, and those looking to escape the modest crowds of the BVI, while Jost Van Dyke attracts partiers to its lively beach bars, along with a smaller contingent of visitors who spend a few days. Among the other islands, Guana, Necker, and Scrub islands are luxe private-island resorts, while Cooper Island is a bit more down-to-earth in terms of price. Norman Island is uninhabited, but it does have a restaurant at Pirate's Bight and a floating bar on a ship moored off its coast.

Most of these islands are linked to Tortola by ferry. Some can be day-trip destinations (Jost Van Dyke, Anegada, and Norman Island are all popular with day-trippers), and Cooper Island attracts many charter boats that moor for the night. Guana has regular ferry service for guests; Necker remains completely private.

Getting Here and Around

You can fly to Anegada on a charter flight (affordable if you are traveling with a group), but all the other islands are reachable only by boat (or perhaps helicopter if

you are visiting Necker Island). Anegada has daily ferry service from Tortola (three times a week from Road Town and four times a week from Trellis Bay). Both services make stops in Virgin Gorda. Jost Van Dyke has regularly scheduled ferry service from Tortola, St. John, and St. Thomas. You can rent a jeep on Anegada, and many people do, especially if they are staying for several days. It's possible to rent a car or jeep in Jost Van Dyke, but it's not really necessary.

CAR
You can rent a car or jeep on either Anegada or Jost Van Dyke. This may make sense in Anegada (which also offers Mini Moke rentals), where you might want to explore a variety of different beaches to maximize your snorkeling opportunities. However, in Jost Van Dyke, it's often just as easy to take a taxi or walk. On either island, both rentals and gas are expensive, so be sure to make room for those costs in your vacation budget.

ANEGADA
D.W. Jeep Rentals
Dean Wheatley can rent you a jeep for $65 per day. ⊠ *The Settlement* ☎ *284/495–9677.*

JOST VAN DYKE
Paradise Jeep Rentals

TOUR—SPORTS | Paradise Jeep Rentals offers the ideal vehicles to tackle Jost Van Dyke's steep, winding roads. Even though Jost is a relatively small island, you really need to be in shape to walk from one bay to the next. This outfit rents two-door Suzuki Jimmys for $65 per day, four-door Grand Vitaras for $75, and eight-seat Kia Mojaves for $90. Discounts are available for rentals of six or more days. It's next to the fire station in Great Harbour. Reservations are a must. ⊠ *Great Harbour* ☎ *284/547–1040.*

Essentials

ABOUT THE HOTELS AND RESTAURANTS

Both Anegada and Jost Van Dyke offer a choice of resorts and independent restaurants and bars; however, true luxury is in short supply. Some of the other smaller islands in the BVI are private and have a single resort, including the luxe choices Necker Scrub, and Guana islands, as well as the more modest Cooper Island.

Hotel reviews have been shortened. For full information, visit Fodors.com.

BANKS AND ATMS

Be sure to take cash if you travel to the smaller islands in the BVI. None has an ATM or a bank, though most resorts and some stores take credit cards.

WHAT IT COSTS in U.S. Dollars

	$	$$	$$$	$$$$
RESTAURANTS				
	under $13	$13–$20	$21–$30	over $30
HOTELS				
	under $276	$276–$375	$376–$475	over $475

Jost Van Dyke

Named after an early Dutch settler, Jost Van Dyke is a small island northwest of Tortola and is *truly* a place to get away from it all. Mountainous and lush, the 4-mile-long (6½-km-long) island—with fewer than 300 full-time residents—has one tiny resort, some rental cottages and villas, a campground, a couple dozen cars, and a single road. There are no banks or ATMs on the island, and many restaurants and shops accept only cash. Life definitely rolls along on "island time," especially during the off-season from August to November, when finding a restaurant open for dinner can be a challenge. Electricity came to Jost in the 1990s, and water conservation is encouraged, as the primary sources are rainwater collected in basementlike cisterns and desalinized seawater. Jost is one of the Caribbean's most popular anchorages, and there is a disproportionately large number of informal bars and restaurants, which have helped earn Jost its reputation as the "party island" of the BVI.

GETTING HERE AND AROUND

The only way to get to Jost Van Dyke is by ferry or private boat. Day-sail operators, both in the USVI and the BVI, take guests here daily, and there are regularly scheduled ferries from West End, Tortola (25 minutes); St. John (30 minutes); and St. Thomas (60 minutes, via St. John). Ferries from Tortola run several times daily from West End; the St. Thomas/St. John ferry runs generally just once a day, six days per week. Always check the schedules, as they change. Once on the ground, you can walk most everywhere you might need to go, but you can also hire a taxi driver if you want to avoid some steep uphills on foot.

8

Other British Virgin Islands JOST VAN DYKE

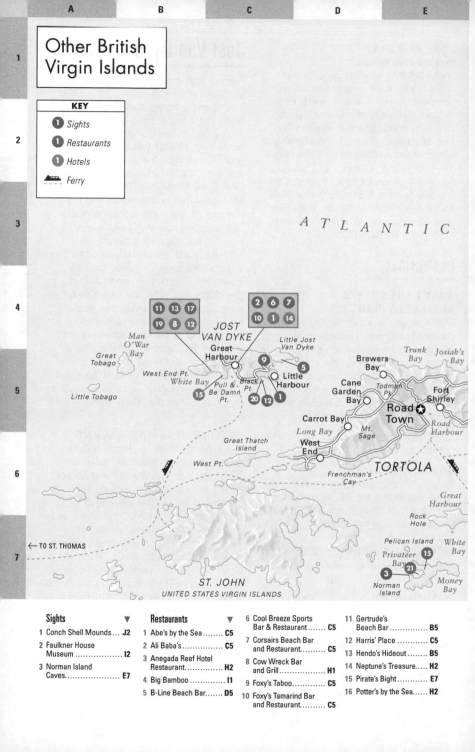

Other British Virgin Islands

KEY
- **1** Sights
- **1** Restaurants
- **1** Hotels
- Ferry

A T L A N T I C

11 13 17
19 8 12

2 6 7
10 1 14

JOST VAN DYKE

Man O'War Bay

Great Tobago

Great Harbour

West End Pt.

White Bay

9

Pull & Be Damn Pt.

Black Pt.

Little Jost Van Dyke

5

Little Harbour

Trunk Bay

Josiah's Bay

Brewers Bay

Cane Garden Bay

Todman Pk.

Fort Shirley

Road Town ★

15

Little Tobago

20 12 1

Carrot Bay

Long Bay

Mt. Sage

Road Harbour

Great Thatch Island

West End

TORTOLA

West Pt.

Frenchman's Cay

Great Harbour

Rock Hole

← TO ST. THOMAS

Pelican Island

White Bay

Privateer Bay

15

3 21

Money Bay

ST. JOHN
UNITED STATES VIRGIN ISLANDS

Norman Island

Sights ▼

1 Conch Shell Mounds... **J2**

2 Faulkner House Museum **I2**

3 Norman Island Caves.................... **E7**

Restaurants ▼

1 Abe's by the Sea........ **C5**

2 Ali Baba's **C5**

3 Anegada Reef Hotel Restaurant.............. **H2**

4 Big Bamboo **I1**

5 B-Line Beach Bar....... **D5**

6 Cool Breeze Sports Bar & Restaurant....... **C5**

7 Corsairs Beach Bar and Restaurant.......... **C5**

8 Cow Wreck Bar and Grill.................. **H1**

9 Foxy's Taboo............. **C5**

10 Foxy's Tamarind Bar and Restaurant.......... **C5**

11 Gertrude's Beach Bar **B5**

12 Harris' Place **C5**

13 Hendo's Hideout **B5**

14 Neptune's Treasure..... **H2**

15 Pirate's Bight............ **E7**

16 Potter's by the Sea...... **H2**

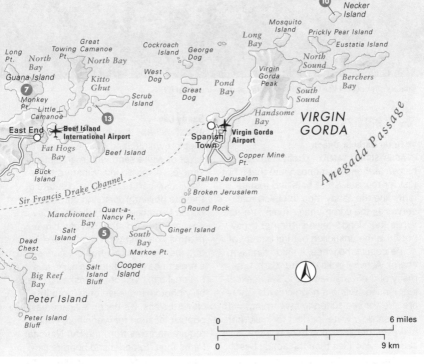

17 Seddy's One Love Bar and Grill............ **B5**	**Hotels** ▼	**6** Cow Wreck Beach Resort........... **H1**	**12** Perfect Pineapple Guest Houses **B5**
18 Sid's Pomato Point Restaurant.............. **H1**	**1** Ali Baba's Heavenly Rooms.................. **C5**	**7** Guana Island Resort.... **F4**	**13** Scrub Island Resort, Spa and Marina......... **G4**
19 Soggy Dollar Bar........ **B5**	**2** Anegada Beach Club... **H1**	**8** Ivan's Stress Free Guest House............ **B5**	**14** Sea Crest Inn............. **C5**
20 Sydney's Peace and Love......... **C5**	**3** Anegada Reef Hotel.... **H2**	**9** Keel Point Cottages **H1**	**15** White Bay Villas and Seaside Cottages....... **B5**
21 Willy T.................... **E7**	**4** Big Bamboo **I1**	**10** Necker Island **I3**	
22 The Wonky Dog......... **H2**	**5** Cooper Island Beach Club.............. **G6**	**11** Neptune's Treasure..... **H2**	

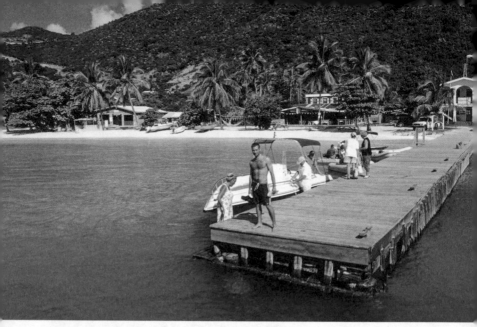

Boaters dock at Jost Van Dyke, known as the party island of the BVI.

Beaches

★ Great Harbour Beach

BEACH—SIGHT | FAMILY | Great Harbour has an authentic Caribbean feel that's not just for tourists. Small bars and restaurants line the sandy strip of beach that serves as the community's main street. While the island's main settlement may not have the unspoiled natural beauty of some popular beaches, it holds a quaint charm. Activity picks up after dark, but many of the restaurants also serve excellent lunches without huge crowds. There are a few areas suited to swimming, with calm, shallow water perfect for children; however, the attraction here is more about the facilities than the actual beach. Ali Baba and SeaCrest Inn have rooms on the bay. Bring your bug spray for sand flies in the early evenings. **Amenities:** food and drink; toilets. **Best for:** walking; swimming. ⊠ *Great Harbour.*

Sandy Cay

BEACH—SIGHT | Just offshore, the little islet known as Sandy Cay is a gleaming sliver of white sand with marvelous snorkeling and an inland nature trail. Previously part of the private estate of the late philanthropist and conservationist Laurance Rockefeller, the Cay is now a protected area. You can hire any boatman on Jost Van Dyke to take you out; just be sure to agree on a price and a time to be picked up again. As this is a national park, visitors are asked to "take only photos and leave only footprints." Nevertheless, it's become an increasingly popular location for weddings, which require approval from the BVI National Parks Trust. Experienced boaters can rent a boat or dinghy to go here, but be aware that winter swells can make beach landings treacherous. **Amenities:** none. **Best for:** snorkeling; swimming; walking.

★ White Bay Beach

BEACH—SIGHT | FAMILY | On the south shore, this long stretch of picturesque white sand is especially popular with boaters who come ashore for a libation at one of the many beach bars that offer refuge from the sun. Despite the sometimes rowdy bar scene, the beach is large enough to find a quiet spot, particularly late in the day when most of the day-trippers disappear and the beach becomes serene. Accommodations directly on or just steps from the sand include the White Bay Villas, Perfect Pineapple, and the Pink House Villas. Swimmers and snorkelers should be cautious of boat traffic in the anchorage. **Amenities:** food and drink; toilets. **Best for:** partiers; swimming; walking. ✉ *White Bay.*

🍴 Restaurants

Restaurants on Jost Van Dyke are informal (some serve meals family-style at long tables), but charming. The island's a favorite charter-boat stop, and you're bound to hear people exchanging stories about the previous night's anchoring adventures. Reservations are not mandatory, but it's a good idea to call ahead in season for dinner. In all cases dress is casual. Most of the restaurants are also known for their nightlife, particularly during the weekends. Meal prices are fairly consistent across the island, with dinner entrées usually varying by a few dollars.

Abe's by the Sea

$$$$ | ECLECTIC | Many sailors who cruise into this quiet bay come so they can dock right at this open-air eatery to enjoy the conch, lobster, and other fresh catches. Chicken and ribs round out the menu, and affable owners Abe Coakley and his wife, Eunicy, add a pinch of hospitality that makes a meal into a memorable evening. **Known for:** fresh seafood; outdoor dining; hospitality. $ *Average main: $40* ✉ *Little Harbour* ☎ *284/544–9981, 284/543–3362.*

Ali Baba's

$$$ | SEAFOOD | Lobster is the main attraction at this beach bar with a sandy floor, which is just some 20 feet from the sea. Grilled local fish, including swordfish, kingfish, and wahoo, are caught fresh daily. **Known for:** chicken roti; barbecue ribs; potent rum punch. $ *Average main: $30* ✉ *Great Harbour* ☎ *284/495–9280* ⊕ *www.alibabasrestaurantandbarbvi.com* ▤ *No credit cards.*

B-Line Beach Bar

$$ | ECLECTIC | The simple, open-air B-Line Beach Bar brings "getting away from it all" to a new level—if you're on mainland Jost Van Dyke you'll have to charter a dinghy or boat, or wade (at low tide) across the few hundred meters of water between Little Jost Van Dyke and Jost Van Dyke. Here you can have an ice-cold beer, an assortment of rums, and great grilled food like barbecued ribs and chicken on a beautiful, remote beach. **Known for:** remote setting; beach bar atmosphere; good rum selection. $ *Average main: $13* ☎ *284/343–3311.*

Cool Breeze Sports Bar & Restaurant

$$$ | BARBECUE | This brightly colored eatery with a pool table and big-screen TVs for watching sports is frequented by locals and visitors alike. The establishment offers full dinner options, serving fresh grilled lobster, barbecue, and baby back ribs. **Known for:** local scene; Caribbean-style barbecue; live sports on TV. $ *Average main: $29* ✉ *Great Harbour* ☎ *284/440–0302* ⊕ *www.coolbreezejvd.com* ▤ *No credit cards.*

Corsairs Beach Bar and Restaurant

$$$$ | ECLECTIC | On an island known for seafood, it's the pizza that draws raves at this friendly beach bar considered by some to be Jost's version of *Cheers.* If pizza doesn't appeal, the lunch and dinner menus have a wide variety of selections with an eclectic, Continental flair. Bring an appetite to breakfast, when the choices include hearty omelets and breakfast burritos. **Known for:**

The Famous Foxy Callwood

It's the laid-back attitude of Jost Van Dyke, which boasts a beach as its main street and has had electricity only since the 1990s, that makes the famous feel comfortable and everyday folk feel glorious. At no locale is this more true than at Foxy's Tamarind. Foxy Callwood, a seventh-generation Jost Van Dyker and calypsonian extraordinaire, is the star here, strumming and singing rib-tickling songs full of laughable lyrics that attract a bevy of boaters, and even celebrities like Tom Cruise, Kelsey Grammer, and Steven Spielberg.

What began in 1968 as a lemonade-stand-size bar, albeit with "modern" fixtures like a galvanized roof and plywood walls, has evolved into a bona fide beach bar with sandy floors, wattle walls, and a thatched roof that defines the eastern end of the beach at Great Harbour. Since Jost lacks the bustle of St. Thomas, cachet of St. John, or grace of Tortola, islanders like Foxy knew they needed to carve out their own unique niche—and have done so by appearing to have done nothing at all. Unhurried friendliness and a slice of quintessential Caribbean culture flow freely here.

Foxy, who fished for a living before he started singing for his supper, has traveled the world and has the world come to him for endless parties for Halloween, Labor Day weekend, and the New Year. *The New York Times* named Foxy's one of its three top picks for ringing in the millennium, and even Queen Elizabeth chose to honor Foxy, making him a Member of the Order of the British Empire (MBE) in 2009. A local newspaper headline from the occasion read: "Is Foxy Wearing Shoes?"

So what makes Foxy and his bar so popular, some 50-plus years on? He sums it up himself: "It's the quantity of people and the quality of the party. You can dance on the tables and sleep on the beach. No one is going to bother you."

pirate-themed decor; hearty breakfast; pizza. ⑤ *Average main: $38* ⊠ *Great Harbour* ☎ *284/495–9294* ⊕ *www.corsairs-bvi.com.*

Foxy's Taboo
$$ | **MEDITERRANEAN** | **FAMILY** | It's well worth the winding, hilly drive or sometimes rough sail to get to Taboo, where there's a sophisticated menu and friendly staff with a welcoming attitude. You'll find specialties with a Mediterranean twist like eggplant cheesecake, kebabs, hummus, and veggie-stuffed pitas.
Known for: Mediterranean fare with flair; scenic views; friendly staff. ⑤ *Average main: $15* ⊠ *East End* ☎ *284/441–1423* ⊕ *foxysbvi.com/foxys-taboo.*

Foxy's Tamarind Bar and Restaurant
$$$ | **ECLECTIC** | **FAMILY** | The big draw here is the owner, Foxy Callwood, a famed calypso singer who will serenade you with funny songs as you fork into grilled chicken, burgers, barbecue ribs, and lobster. Check out the pennants, postcards, and weathered T-shirts that adorn every inch of the walls and ceiling of this large, two-story beach bar; they've been left by previous visitors who are mostly either day-trippers from elsewhere in the Virgin Islands or yacht owners. **Known for:** Foxy, a Virgin Islands icon; live music and performances; happy hour and locally brewed beer. ⑤ *Average main: $30* ⊠ *Great Harbour* ☎ *284/442–3074* ⊕ *foxysbvi.com.*

Gertrude's Beach Bar

$$$ | **BURGER** | A casual bar and restaurant right on White Bay Beach, Gertrude's will make you feel at home with burgers, conch fritters, and rotis. It's open for lunch and dinner, but it's a good idea to call ahead for dinner reservations. **Known for:** beachfront setting; giant Adirondack chair; conch fritters and burgers. ⓢ *Average main: $25* ✉ *White Bay* ☎ *284/346–1626, 284/543–1626.*

Harris' Place

$$$$ | **ECLECTIC** | **FAMILY** | Owner Cynthia Harris is as famous for her friendliness as she is for her food. Lobster in a garlic butter sauce, and other freshly caught seafood, as well as pork, chicken, and ribs, are on the menu. **Known for:** fresh seafood; live music; homemade key lime pie. ⓢ *Average main: $50* ✉ *Little Harbour* ☎ *284/344–8816* ⊕ *www.harrisplacejvd.com.*

Hendo's Hideout

$$$$ | **AMERICAN** | **FAMILY** | Hendo's Hideout is a beach bar that brings an upscale but family-friendly vibe to White Bay beach. The menu of salads, sandwiches, and seafood is similar to other nearby establishments on this popular sandy stretch; however, the handsome wood bar, lounge area, and hammocks nestled in among the palm trees make you feel as if you are at a small resort. **Known for:** beachside dining; family-friendly atmosphere; pulled-pork nachos. ⓢ *Average main: $38* ✉ *White Bay* ☎ *284/340–0074* ⊕ *www.hendoshideout.com* ☽ *No dinner Mon.–Wed.*

Seddy's One Love Bar and Grill

$$$ | **ECLECTIC** | Menu items at this beachfront eatery include freshly caught seafood, quesadillas, sandwiches, and salads. The Food Network's Alton Brown once sought out this beachfront eatery and featured its stewed conch on a flavor-finding trip. **Known for:** beachy decor; Bushwacker cocktails; the year-round Christmas tree out front. ⓢ *Average main: $28* ✉ *White Bay* ☎ *937/470–8523* ⊕ *www.seddysonelovebarandgrill.com.*

★ Soggy Dollar Bar

$$ | **CARIBBEAN** | Caribbean-style, casual beach fare rules here, with the emphasis on lunch service and an appetizer-oriented menu (call them tapas if you'd like) served from later afternoon to early evening. Don't miss the Painkiller cocktail, the semi-official drink of the BVI, invented here. **Known for:** Painkiller cocktails, invented here; lively beach party; wading ashore from your boat—that's where the name comes from. ⓢ *Average main: $15* ✉ *White Bay* ☎ *284/495–9888* ⊕ *www.soggydollar.com.*

Sydney's Peace and Love

$$$$ | **CARIBBEAN** | Here you can find great local lobster and fish, as well as barbecue chicken and ribs with all the fixings, including peas and rice, corn, coleslaw, and potato salad. A popular pig roast happens on Monday and Saturday nights. **Known for:** local flair; fresh lobster; jukebox. ⓢ *Average main: $35* ✉ *Little Harbour* ☎ *284/344–2160.*

 Hotels

Ali Baba's Heavenly Rooms

$ | **B&B/INN** | Just above Ali Baba's restaurant, owner Wayson "Baba" Hatchett offers three simple but attractive rooms, each equipped with air-conditioning and a private bath. **Pros:** convenient location; air-conditioning; private bath. **Cons:** noisy area of Great Harbour; small; basic decor. ⓢ *Rooms from: $160* ✉ *Great Harbour* ☎ *284/495–9280* ⊕ *www.alibabasrestaurantandbarbvi.com* ⇄ *3 rooms* ⦿ *No meals.*

Ivan's Stress Free Guest House

$ | **RENTAL** | Ivan's will give you a quintessential Caribbean experience in a comfortable guesthouse setting. **Pros:** steps away from the best beach on the island;

Camping on Jost Van Dyke

Ivan's White Bay Campground. This bar, restaurant, and campground is a popular destination on Jost Van Dyke for those who don't mind roughing it. You can pitch your tent 6 feet from the sea or farther back under the seagrape trees where there's an electric hookup and lamp. Or opt for a primitive cabin, where you can find just a bed, fan, light, and bucket of water to wash the sand off your feet. There's an outhouse, a sun shower (basically a plastic sack hung from a tree branch), and a communal kitchen stocked with pots and pans. Expect to pay $20 for a bare site, $40 for an equipped site, or $65–$75 for a cabin. Camping reservations are essential. *White Bay 284/513–1095* ⊕ *www.ivanscamp-ground.com.*

you can meet new friends at Ivan's convivial bar; air-conditioning. **Cons:** basic furnishings; not within walking distance to other restaurants and nightlife (except Ivan's); no pool or other outdoor amenities. ⑤ *Rooms from: $150* ⊠ *White Bay* ☎ *284/495–9358* ⊕ *www.ivansstressfree-guesthouse.com* ⊟ *No credit cards* ⤴ *4 rooms* ⦿ *No meals.*

Perfect Pineapple Guest Houses

$ | **B&B/INN** | One-bedroom suites, as well as one- and two-bedroom guesthouses, all come equipped with private bath, air-conditioning, stove, satellite TV, and refrigerator. **Pros:** located just steps from the popular White Bay beach; air-conditioning; owner's taxi service will deliver you anywhere on the island. **Cons:** rooms have only basic furnishings; in need of updating; nothing fancy. ⑤ *Rooms from: $170* ⊠ *White Bay* ☎ *340/514–0713* ⊕ *www.perfectpineapple.com* ⤴ *6 rooms* ⦿ *No meals.*

Sea Crest Inn

$ | **RENTAL** | Sea Crest offers the cheapest lodging on Jost Van Dyke, save for camping, and the location is smack-dab in the hub of Great Harbour. **Pros:** hospitable host; affordable rates; walking distance to restaurants and ferry. **Cons:** noise from nearby bar; basic rooms; taxi required to reach the beach bars of White Bay. ⑤ *Rooms from: $200* ⊠ *Great Harbour* ☎ *284/443–5300, 340/775–6389* ⊕ *www.seacrestinn.net* ⤴ *4 1-bedroom apartments* ⦿ *No meals.*

White Bay Villas and Seaside Cottages

$$$ | **RENTAL** | **FAMILY** | Beautiful views and friendly staff keep guests coming back to these hilltop one- to three-bedroom villas and cottages, the nicest accommodations on the island. **Pros:** incredible views; full kitchens; friendly staff. **Cons:** 10- to 15-minute walk to White Bay and Great Harbour's restaurants and beaches; rental car recommended; steep access roads. ⑤ *Rooms from: $389* ⊠ *White Bay* ☎ *340/642–4484, 800/778–8066* ⊕ *www.jostvandyke.com* ⤴ *20 units* ⦿ *No meals.*

ⓨ Nightlife

Jost Van Dyke is the most happening place to go barhopping in the BVI, so much so that it is an all-day enterprise for some. In fact, yachties will sail over just to have a few drinks. All the spots are easy to find, clustered in three general locations: Great Harbour, White Bay, and Little Harbour (*see Restaurants, above*). On the Great Harbour side you can find Foxy's, Corsairs, and Ali Baba's; on the White Bay side are the One Love Bar and Grill and the Soggy Dollar Bar, where legend has it the famous Painkiller was first concocted; and in Little Harbour are Harris' Place, Sydney's Peace and Love, and Abe's By The Sea. Foxy's Taboo is on Diamond Cay on the east end of the island, looking across shallow Long Bay at Little Jost Van Dyke, home of the B-Line beach bar. If you can't make it to Jost Van Dyke, you can have a Painkiller at almost any bar in the BVI.

🛍 Shopping

The FoxHole Boutique

GIFTS/SOUVENIRS | Australian-born Tessa, who is married to Foxy Callwood, first arrived here back in the 1970s, and her shop offers a surprisingly large selection for such an out-of-the-way island. As a complement to Foxy's Tamarind Bar Restaurant, the boutique offers a wide selection of "Foxy's specific" merchandise both in store and online. The large store also offers Cuban cigars, gift items, Foxy's own Firewater rum, and women's and men's clothing (including hats, board shorts, and sandals). Tessa has a unique style that's evident in the interesting handbags, accessories, and jewelry that she's found around the Caribbean and the world. ✉ *Great Harbour* ☏ *284/442–3074* ⊕ *www.shopfoxysbvi.com.*

 Activities

Foxy's Charters

Foxy's operates day tours to surrounding islands as well as water-taxi service between the USVI and BVI. ✉ *Great Harbour* ☏ *284/346–0356* ⊕ *www.foxyscharters.com.*

JVD Scuba and BVI Eco-Tours

TOUR—SPORTS | Check out the undersea world around the island with dive master Colin Aldridge. One of the most impressive dives in the area is off the north coast of Little Jost Van Dyke. Here you can find the Twin Towers: a pair of rock formations rising an impressive 90

feet. A one-tank dive costs $90, a two-tank dive $135, and a four-hour beginner course is $150 plus the cost of equipment. Colin and crew also offer day trips to Sandy Cay and Sandy Spit, Norman Island, Virgin Gorda (The Baths), and newly opened dive sites in the northwest British Virgin Islands. You can also rent snorkel equipment, dive gear, stand-up paddleboards, kayaks, dinghies, and outboard boats here. ✉ *Great Harbour* ☏ *284/443–2222, 757/287–2731 U.S. phone* ⊕ *jostvandykescuba.com.*

Ocean Spa

SPA/BEAUTY | When life gives you hurricanes, turn the debris into a spa. That's what Jost Van Dyke resident Dale Mapp did following 2017's Hurricane Irma, salvaging various pieces of flotsam and jetsam and turning them into a floating spa permanently anchored in the waters of White Bay. The spa has two treatment rooms with sections of see-through flooring and windows open to allow in cooling breezes, as well as space on the open deck for an alfresco treatment. Services include a variety of massages, including a romantic moonlight couples treatment followed by champagne. ✉ *White Bay* ☏ *284/340–0772.*

Paradise Jeep Rentals

TOUR—SPORTS | Paradise Jeep Rentals offers the ideal vehicles to tackle Jost Van Dyke's steep, winding roads. Even though Jost is a relatively small island, you really need to be in shape to walk from one bay to the next. This outfit rents two-door Suzuki Jimmys for $65 per day, four-door Grand Vitaras for $75, and eight-seat Kia Mojaves for $90. Discounts are available for rentals of six or more days. It's next to the fire station in Great Harbour. Reservations are a must. ✉ *Great Harbour* ☏ *284/547–1040.*

Anegada

Anegada lies low on the horizon about 14 miles (22½ km) north of Virgin Gorda. Unlike the hilly volcanic islands in the chain, this is a flat coral-and-limestone atoll. Nine miles (14 km) long and 2 miles (3 km) wide, the island rises no more than 28 feet above sea level. In fact, by the time you're able to see it, you may have run your boat onto a reef. (More than 300 captains unfamiliar with the waters have done so since exploration days; note that bareboat charters don't allow their vessels to head here without a trained skipper.) Although the reefs are a sailor's nightmare, they are a primary attraction for many visitors. Snorkeling, especially in the waters around Loblolly Bay on the north shore, is a transcendent experience. You can float in shallow, calm water just a few feet from shore and see one coral formation after another, each shimmering with a rainbow of colorful fish. Many local captains are happy to take visitors out bonefishing or sport-fishing. These experiences are complemented by ever-so-fine, ever-so-white sand (the northern and western shores have long stretches of beach) and the occasional beach bar (stop in for burgers, local lobster, or a frosty beer). Several years ago, flamingos were reintroduced to the island. Seeking out the large, bright-pink birds in Anegada's salt ponds has become a popular diversion from the island's beaches when touring by vehicle.

The island's population of about 300 lives primarily in a small south-side village called The Settlement, which has a handful of grocery stores, a bakery, and a general store. Many restaurants and shops take only cash. Mosquitoes and sand flies can be murderous around dusk and dawn on Anegada; never come here without bug repellent and long-sleeved clothing. ■TIP→ **Note that the island has no banks or ATMs, and that many restaurants and shops take only cash.**

GETTING HERE AND AROUND

You can get to Anegada from Tortola by ferry or private boat. The Road Town Fast Ferry does two round-trips per day on Monday, Wednesday, and Friday. Anegada Express sails from Trellis Bay to Anegada, with stops on Virgin Gorda on both legs of the trip, on Tuesday, Thursday, Saturday, and Sunday. There are morning and afternoon departures, making it possible to visit the island for the day. VI Airlink has scheduled flight to Anegada three times a week. It's also possible to fly on a charter from Beef Island or St. Thomas; the flight from Beef Island takes only 10 minutes, and can be reasonably priced per person if you are traveling with a small group.

 Sights

Conch Shell Mounds
ARCHAEOLOGICAL SITE | The vanished indigenous residents of Anegada left their mark on the low-lying island by creating piles of thousands of conch shells that remain visible today. More modern fisherman also have created large piles of pink, sun-bleached conch shells in the shallow emerald waters off the island's southeast tip, creating an artificial island that can be visited (in combination with snorkeling and a look at Anegada's resident flamingos, which tend to congregate in nearby waters) on a tour with Kelly's Land and Sea Tours (284/496–0961). ⊠ East End.

Faulkner House Museum
MUSEUM | Theodolph Halburn Faulkner, a native of tiny Anegada, played an outsized role in winning freedom and democracy for the people of the British Virgin Islands, leading a 1949 march of more than 1,500 people to Road Town to demand a constitution and legislative representation. Faulkner's modest home in The Settlement—the first built of concrete on the island—is preserved as a museum detailing this history and offering a window into life on Anegada

Anegada has miles of beautiful white-sand beaches.

as it was in the middle of the previous century. ☎ *284/499–1496 Iverson Smith of BVI Tourism* ⊘ *Closed weekends.*

Beaches

Cow Wreck Beach

BEACH—SIGHT | Named for the cow bones that once washed ashore, this stretch of soft white sand on the island's northwest coast has a casual beach bar and restaurant. Cow Wreck Beach Resort is located directly on the beach, and small crowds congregate near the bar, but there's also plenty of room for those looking for solitude. Look for the palm-thatched benches that provide some shade on the beach. **Amenities:** food and drink; toilets. **Best for:** snorkeling; walking. ⊠ *Cow Wreck Bay.*

Loblolly Bay

BEACH—SIGHT | A curve of shore on Anegada's northern coast, this bay is home to the best snorkeling on the island. This is a place for solitude, but with a dash of convenience thrown in. Loblolly has a popular beachfront restaurant, Big Bamboo, showers, a gift shop, and snorkel rentals. The cottages at Big Bamboo are steps from the beach. Some palm-thatched shelters on the beach offer shade. **Amenities:** food and drink; showers; toilets; water sports. **Best for:** swimming; snorkeling; walking. ⊠ *Loblolly Bay.*

Pomato Point

BEACH—SIGHT | A powder white-sand beach on Anegada's western shore, Pomato Point has the best sunset views. There is no easily accessible reef, but the water is calm (making it a good choice for children) and the views of Tortola and Jost Van Dyke are beautiful. Sid's Pomato Point Restaurant is on the beach, and nearby Setting Point offers several other restaurant options, along with lodging. **Amenities:** food and drink. **Best for:** swimming; walking. ⊠ *Setting Point.*

🍴 Restaurants

There are between 6 and 10 restaurants open at any one time, depending on the season and on whim. Check when you're on the island. Fresh fish and lobster are the specialties of the island. The going rate for a lobster dinner is $50, and it's almost always the most expensive thing on any restaurant menu.

★ Anegada Reef Hotel Restaurant

$$$$ | SEAFOOD | Seasoned yachties gather here nightly to share tales of the high seas; the open-air bar is the busiest on the island. Dinner is by candlelight under the stars and always includes famous Anegada lobster, steaks, and succulent baby back ribs—all prepared on the large grill by the little open-air bar. **Known for:** grilled lobster; fun atmosphere; open-air bar. ⑤ *Average main: $38 ⊠ Setting Point* ☎ *284/495–8002* ⊕ *www.anegadareef.com.*

Big Bamboo

$$$ | SEAFOOD | FAMILY | This beachfront bar and restaurant tucked among seagrape trees at famous Loblolly Bay is the island's most popular destination for lunch. After you've polished off a plate of succulent Anegada lobster, barbecue chicken, or fresh fish, you can spend the afternoon on the beach, where the snorkeling is excellent and the view close to perfection, or browsing through the gift shop. **Known for:** spectacular beach; free shuttle from ferry; frozen drinks. ⑤ *Average main: $22 ⊠ Loblolly Bay* ☎ *284/499–1680, 284/346–5850* ⊕ *www. bigbambooanegada.com.*

Cow Wreck Bar and Grill

$$$$ | SEAFOOD | Named for the cow bones that once washed up on shore, this wiggle-your-toes-in-the-sand beachside eatery on the northern shore is a fun place to watch the antics of surfers and kiteboarders skidding across the bay. Tuck into conch ceviche, lobster fritters, or the popular hot wings for lunch. **Known for:** snorkeling on-site; beach vibes; homemade coconut pie. ⑤ *Average main: $36 ⊠ Cow Wreck Bay* ☎ *284/442–7180, 954/600–6616* ⊕ *www.cowwreckbeachbvi.com.*

★ Neptune's Treasure

$$$$ | SEAFOOD | FAMILY | The owners, the Soares family, have lived on the island for more than half a century, and catch, cook, and serve the seafood at this homey bar and restaurant a short distance from Setting Point. The fresh lobster, swordfish, tuna, and mahimahi are all delicious. **Known for:** authentic local feel; fresh baked goods; locally harvested seafood. ⑤ *Average main: $32 ⊠ Pomato Point* ☎ *284/495–9439 Pam's Kitchen, 284/345–5436* ⊕ *www. neptunestreasure.com.*

Potter's By the Sea

$$$$ | SEAFOOD | Friendly staff and a lively atmosphere just a few steps from the dock complement freshly grilled lobster and other seafood selections such as snapper and grouper. Potter's also offers a beach shuttle, free Wi-Fi, and live music (ask about the schedule when you call ahead for dinner reservations). **Known for:** local vibe; waterfront dining; local seafood. ⑤ *Average main: $45 ⊠ Setting Point* ☎ *284/341–9769* ⊕ *pottersanegada.com.*

Sid's Pomato Point Restaurant

$$$$ | SEAFOOD | This relaxed restaurant and bar sits on one of the best beaches on the island and enjoys Anegada's most dramatic sunset views. Entrées include fish tacos and freshly caught seafood. **Known for:** historic artifacts on display; sunset views; beautiful beach location. ⑤ *Average main: $38 ⊠ Pomato Point* ☎ *284/441–5565.*

The Wonky Dog

$$$$ | SEAFOOD | The laid-back, low-key vibe of this Setting Point bar and restaurant is infectious. Lobster served on a seaside rooftop pairs with draft beer and craft cocktails. **Known for:** friendly atmosphere; live music; lobster. ⑤ *Average main: $42 ⊠ Setting Point* ☎ *284/547–0539, 284/441–0539, 284/344–1265* ⊕ *www.thewonkydog.com.*

Hotels

Anegada Beach Club
$ | RESORT | This is a laid-back beach club setting with well-equipped rooms and luxury "palapa retreats" overlooking the dunes. **Pros:** option to adjoin king and junior suites makes this a great spot for families; bar and restaurant on-site; plenty of outdoor activities. **Cons:** remote location; pricey; small pool. ⑤ *Rooms from: $235* ✉ *Keel Point* ☎ *284/346-4005, 284/340-4455* ⊕ *www.anegadabeachclub.com* ⊐ *23 units* ⁞○⁞ *No meals.*

Anegada Reef Hotel
$ | HOTEL | Head here if you want to bunk in comfortable lodging near Anegada's most popular anchorage; this venerable hotel, a destination for more than 40 years, still feels like the nerve center for the island. **Pros:** everything you need is nearby; nice sunsets; rents cars and arranges tours. **Cons:** basic rooms; no beach; often a party atmosphere at the bar. ⑤ *Rooms from: $225* ✉ *Setting Point* ☎ *284/495-8002* ⊕ *www.anegadareef.com* ⊐ *16 rooms* ⁞○⁞ *Free Breakfast.*

Big Bamboo
$ | RENTAL | Location is this property's finest attribute: the four circular villas are just steps from beautiful Loblolly Bay. Painted in the Big Bamboo's signature green and blue, these one- and two-bedroom units offer full kitchens, spacious bedrooms, and the opportunity to wake up to one of the prettiest views on the island. **Pros:** beachfront location; near restaurant and snorkeling; nice views from balconies. **Cons:** some may feel isolated; beach popular during the day; simple furnishings in rooms. ⑤ *Rooms from: $250* ✉ *Loblolly Bay* ☎ *284/346-5850, 284/499-1680* ⊕ *www.bigbambooanegada.com* ⊐ *4 villas* ⁞○⁞ *No meals.*

Cow Wreck Beach Resort
$ | RENTAL | Brightly painted, furnished one- or two-bedroom villas with full kitchens are available at this resort, but the best attribute is its location at Cow Wreck Beach. **Pros:** secluded location; great snorkeling; on-site restaurant. **Cons:** the island's free-roaming livestock sometimes leave "presents" behind; location too remote for some; need a car to get around, but vehicle-rental service is available. ⑤ *Rooms from: $200* ✉ *Cow Wreck Bay* ☎ *284/442-7180, 954/600-6616* ⊕ *www.cowwreckbeachbvi.com* ⊐ *7 units* ⁞○⁞ *No meals.*

Keel Point Cottages
$ | RENTAL | FAMILY | Picture yourself nearly alone in a tropical paradise; if that's your dream, then this may be your place. **Pros:** right on the water; new, well-kept property; rental car included. **Cons:** no on-site dining options (except your kitchen); far from restaurants and town; simple furnishings. ⑤ *Rooms from: $260* ✉ *Keel Point* ☎ *284/441-0296, 284/341-3128* ⊐ *4 cottages* ⁞○⁞ *No meals.*

Neptune's Treasure
$ | B&B/INN | FAMILY | Basic waterfront rooms with simple furnishings and lovely views of the ocean are the hallmark of this family-owned guesthouse. **Pros:** waterfront property with nice sunset views; run by a family full of tales of the island; good restaurant. **Cons:** simple rooms; narrow beach; no pool. ⑤ *Rooms from: $170* ✉ *Pomato Point* ☎ *284/345-5436, 284/495-9439* ⊕ *www.neptunestreasure.com* ⊐ *9 rooms, 1 cottage* ⁞○⁞ *No meals.*

Shopping

Faulkner's Country Store
FOOD/CANDY | Stop here for a taste of old-time Anegada or just to buy groceries or other necessities. ✉ *The Settlement.*

Activities

Anegada Fly Fishing Guide Service
FISHING | Kevin and Garfield Faulkner take visitors fly-fishing for bonefish, tarpon, and other game fish in Anegada's flats and reefs. Trips range from four to eight hours and start at $400 for up to two

anglers. ⊠ *The Settlement* ☎ *284/540–5100, 284/340–5100* ⊕ *www.anegadafly-fishing.com.*

Anegada Reef Hotel

FISHING | Call the hotel to arrange bonefishing and sportfishing outings with seasoned local guides. ⊠ *Setting Point* ☎ *284/495–8002* ⊕ *www.anegadareef.com.*

Danny's Bonefishing

FISHING | Danny Vanterpool offers half-, three-quarter-, and full-day bonefishing excursions around Anegada. The cost is $400 for a half day (four hours) and $600 for a three-quarter-day (six hour) fishing trip. ☎ *284/441–6334, 284/344–1226* ⊕ *www.dannysbonefishing.com.*

Other British Virgin Islands

Of the 50-odd islands in the British Virgin Islands chain only 15 are inhabited, and several of those are privately owned, having been turned into private-island resorts. Some of these—most notably Necker Island, which is owned by Sir Richard Branson and often visited by celebrities, are well-known among the jet-set crowd; others are not as well-known but equally beautiful.

Cooper Island

This small, hilly island on the south side of the Sir Francis Drake Channel, about 8 miles (13 km) from Road Town, Tortola, is popular with the charter-boat crowd. There are no paved roads (which doesn't really matter, as there aren't any cars), but you can find a beach restaurant, rum bar, brewery, coffee shop, a casual hotel, a few houses (some are available for rent), and great snorkeling at the south end of Manchioneel Bay.

GETTING HERE AND AROUND

Unless you have your own sailboat, the only way to reach Cooper Island is on a private ferry from Road Harbour Marina. The 35-minute ride is included in the cost of your vacation at Cooper Island Beach Club if your schedule meshes with the hotel's boat service.

 Hotels

★ Cooper Island Beach Club

$$ | RESORT | Relaxation is the focus at this small resort, but folks who want to simply swim, snorkel, or chill on the beach can also feel right at home in comfortable rooms with attractive recycled furniture, tile floors, and lovely sea views. **Pros:** laid-back vibe; easy access to diving, snorkeling, and other water sports; excellent brewery and rum bar. **Cons:** rooms have no air-conditioning; island beyond the resort is not accessible; minimal nightlife. ⑤ *Rooms from: $310* ⊠ *Manchioneel Bay* ☎ *284/345–6725, 800/542–4624* ⊕ *www.cooperislandbeachclub.com* ⇥ *8 rooms* ⦿ *Free Breakfast.*

Guana Island

Guana Island sits off Tortola's northeast coast. Sailors often drop anchor at one of the island's bays for a day of snorkeling and sunning. The island is a designated wildlife sanctuary, and scientists often come here to study its flora and fauna. It's home to a back-to-nature resort that offers few activities other than relaxation. Unless you're a hotel guest or a sailor, there's no easy way to get onto the island.

GETTING HERE AND AROUND

Unless you have your own sailboat, the best way to reach Guana Island is by the resort's private ferry, which will pick you up at Beef Island, Tortola, if you are a guest. You can also take a water taxi from St. Thomas.

Take the ferry from Tortola to reach lush Guana Island, designated a wildlife sanctuary.

Hotels

★ Guana Island Resort

$$$$ | RESORT | This charming resort is perfect for those wanting to hike, snorkel, swim, and relax at the beach in comfort. **Pros:** secluded feel; lovely grounds; good for nature lovers. **Cons:** very expensive; no TVs or radios in rooms; minimal nightlife. ⑤ *Rooms from: $1,650* ☎ *284/494–2354, 800/544–8262* ⊕ *www.guana.com* ⇨ *21 rooms* ⑩ *All-inclusive.*

Scrub Island

The main resort is located at the marina, while a hilly road leads to the spa, villas, and several secluded beaches. A narrow strip of land connects Big Scrub Island, where the resort is, to the mostly undeveloped Little Scrub Island. The island is close enough to Tortola to spend a day exploring but there are enough activities that you might not want to leave.

GETTING HERE AND AROUND
Scrub Island is easily reachable from Beef Island by the resort's private ferry. The dock is just minutes from the airport.

Hotels

★ Scrub Island Resort, Spa and Marina

$$$ | RESORT | Part of Marriott's Autograph Collection, this swanky resort is located on a 250-acre island near Tortola's Beef Island Airport. **Pros:** full-service marina; lots of activities; spa. **Cons:** need ferry to get there; expensive; can be many guests. ⑤ *Rooms from: $391* ☎ *877/890–7444, 284/394–3440* ⊕ *www.scrubisland. com* ⇨ *62 units* ⑩ *No meals.*

Necker Island

Necker Island sits off Virgin Gorda's northeast coast, reachable only by private ferry or helicopter. A mere speck in the British Virgin Islands, it's home to Sir Richard Branson's private estate. When he's not in residence, you and your friends are welcome to enjoy its gorgeous beaches and myriad amenities—for a hefty price tag.

GETTING HERE AND AROUND
Guests (and only guests) of Necker Island will be whisked away from Beef Island or Virgin Gorda on a private boat or helicopter.

Hotels

Necker Island
$$$$ | **RESORT** | You probably won't run into British magnate Sir Richard Branson, but you can live in his luxurious style when you rent his estate on Necker Island. **Pros:** gorgeous rooms; an island for you and a few dozen friends; spectacular views. **Cons:** very expensive; need boat to get here; limited availability for non-group stays. ⑤ *Rooms from: $102,500* ☎ *212/994–3070, 877/577–8777* ⊕ *www. virginlimitededition.com/en/necker-island* ⤴ *20 rooms total: 11 in Great House, plus 9 in cottages and the Temple House* ⑩ *All-inclusive* ⌇ *Rate is per night for up to 40 people; individual rooms start at $5,000 nightly.*

Norman Island

This uninhabited island is the supposed setting for Robert Louis Stevenson's *Treasure Island.* The famed caves at Treasure Point are popular with day sailors and powerboaters. There are nearly 12 miles (20 km) of hiking trails on the island. If you land ashore at the island's main anchorage in the Bight, you'll find a restaurant and behind it a trail that winds up the hillside and reaches a peak with a fantastic view of the Sir Francis Drake Channel to the north. Another trail (a dirt road, actually) leads to Turtle Cove. Call Pirate's Bight for information on ferry service to accommodate day-trippers.

GETTING HERE AND AROUND
The only way to reach this island is by private boat or on a charter boat that puts you aboard the *Willy T.* for a meal and drinks. The Norman Island Ferry leaves from Hannah Bay, Tortola, and arrives at Pirates Bight.

Sights

★ Norman Island Caves
CAVE | A popular day trip for sailors, the caves at Treasure Point are a good place for snorkeling among tropical fish and coral formations. Although the caves inspired Robert Louis Stevenson's *Treasure Island*, you probably won't find any gold doubloons hidden inside. The only way to arrive is by boat; inquire about excursions at Pirate's Bight. ⊠ *Treasure Point.*

⑪ Restaurants

Pirate's Bight
$$$$ | **SEAFOOD** | This breezy, open-air dining establishment boasts quirky beach-bar eccentricities (a cannon is fired at sunset and bar goers play games like "Giant Jenga"), all while maintaining a slightly refined feeling. The owners offer ferry service from Hannah Bay on Tortola, giving the restaurant the feel of a casual day resort. **Known for:** beach club setting; fun atmosphere; live entertainment. ⑤ *Average main: $32* ⊠ *The Bight* ☎ *284/443–1305, 284/344–1688* ⊕ *www. piratesbight.com.*

Willy T
$$ | **ECLECTIC** | *Willy T* is a floating bar and restaurant that's anchored in Pirate's Bight. The current boat is new; its predecessor, sunk in 2017's Hurricane Irma, lies nearby at the bottom of the Bight and is now a dive site, complete with skeleton crew. **Known for:** conch fritters; West Indian roti; party atmosphere. ⑤ *Average main: $16* ☎ *284/340–8603 for boaters, use VHF Channels 16/74* ⊕ *willy-t.com.*

Index

Photo Credits

Front Cover: Don Hebert [Description: Hawks Nest Bay, Virgin Island.]. **Back cover, from left to right:** BlueOrange Studio/Shutterstock, U.S. Virgin Islands Dept of Tourism, emperorcosar/Shutterstock. **Spine:** Sasha Buzko/Shutterstock. **Interior, from left to right:** SuperStock / age fotostock (1). Eric Rubens/Shutterstock (2). Shirley Vanderbilt / age fotostock (5). **Chapter 1: Experience the U.S. and British Virgin Islands:** Ellen Rooney / age fotostock (6). Jon Arnold Images Ltd / Alamy (8). Gary Felton (9). Gary Felton (9). TalbotImages/iStockphoto (10). emperorcosar/Shutterstock (10). LOW FLITE/iStockphoto (10). Michael BVI/Shutterstock (11). Darryl Brooks/Dreamstime (12). Jennifer Pitiquen/Dreamstime (12). USVI DoT (12). Ken Hayden Photography (13). C. Kurt Holter/Shutterstock (13). Carlos Villoch - MagicSea.com / Alamy (14). Vlad Ispas/Dreamstime (14). Shutterdo/Dreamstime (15). Malachi Jacobs/Shuttersotck (18). BlueOrange Studio/Shutterstock (18). emperorcosar/Shutterstock (18). Luebeck.er/Shutterstock (18). Irishka777 /Dreamstime (19). bcampbell65/Shutterstock (20). ESB Professional/Shutterstock (20). Nicole R Young/Shutterstock (20). LOW FLITE/iStock Editorial (21). emperorcosar/Shutterstock (21). **Chapter 3: St. Thomas:** Vale_T/iStockphoto (45). Jeff Greenberg / age fotostock (48). Olga Lyubkina/Shutterstock (49). Atlantide S.N.C. / age fotostock (49). Gang Liu/Shutterstock (54-55). Thomas USVI/Shutterstock (60). Michael DeFreitas / age fotostock (67). Andrei Medvedev / Shutterstock (81). World Pictures / Alamy (82). Vlad Ispas/Shutterstock (86). **Chapter 4: St. John:** Terri Butler Photography/Shutterstock (89). Gavin Hellier / age fotostock (98). Walter Bibikow / age fotostock (105). Ciaoarturo/Dreamstime (109). Ken Brown/iStockphoto (112-113). Carlos Villoch - MagicSea.com / Alamy (115). Kendra Nielsam/Shutterstock (117). divemasterking2000/Flickr (119). Julie de Leseleuc/iStockphoto (120). Shirley Vanderbilt / age fotostock (120). Marjorie McBride / Alamy (120). divemasterking2000/Flickr (121). David Coleman/iStockphoto (122). Steve Simonsen (122). nik wheeler / Alamy (125). **Chapter 5: St. Croix:** NAPA/Shutterstock (127). Walter Bibikow / age fotostock (136). Danita Delimont / Alamy (145). The Buccaneer (147). Napa735/Dreamstime (150). Marc Muench / Alamy (156). Stephen Frink Collection / Alamy (158). Julie Hewitt / Alamy (161). **Chapter 6: Tortola:** Alvaro Leiva / age fotostock (163). Alvaro Leiva / age fotostock (175). Irishka777/Dreamstime (179). Eric Sanford / age fotostock (181). Steve Dangers/iStockphoto (182). Randy Lincks / Alamy (182). Slavoljub Pantelic/iStockphoto (183). Doug Scott / age fotostock (183).Doug Scott / age fotostock (184). Giovanni Rinaldi/iStockphoto (186). Walter Bibikow / age fotostock (187). Jason P Ross/Dreamstime (188). World Pictures / Alamy (191). Fotograferen.net / Alamy (194). **Chapter 7: Virgin Gorda:** BlueOrange Studio/Shutterstock (197). Carlos Villoch - MagicSea.com / Alamy (203). BVI Tourist Board (205). Ellen Rooney / age fotostock (208). COPYRIGHT Ken Hayden Photography (210). Larwin/Shutterstock (212). **Chapter 8: Other British Virgin Islands:** Napa735/Dreamstime (215). Andre Jenny / Alamy (222). Kreder Katja / age fotostock (224-225). shalamov/iStockphoto (231). Andrea Haase/Dreamstime (235). **About Our Writers:** All photos are courtesy of the writers.

Every effort has been made to trace the copyright holders, and we apologize in advance for any accidental errors. We would be happy to apply the corrections in the following edition of this publication.

Notes

Notes

Notes

Notes

Notes